D0548205

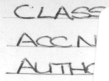

# A CONCISE GUIDE

## to

# PLASTICS

*by*

HERBERT R. SIMONDS
*Consulting Engineer*
*Stepney, Connecticut*

REINHOLD PUBLISHING CORPORATION
NEW YORK
CHAPMAN & HALL, LTD., LONDON

Copyright 1957 by
REINHOLD PUBLISHING CORPORATION

———————

Library of Congress Catalog Card Number: 57-13169

REINHOLD PUBLISHING CORPORATION
Publishers of Chemical Engineering Catalog, Chemical Materials Catalog, "Automatic Control," "Materials in Design Engineering," "Progressive Architecture"; Advertising Management of the American Chemical Society

Printed in the U.S.A.

# FOREWORD

The continued growth of the plastics industry indicates that plastics are being used more and more extensively—as industrial and electrical components; in consumer goods as housewares, toys, hardware; in building as fenestration; as plastics pipe; in communications and in transportation. Indeed, at home, at work and at play, plastics are encountered in an ever-increasing variety of applications.

For those being introduced to the multi-faceted plastics industry who are seeking more information on the industry, its materials, on the materials producing companies, the processing methods and the industry's products this concise volume has been written.

Since plastics are a product of the chemical industry, to the uninitiated their nomenclatures may be confusing—the many types complicate the problem of identifying performance capabilities and performance potentialities. By including condensed tables of properties and a description of them, and by listing typical applications, the author has provided information to orient the reader.

The volume includes a list of the U.S. manufacturers of plastics. In addition to including information on the materials they produce, historical, personnel and financial facts are incorporated. This section will be of interest as a reference to those interested in such information on this segment of the industry.

In writing this book, the author has enjoyed the cooperation of many competent authorities in the industry. The forecasts for the future are likely to stimulate the reader's thinking.

There are now many plastics materials and from these a vast number of articles are made. Still others are to come. As this "Concise Guide to Plastics" reveals, the industry is sizeable, it is vigorous, and it is growing. Its progress depends upon well designed, soundly engineered applications. As a preliminary source for information on plastics and as a guide, this volume will serve usefully.

WM. T. CRUSE
*Executive Vice President*
The Society of the Plastics Industry, Inc.

# PREFACE

At the 1956 Plastics Exhibit at the New York Coliseum there undoubtedly were in attendance many people not directly associated with plastics; I think it is safe to say that nearly all of these had an interest in plastics or they would not have been there. At the Reinhold Publishing Corporation booth a record was kept of questions and interviews and, to the surprise of everyone, it was discovered that most queries were from people knowing very little about plastics and knowing even less about chemistry.

From an analysis of the interviews it was evident that there was a need for a short book which would help to orient a newcomer to the widespread and rather complex industry devoted to the production of plastics materials and plastics products. Accordingly, the present book has been planned to fill this need. Without going too deeply into details about any one subject this book attempts to give readers a useful understanding of the industry as a whole and a comprehensive starting point for those first approaching plastics. As its name indicates the book's function is essentially that of a guide.

Those wishing to know more about the properties and the uses of any one particular material are referred to a new series of books known as the "Reinhold Plastics Applications Series," now in the process of publication. The first of this Series, a book on Polyethylene, has already appeared. The others which are scheduled for appearance during the next ten or twelve months will cover acrylics, cellulosics, epoxies, fluorocarbons, laminates, polyamides, polyesters, polystyrene, polyurethane, gum plastics, silicones and vinyls.

The fountainhead for most of the information about the materials of the plastics industry is the relatively small group of plastics materials manufacturers, which group, according to most authorities, numbers but slightly over 100 companies. Forty-three of the most important of these companies have cooperated by submitting statements which appear in Chapter 8, and which have been interpreted and analyzed elsewhere in this book.

Readers will find in these statements authoritative information about the materials each company produces as well as the trade names it uses to cover such materials. Further trade name information will be found in Chapter 10 which is thought to contain the most complete list of trade names, of strictly plastics materials, yet to be published.

The arrangement of the text with, for instance, separate chapters for processing and application, has made some duplication unavoidable and therefore full use of the index is urged. The list of chapters will give an idea of the general scheme of presentation.

July 1, 1957                                              HERBERT R. SIMONDS
Stepney, Connecticut

## ACKNOWLEDGMENTS

Much of the information for a book of this type originates with the material manufacturers, and it is to the 103 such manufacturers that I am chiefly indebted for help in the preparation of the present volume. This applies especially to the 43 companies whose statements appear in Chapter 8.

Three leading Associations in the plastics field have been most helpful. These are: The Society of the Plastics Industry, Inc., 250 Park Avenue, New York; The Society of Plastics Engineers, Inc., Greenwich, Connecticut; and Manufacturing Chemists' Association, 1625 Eye Street, N.W., Washington 6, D. C. I also wish to express my appreciation for the help given by the three principal magazines in the industry, *Modern Plastics,* 575 Madison Avenue, New York; *Plastics World,* Cos Cob, Connecticut; and *Plastics Technology,* 386 4th Avenue, New York.

The technical men who cooperated with specific sections in the book have been credited with footnotes at such sections. However, I particularly want to thank Dr. Irving Skeist, Skeist Laboratories, Newark, New Jersey; Dr. W. Mayo Smith, Escambia Chemical Corporation, Cambridge, Massachusetts; J. H. Thomas, Vice President, Resins & Chemicals Division, Jones-Dabney Company, Louisville, Kentucky; Maurice C. Hommel, Dow Corning Corporation, Midland, Michigan; Dr. Walter D. Paist, Plastics Division, Celanese Corporation of America, New York; George K. Scribner, Boonton Molding Company, Boonton, New Jersey; Dr. C. A. Sperati, Polychemicals Department, E. I. du Pont de Nemours & Company, Wilmington, Delaware; George W. Rhine, *Plastics World,* Cos Cob, Connecticut; and Dr. R. B. Greene, Barrett Division, Allied Chemical & Dye Corporation, New York.

In addition, I am grateful for help from the various authors of a new series known as the "Reinhold Plastics Applications Series," of which the first book on "Polyethylene" by Theodore Kresser has just been published.

HERBERT R. SIMONDS

# CONTENTS

# 1. INTRODUCTION

The plastics industry—a young industry—is growing more rapidly than most other American industries and is expanding at an astonishing rate both in the number of different materials commercially available and in the fields of their application. Today, judged by total sales, it comprises one of the few billion dollar industries and its growth has been so rapid in recent years that public acceptance has outstripped public knowledge. Thus, many of the widely disparate materials enjoying the general term "plastics" have a common image in the consumer's mind. This creates a problem in identification as well as in application.

An analogy with the metal industry may help to make this problem clear. Both soft lead and hard tungsten, for instance, are included under the term "metals," but their properties are so well known that few people would refer to either as a metal without some qualification. Yet many people still refer to, say, polyethylene, merely as a plastic. To correct this, manufacturers and plastics engineers are endeavoring to educate users to adopt more specific terminology. In addition, they are trying to acquaint consumers and fabricators alike with the essential properties of the more common materials such as the vinyls and the phenolics. To this end manufacturers have been doing more and better labeling of their end products. These certainly are moves in the right direction and the industry as a whole has made encouraging strides since the introduction of phenolics in 1909. However, some difficulties still exist for the designer first entering the field because variations in physical properties occur within each specific type. Group and type characteristics will be found in Chapter 2. If these meet general requirements, additional information can be secured by noting the applications in Chapter 5 and the comparative tables in Chapter 7. Finally, when selection of a material has been narrowed down the manufacturer should be consulted for recommended detailed specifications.

To illustrate, the cellulosics form a typical group or family of plastics.

1

As a group they are sturdy materials, readily colored, hard-surfaced and relatively low in price. Within this group are the acetates, the butyrates, ethyl cellulose and the nitrates—each with its distinct properies. Furthermore, each of these may be varied to a considerable extent by the producer. One producer, for instance, lists five different acetates among his products. Others often advertise "materials compounded to meet your specifications." The buyer as well as the user of the end products should know that a urethane product, for example, is not much like a phenolic product, although they are both plastics. To know the right plastic to use for a specific application is, of course, not only highly important to the fabricator but also to the consumer. To impart such knowledge to both fabricator and consumer is the object of this book.

Chapter 2 describes the properties of most commercial plastics. It presents a longer list than needed for the average buyer, as a few of these may be regarded as specialized materials. Some authorities list just 12 household plastics which they say should be better known. These are partly thermoplastic and partly thermosetting as indicated in Tables 1.2 and 1.3.

**What Are Plastics?**

The generic term "plastics" refers to a group of organic synthetic materials (p. 14) which group itself constitutes the best definition of the term. The American Society for Testing Materials has the following rather complicated description:

"A plastic is a material that contains as an essential ingredient an organic substance of large molecular weight, is solid in its finished state, and at some stage in its manufacture or in its processing into finished articles, can be shaped by flow."

The modern plastics industry may be said to have started in 1930 when diversified products of plastics research laboratories first came into commercial use in appreciable volume. The commercial materials available that year included the nitrates, the phenolics, the acetates, casein, the ureas and the alkyds. Table 1.1 shows the approximate dates when many of today's plastics first became commercially available in the United States.

Plastics are synthetic in the sense that they do not occur naturally. The molecules are composed principally of carbon, hydrogen, nitrogen, and oxygen, which are derived from petroleum, coal, salt, and air and water. Their properties depend to some extent on the size of the molecules of which they are composed. In the early stages of manufacture most plastics are monomers, composed of small single molecules, but under the influence of heat, or of heat and pressure, or of chemical catalysts these small molecules combine to form long-chain molecules which make up solid or semi-solid structures. This process is called "polymerization." Dissimilar monomers may be jointly polymerized, and the process is then called "copolymerization." Usually no water or other substances are given off during the process. When substances are given off the process is called a "condensation reaction" instead of polymerization.

TABLE 1.1. PROGRESS IN PLASTICS DEVELOPMENT

Approximate Dates Covering Introduction of Some Commercial Plastics

| Year | Plastic | Typical Application |
|------|---------|---------------------|
| 1870 | The nitrates (Celluloid) | Eyeglass frames |
| 1909 | The phenolics | Telephone hand set |
| 1909 | Cold molded | Electric heater parts |
| 1919 | Casein | Knitting needles |
| 1919 | Vinyl acetates | Adhesives |
| 1927 | The acetates | Safety glass interlayer |
| 1928 | The ureas | Lighting fixtures |
| 1931 | The acrylics | Brush backs, displays |
| 1935 | Ethyl cellulose | Flashlight cases |
| 1936 | Polyvinyl chloride | Raincoats |
| 1938 | Vinyl butyral | Safety glass |
| 1938 | Polystyrene | Housewares |
| 1938 | Polyamides (nylon) | Fibers |
| 1939 | Polyamide molding powders | Gears |
| 1939 | Melamines | Tableware |
| 1939 | Polyvinylidene chloride (saran) | Auto seat covers |
| 1942 | Polyethylene | Squeeze bottles |
| 1942 | Polyesters | Large forms |
| 1943 | Silicones | Motor insulation |
| 1943 | Tetrafluoroethylene | Gaskets |
| 1947 | Organosols and plastisols | Coatings, films |
| 1947 | Epoxies | Molding compound, adhesives |
| 1948 | Chlorotrifluoroethylene | Gaskets and valve seats |
| 1953 | Urethanes | Sheets and foams |
| 1955 | Urethanes | Molding powder |

The use of the term "resin" is sometimes confusing. It may be synonymous with "plastic" but it usually refers to the liquid polymers which are the starting materials in the production of molded or fabricated solid or semi-solid products. For example, a bath of liquid polyester for impregnating fabrics for use in the production of a boat or a fender, is referred to as a "resin bath." The term resin is not used in referring to the cellulosics. The most common over-all advantages of plastics as a group are: light weight, good physical properties, good range of color, adaptability to mass production methods, and, often, lower cost.

Some materials which belong to the broad family of plastics are based on inorganic rather than organic molecules, and this further complicates a definition for plastics. Typical of the inorganic group are the silicones. As stated earlier, the best definition of "plastics" is the total list (given in Chapter 2) of materials now generally recognized as such. If one knows these materials he has a pretty good idea of the meaning of the word "plastics" but he still may have a far from complete understanding of the entire plastics industry in which the methods of fabrication and the intermediate shapes and forms play such an important role.

The industry likes to include many products which in the popular mind seem far removed from plastics. Thus, certain types of printing ink, organic coatings, and adhesives are often included as plastics.

Most basic materials for the plastics industry—the resins and molding powders—are produced by a branch of the chemical industry, and thus both industries—plastics and chemicals—are closely associated. Many resins are filled or reinforced or extended by non-plastic materials, chief of which are wood flour used in phenolics and in some of the other thermosetting plastics, and glass fibers and fabrics used in connection with several of the newer thermoplastic resins. These materials, known as "fillers" play an important part in the over-all plastics picture. (See Fillers, Chapter 3.)

At this point the terms thermosetting and thermoplastic should be explained.

*Thermosetting* is a term applied to resins (plastics) which solidify or set on heating and cannot be remelted. The thermosetting property usually is associated with a cross-linking reaction which forms a three-dimensional network of polymer molecules. Typical of the thermosetting materials are the phenolics and the ureas. In general, thermoset materials cannot be reshaped once they have been fully cured.

*Thermoplastic* is a term applied to resins (plastics) that may be softened by heat and which upon cooling regain their original properties, even if the process is repeated. Typical of this group are polystyrenes, acrylics, and vinyls.

Some terms often used in connection with plastics are described briefly in Table 1.4.

*Plastics,* generally speaking, are light weight; for their weight, they are prodigiously strong. There are many plastics (32 commercial varieties,

as listed in Chapter 2) and each has its individual characteristic properties. Thus, by studying the tables in Chapter 7, the properties in Chapter
2, and the applications in Chapter 5, it usually is possible to select the
type which may be best for a given job. A recent case in the medical
field may emphasize the value of securing the right plastic.

According to a recent announcement the choice of a plastic in one
instance probably saved many lives. Charles Holter, seeking a material
for a tiny valve used in draining fluid from the brain in treating hydro-
cephalic babies, tried several plastics which failed for one reason or
another. Finally, engineers from Lee Rubber & Tire Company suggested
silicone, which proved successful, solving a problem which had baffled
surgeons for years.

Because terms for the various plastics differ with the users the following brief forms used in this book* should be noted.

Acrylic—methyl methracrylate or acrylate
Acetate—cellulose acetate
Butyrate—cellulose acetate butyrate
Nitrate—cellulose nitrate or nitrocellulose or pyroxylin
Melamine—melamine-formaldehyde,     (sometimes     called     melamine
    resins)
Phenolic—phenol-formaldehyde
Urea—urea-formaldehyde
Fluorocarbons—chlorotrifluoroethylene  and  tetrafluoroethylene

## The Extent of the Industry

Plastics start where chemicals leave off and continue through to the
finished products. In the earliest stage are the molding powders and resins
produced in the main by perhaps 100 chemical or plastics companies. (A
total of 103 such companies have been listed.) These may be considered
a sort of reservoir of unfinished material waiting to be processed. The
molding powders are purchased by molders, extruders and others scattered
across the country. The resins are purchased by a still larger group of
processors ranging from boat manufacturers on one hand to packaging
film producers on the other. Of the molders and extruders nearly 50 per
cent are injection molders, 30 per cent compression molders, and 20 per
cent extruders. These figures are somewhat arbitrary in the sense that
many molders do compression and injection molding and some do extrusion. Transfer and jet molding are included under compression molders.
There are others, for example, the cold-molding operators, who use mold-

---

* Some tables and quoted items may continue to use the longer forms.

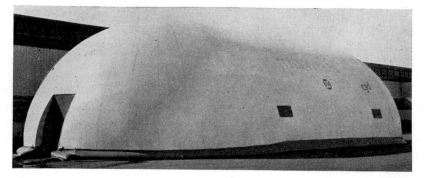

Figure 1.1. This portable warehouse is entirely supported by air. It is made of Fiberthin, a paper-thin tough vinyl-coated nylon fabric produced by the coated fabrics department of U. S. Rubber at Mishawaka, Indiana. The structure is held to the ground by a tube at its base which is filled with water. A small blower keeps up the supporting air pressure, which is low. Passage through the door does not disturb the stability of the structure.

## TABLE 1.2. THE COMMON THERMOPLASTICS
(remeltable)

| Term | Features | Some Trade Names |
|---|---|---|
| Acrylics | crystal-like, warm | Lucite—Du Pont<br>Plexiglas—Rohm & Haas |
| Acetates | tough, hard, easily colored | Lumarith—Celanese<br>Plastacele—Du Pont<br>Vuepak—Monsanto |
| Butyrates | tough, good weatherability | Tenite Butyrate—Eastman |
| Cellulose propionate | no odor, stable, bright finish | Forticel—Celanese |
| Cellulose nitrate | tough, hard surface, inflammable | Nixon C/N—Nixon Nitration<br>Herculoid—Hercules Powder |
| Ethyl cellulose | tough, stands hard treatment | Hercocel E—Hercules Powder<br>Nixon E/C—Nixon Nitration |
| Polyamides (nylon) | strong and extra tough; stands high temperature | Zytel—Du Pont<br>Plaskon—Barrett Division |
| Polyethylene | light weight and squeezable | Poly-eth—Spencer<br>Alathon—Du Pont |
| Polystyrene | brilliant, rigid, colorful | Styron—Dow<br>Lustrex—Monsanto |
| Vinyls | versatile, multi-purpose, colorful | Exon—Firestone<br>Marvinol—Naugatuck |

NOTE: Most materials have many trade names associated with them. Names listed here have been selected arbitrarily and are not to be considered as in any way leading or most common. See Chapter 10, p. 272, for other names.

ing powders. Then there are the producers of cast materials and the formulators of organosols and plastisols, to mention but a few of those who produce the many semi-finished materials of the industry. Many of the unit forms of plastics are described in Chapter 3. Molded forms are difficult to classify because some are intermediate or unfinished whereas many are finished materials which are packaged for the ultimate consumer right at the molders plant.

The last and largest group active in the plastics industry comprises the fabricators, and they are so widely diversified that they can scarcely be called a group.

There are other complications. Some of the producers of molding powder are also molders and many of the molders are also fabricators.

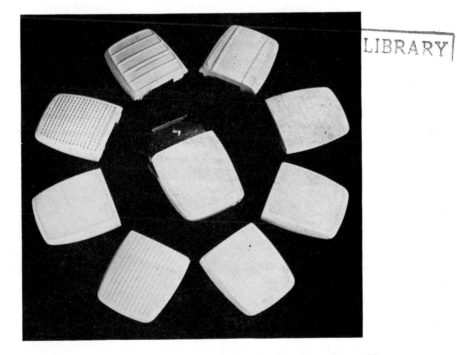

Figure 1.2. Electric razor parts molded of melamine plastics. According to Norman Gray of Schick, Inc., "no other material could give us in one unit a dimensionally accurate chassis on the inside and at the same time a colorful, easy-to-hold handle on the outside." He goes on to say that melamine has proved completely resistant to perspiration, tarnishing, scratching, and the corrosive onslaughts of shaving aids and lotions, in addition to which it possesses the required electrical and mechanical properties. It is produced by transfer molding. Melamine molding compound molds more readily by transfer than urea does.

*(Courtesy Bakelite Co.)*
Figure 1.3. Using polyethylene film for glazing, simple greenhouses like this have been constructed for as little as $50.00.

TABLE 1.3. THE COMMON THERMOSETTING PLASTICS
(non-remeltable)

| Term | Features | Some Trade Names |
|------|----------|------------------|
| Casein | the button plastic, variegated effects | Ameroid—American Plastics Corp., New York, N. Y.<br>Galorn—George Morrel Corp., Muskegon Heights, Mich. |
| Epoxies | coatings, tooling and for reinforced materials | Epon—Shell Chemical<br>C-8 epoxy—Bakelite |
| Melamines | sturdy, hard, rich, durable | Melmac—American Cyanamid<br>Resimene—Monsanto |
| Phenolics | extra stronge, durable, good insulator | Resinox—Monsanto<br>Bakelite Phenolic—Bakelite |
| Polyesters | weather resistant, choice for reinforced material | Laminac—American Cyanamid<br>Vibrin—Naugatuck Chemical |
| Ureas | hard, smooth surfaced, colorful, stable | Beetle—American Cyanamid<br>Plaskon Urea—Barrett Division |

NOTE: The trade names listed here are arbitrary only. For other trade names see the trade name section, p. 272. Epoxies in some forms may be thermoplastic.

No clear line of distinction can be drawn between plastics production and the production of some closely associated materials. Nylon molding powder is a plastic but what about nylon textile fibers? Epoxy resins start as plastics and may end up as coatings or adhesives, and the point where they are no longer plastics has not been defined.

Recently plastics have been claimed to be growing five times as fast as all industry combined. Within ten years the annual production of all plastics materials has jumped from about 1,000,000,000 to close to 4,000,000,000 pounds.

The impressive sales figures given in Chapter 4 which show plastics to be a billion dollar industry do not cover the extensive tool and equipment business which is an essential concomitant. The use of plasticizers for plastics is increasing at a higher rate than that of plastics as a whole.

## The Make-up of the Industry*

Today, a minimum of 5,000 companies in the United States are engaged in some plastics activity. These divide into three categories, which sometimes overlap: (1) the plastics materials manufacturer who produces the basic plastics resins or compounds; (2) the processor who converts plastics into solid or semi-solid form; and (3) the fabricator or finisher who further fashions and decorates the product. Exceptions to the above classifications are many. The company which formulates plastics-type coating materials may be considered part of the plastics industry, although he does not deal with a solid or semi-solid product.

## The Materials Manufacturer

The primary function here is the formulation of a plastic from basic chemicals. The plastic usually is sold in the form of granules, powder, pellets or flake. However, some of the materials manufacturers go a step further and produce sheets, rods, film, and similar materials from the molding compounds. In 1956 The Society of the Plastics Industry listed 103 companies in this group. Of these, 43 companies have been suggested as the leading materials manufacturers of the industry. (These are listed and described in Chapter 8.) Most of them are chemical manufacturing companies. However, some companies purchase the chemicals from which they formulate the resins and compounds; others purchase resins, limiting their work to the formulation of molding compounds.

---

* Prepared in cooperation with The Society of the Plastics Industry.

**The Processor**

Processors of plastics may be divided into six rather distinct classifications:

(1) *Molders* who form end products in molds of the desired shape. These number about 1200.

(2) *Extruder*s who, by means of extruding machines, produce sheets, film, wire covering, special shapes and similar materials. A subgroup (not usually referred to as extruders) produces fibers and monofilaments, as explained in Chapter 3. The conventional extruders number about 250.

(3) *Film and sheet makers*. These are considered here as a separate group, although some are included under extruders. This group includes those who make sheets and film either by casting or calendering or by extruding. There are about 60 companies in this group.

(4) *High-pressure laminators*. This group, comprising about 50 companies, forms sheets, rods and tubes from paper, cloth, wood, and other materials, by impregnating the materials with liquid resins and producing the end products by means of heat and high pressure.

(5) *Reinforced plastics manufacturers* who combine liquid resins with such materials as glass fibers, cloth, sisal and hemp fibers, and even such materials as wood flour, to form the final desired shapes by low pressure means. There are about 120 companies in this group.

(6) *Coaters,* numbering about 80, who make use of spread coating, dipping or calendering to coat fabric and paper with plastics.

TABLE 1.4. DEFINITIONS OF SOME PLASTICS TERMS

| | |
|---|---|
| *Accelerator* | a substance which speeds up reactions either in polymerizing of resins or vulcanization of rubbers. |
| *A-Stage resin* | a thermosetting resin before it is cured or made into molding powder. |
| *Autioxidant* | any of a class of compounds added to other substances to retard oxidation. |
| *Binder* | the resin in a molding composition is known as a binder. It holds together fillers and other ingredients. |
| *Bleeding* | diffusion of color out of plastic part into surrounding surface or part. |
| *Blow molding* | shaping thermoplastic materials into hollow form by air pressure and heat. Usually performed on sheets or tubes. |
| *B-Stage resin* | intermediate stage between A-Stage and C-Stage. Phenolic molding powders are usually in B-Stage. |

| | |
|---|---|
| *Bulk factor* | ratio of the volume of a molding powder to that of articles produced therefrom. |
| *Calendering* | producing film or sheeting between rotating hot rolls. |
| *Catalyst* | a substance which changes the rate of a chemical reaction without itself undergoing permanent change in its composition. |
| *Cold flow* | permanent change in dimension of a plastic under stress without heat. |
| *Cold-molded plastics* | bituminous or inorganic materials molded at high pressure and room temperature and cured by baking afterwards. |
| *Creep* | synonymous with cold flow. |
| *C-Stage* | final stage in the reactions of a thermosetting resin. A fully cured stage. |
| *Cure* | changing physical properties of a material by chemical reaction —usually to a harder or more permanent form. Sometimes synonymous with set. |
| *Dielectric strength* | maximum voltage a plastic material can resist. Test usually is on ⅛ in. thick sheet. Result is expressed in volts per mil. |
| *Estron* | acetate rayon. |
| *Extenders* | low cost materials used to dilute or extend high cost resins without much lessening of properties. |
| *Hobbing* | forming a mold cavity by pressing a hard steel master model into a soft steel blank, which is then hardened and polished. |
| *Inhibitor* | a substance that slows down chemical reaction—often used to prolong shelf or storage life. |
| *Jet molding* | this and other types of molding are described in Chapter 6. |
| *Latex* | water suspension of fine particles of rubber or rubber-like plastics. |
| *Monofilament* | a single fiber or filament of indefinite length generally produced by extrusion. |
| *Organosol* | finely divided or colloidal dispersion of a resin in a plasticizer, with solvents or other materials. See Plastisol. |
| *Paste resins* | another term for organosols. |
| *Plasticizers* | materials added to a plastic to improve flexibility or to facilitate compounding. |
| *Plastisols* | colloidal dispersion of a resin in a plasticizer without solvent. |
| *Post forming* | phenolic laminates and some other thermosetting sheet materials may be formed into simple shapes by heat and pressure after initial care. |
| *Preform* | a compressed tablet of molding powder to facilitate handling and weighing in the molding operation. |
| *Slush molding* | forming hollow shapes by pouring resin into female mold, allowing to form a shell and then pouring out excess. |
| *Sprue* | material left in orifice between entrance and mold parting line in molding. Most common in injection molding. |

### The Fabricator and Finisher

Because of an overlapping of both activity and of terminology no clear cut division actually exists here. This group includes the miscellaneous companies which, for the most part, take the films, sheets, tubes and rods produced by those known as processors and makes them into finished products. Examples include manufacturers of shower curtains (film), luggage (sheets), flash lights (tubes), and towel racks (rods). Fabricators often do their own casting from molding powders and finishers often take complete moldings from an earlier processor. A division under the heading "finisher" might read "decorator," and still be considered as part of the plastics industry. Some printers working with films, sheets, and other plastics materials fall into this classification, and closely associated with them are the embossers, who produce a textured pattern on a plastic surface (e.g., luncheon mats). While this classification is poorly defined The Society of The Plastics Industry lists about 1500 companies working on rigid plastics sheets and another 1500 engaged in finishing film and non-rigid sheeting.

### The Chemical Companies

Most of the primary producers are large chemical companies whose plastics production is actually a relatively small part of their total business. Of the ten leading plastics materials producers only one has plastics sales representing as much as 32 per cent of its total sales. The average proportion of plastics sales to total sales among this group is 17 per cent,

TABLE 1.5. PRODUCTION PER MONTH, MAY 56*

The eight most used plastics (other than coatings)
— in pounds —

| | |
|---|---|
| Vinyls | 64,000,000 |
| Polystyrene | 58,000,000 |
| Polyethylene | 47,000,000 |
| Phenolics | 44,000,000 |
| Ureas and melamines | 27,000,000 |
| Coumarone—indene and petroleum polymer resins | 21,000,000 |
| Cellulosics | 12,000,000 |
| Polyesters | 7,000,000 |

* For more recent figures see Chapter 4.

and the group's annual sales of *all* products (including non-plastics) come to a little more than 7 billion dollars which, at 17 per cent, means that the plastics sales total about 1.19 billion dollars, or about half of the country's total plastics sales. More about the material producing companies will be found in Chapter 8 and more about their production of plastics will be found in Chapter 4.

## Identification of Plastics

Except for a few of the more common types, it is difficult to identify plastics by any simple tests. A person with a good sense of smell and some knowledge of chemical odors can identify any of several plastics by holding a match to them. Some precaution should be used, however, because cellulose nitrate is almost explosive when dry and in thin sections. An electric soldering iron is a good tool to use for identification. Before it gets red hot, press it against the unknown sample. If it sinks in, the sample is thermoplastic; if not, it is thermosetting. This locates the sample as belonging to one of the groups shown in Tables 1.2 and 1.3—as being either thermoplastic or thermosetting.

A more extensive examination can be made with a bunsen burner. If the sample won't burn (after 10 seconds at edge of flame) it is a vinyl or a fluorocarbon if it was found to be thermoplastic and probably a urea, a melamine, or a phenolic if it was thermosetting. A fishlike odor is indicative of melamine and a phenol odor is of course a phenolic. The absence of either odor should indicate a urea. If the sample burns with a blue flame that dies after removal, a polyamide is indicated. However, if the dying flame is yellow it may indicate any of the following: a casein if the odor is of burning milk, and the material was thermosetting; a vinyl, if the odor is acrid, for a thermoplastic. If there is an acetic acid odor a flame-resistant type of cellulose acetate is indicated.

If the sample had a dying flame and was found to be thermosetting, it probably was a laminated phenolic. In this case, in addition to the characteristic phenol odor, it would have an odor of burning cellulose or of some other filler material. If the sample continued to burn after removal from the flame and was found to be thermosetting, an allyl is indicated.

The search has now been narrowed to perhaps six thermoplastic materials, but these are the hardest to identify accurately. An odor of burnt sugar points to ethyl cellulose; an odor of rancid butter means a butyrate. A yellow flame and an acetic odor indicate a standard type of cellulose acetate or of vinyl acetate. The vinyl acetate has a darker smoke. An odor of illuminating gas indicates polystyrene.

# 2. PROPERTIES OF THE COMMERCIAL PLASTICS

From a total of perhaps fifty plastics types, thirty of the best known have been selected for descriptions in this chapter. In addition, two borderline materials—cellophane and cold-molded—have been included. It is thought that the ones selected cover at least 97 per cent of the present commercial activity in plastics. Other information about these materials not included here and about materials now in research laboratories and perhaps of future importance, will be found in Chapter 9.

The following materials will be described here:

1. Acetates
2. Acrylics
3. Alkyds
4. Allyls
5. Butyrates
6. Casein
7. Cellophane
8. Cellulose nitrate
9. Cellulose propionate
10. Cold-molded
11. Coumarone-indene
12. Ethyl cellulose
13. Epoxies
14. Fluorocarbons
15. Furans
16. Melamines
17. Phenolics
18. Polyamides
19. Polyesters, also citrate polyesters
20. Polyethylene
21. Polystyrene
22. Polyurethanes
23. Polyvinyl acetal
24. Polyvinyl acetate
25. Polyvinyl alcohol
26. Polyvinyl butyral
27. Polyvinyl carbazole
28. Polyvinyl chloride
29. Polyvinyl chloride-vinyl acetate
30. Polyvinylidene chloride
31. Silicones
32. Ureas

## Property Tables

Nearly every plastic type can be produced in a variety of forms, each with differing properties. Often such properties are represented by a spread, for example, molded polyethylene may have its value for mold shrinkage represented as 0.02 to 0.05 in. per in. However, the property tables in this book usually show average values. Thus in the case just cited 0.03 might be given because it is felt that the lower value is more typical of general conditions. The primary purpose of the tables is to give the reader a basis for comparing the different types of materials as well as a general idea of their properties. In most cases the tables are based on producers' charts. Where these show several compositions of one type, as for instance Du Pont's No. 31, 63 and 101 molded nylon, the tables in this book give the composition thought to be most representative of the type as a whole. For more specific properties and for actual specifications, readers are referred to the material manufacturers.

### Acetates (Cellulose Acetate)*

These are versatile, light, stable and low-priced thermoplastic materials noted for their toughness and ease of molding. They are relatively non-flammable and for this reason have replaced cellulose nitrate in many applications, the most notable perhaps being that of photographic film. Movie film, for instance, used to be made of cellulose nitrate; today almost all of it is made of cellulose acetate. The material can be produced clear and thus has competed with the more brilliant but higher priced acrylics for such items as brush backs.

The acetates, of course, have some drawbacks. They are subject to dimensional change due to cold flow, heat, or moisture absorption. They soften at about 176°F and melt at about 500°F. Their specific gravity has an average value of 1.30.

Cellulose acetate is manufactured from cellulose in the form of purified cotton linters or wood pulp as follows:

The cellulose is charged into a Werner-Pfleiderer type stainless steel mixer containing 2.4 parts of acetic acid, and the mixture is stirred for about an hour at 100°F. Four parts of acetic acid and 0.88% sulfuric acid, based on the weight of the cellulose, are added, and the mixture is cooled to 65°F after 45 minutes. After the addition of 2.7 parts of 98% acetic anhydride, the cooling is continued to 60°F. Then 6.12% sulfuric acid, based on the weight of the cellulose, is added, diluted with an equal weight of acetic acid. The temperature is allowed to rise gradually to 95°F over a 2-hour period, at which time the reaction mixture has changed to a viscous dope essentially free from fibers. A mixture of one part of water and two parts of acetic acid is then slowly added while thoroughly

* Prepared in cooperation with James A. Mitchell, and B. P. Rouse, Jr., Tennessee Eastman Company, Division of Eastman Kodak Company, Kingsport, Tennessee.

mixing. This stops the acetylation. If the dope is precipitated at this time, cellulose triacetate is obtained. In most cases, the dope is held in a vessel at 100°F, during which time the cellulose ester hydrolyzes, producing a product with improved solubility properties. This hydrolyzed material is termed "secondary cellulose acetate." At the desired degree of hydrolysis, the dope is precipitated by vigorously mixing it with weak acetic acid. The precipitated cellulose acetate is separated from the weak acid and washed until it is free from traces of uncombined acid. The material is stabilized, centrifuged, or pressed to reduce the water content, and then dried in a moving-belt dryer.

Cellulose acetate of 38 to 40 per cent acetyl content is used in the manufacture of plastics and yarn. Higher acetyl materials, 39 to 42 per cent, are used for film base and for some plastic purposes. Cellulose tri-

Figure 2.1. Acetate sheets are produced by pressing the mixed and plastic material into blocks as it is taken from the rolls. Heated presses such as shown here are used. The blocks are then sliced into sheets of the desired thickness.

acetate, 43 to 44.7 per cent, is used in high quality film bases and in tri-acetate yarns. Cellulose triacetate is not soluble in common solvents such as acetone and cannot be plasticized with the usual plasticizers. It has a higher melting point and is less moisture absorbent.

Cellulose mixed esters are reaction products of both acetic and propionic or butyric acids. Cellulose acetate propionate and cellulose acetate butyrate have a better solubility and a wider range of compatibility with plasticizers than cellulose acetate, which gives them considerable advantage in lacquer formulas and in plastic compositions. They have a much lower moisture absorption than cellulose acetate and are much less affected by moisture.

Cellulose acetate butyrate is the base of the butyrate-type plastics (Tenite Butyrate). It is also used in hot-melt coating applications. A low viscosity acetate butyrate has been especially successful in lacquer and hot-melt applications and has been termed "Half-Second Butyrate." This material is finding use in many cases where improvement over "Half-Second Nitrate" is desired.

Cellulose acetate propionate, cellulose acetate butyrate, and cellulose propionate are made by methods similar to those used in making cellulose acetate, except that propionic and butyric acids and anhydrides are substituted for acetic acid and anhydride. Low viscosity materials such as "Half-Second Butyrate" are made at higher temperatures than materials of normal viscosity. The reaction may be continued until the viscosity is lowered to the desired degree. For more on butyrates see under "Butyrates."

Acetate fibers are produced by forcing an acetone solution of cellulose acetate through orifices of a spinneret into a stream of warm air, which evaporates the solvent. The fiber thus formed can then be handled on conventional winding equipment.

**Color Range of Cellulose Acetate.** Throughout the years the basic color of cellulose acetate plastics has been improved by the manufacturers and at the present time brilliant, water-clear transparent materials are available for many applications. A wide variety of colors can be obtained in any degree of translucency or opacity. The coloring agents commonly used are reasonably stable to elevated temperatures for processing and molding, but since the plasticizers added are not as high boiling as those used for cellulose acetate butyrate or as inherently stable and resistant to ultra-violet exposure or oxidation, limited exposure to outdoor weathering is recommended. Many unusual color effects are possible with cellulose acetate compositions. Blends of two or more colors in predetermined amounts can be made to give various effects.

**Physical Properties of the Acetates.** Cellulose acetate molding compositions are noted for their toughness, high impact strength, and ease of fabrication. Their resistance to impact is usually much greater than that of most noncellulosic plastics. Their limited resistance to cold flow and dimensional changes must be considered and sufficient allowance must be made in the finished item. Fluctuations in dimensions due to thermal expansion and the effect of humidity can often be neglected when the entire item is to be fabricated of the same material. Care must be taken in combining cellulose acetate plastics with other materials such as glass, metal, thermosetting plastics or other thermosplastics to prevent the development of strains due to differences in thermal expansion or to prevent the migration of plasticizer which may have adverse effects on either the bond between the two unlike materials or cause crazing of the surface of the other plastic. Cellulose acetate molding compounds are recommended for applications involving relatively low loads, in which some small changes of dimensions on aging can be tolerated. The wide range of physical properties which may be had in commercially available cellulose molding materials is shown in Table 2.1 and other tables. See Table 2.1 for properties of the acetates.

**Acrylic Resins**

In 1936 the Rohm and Haas Co. of Philadelphia introduced transparent rigid sheeting of methyl methacrylate resin which it called Plexiglas and about this same time E. I. du Pont de Nemours & Company of Wilmington introduced a similar material in the form of sheets, rods, tubes, and molding powder, which it called Lucite. Since then Rohm and Haas has brought out a methyl methacrylate molding powder which, like the sheeting, is called Plexiglas. These two companies have continued to be the principal producers of methyl methacrylate, and thus the two trade names Plexiglas and Lucite have come to be representative of this interesting glass-like material with its unique optical properties. It is unfortunate that there isn't one simple generic name which could be used to replace the awkward term, methyl methacrylate. However since there isn't such a generic term the broader term "acrylic" is often used, and, rather loosely, other terms such as acrylates and methacrylates.

Methyl and ethyl esters are the best known starting materials in the production of acrylics. These colorless materials polymerize readily in the presence of light, heat, or catalysts such as benzoyl peroxide. An inhibitor must be used for storing and shipping to prevent spontaneous and explosive polymerization. In addition to the clarity and unusual optical properties the acrylics have low specific gravity, low water absorption, high dielectric strength, and good shock resistance.

Typical uses include hairbrush backs, display fixtures, airplane windows, contact lenses, dentures, signs, instrument panels, and protective coatings.

Care should be taken to keep the standard commercial acrylic sheets below 190°F although some grades will withstand boiling water. The sheets scratch more easily than glass. The visibility of small scratches may be reduced with wax polishing compounds. Abrasive cleaners must be avoided.

Figure 2.2. Airfield landing light covers are being formed from acrylic sheets. The heated sheets are placed over the lower form and the plunger is then pressed slowly down to a snug fit. The sheets are not too hot for the operator to handle with gloves.

Materials which might be confused with the acrylics are the cast allyls and polystyrene, and so for convenience the physical properties of the three resins—acrylics, polystyrenes and allyls—are presented for comparison in Table 2.1.

Trade names for acrylics include the following: Lucite—Du Pont; Plexiglas—Rohm & Haas Co.; Fiberfil—Fiberfil Corp.; and Gering MMRW—Gering Products, Inc.

Acrylic molding powder is available for injection and compression molding and for extrusion. Molded articles shrink slightly on cooling (0.003 to 0.005 in. per in.) but due to the absence of residual solvents

applications to include almost every conceivable decorative and protective finish. A special type is available for use in flat and semi-gloss wall enamels. Used with alkylated urea resins, they find wide application in white and colored porcelain-like enamels for refrigerators, kitchen appliances, hospital equipment, etc.

One large and important use of alkyd-base enamels is in finishes for automobiles. A new-car finish usually contains an alkylated melamine resin as well as an alkyd resin. The enamel is cured by oven-baking at temperatures ranging from 180 to 300°F. The melamine component gives a fast cure and develops a hard, durable, and mar-resistant finish. Auto refinishing enamels are usually air-dry alkyd resin enamels.

A use for one type of alkyd resin which is increasing rapidly is in the production of fast-curing molding compounds mainly for industrial parts and electrical components.

Non-drying alkyds are used as modifiers in nitrocellulose lacquers to promote adhesion and flexibility and to improve exterior durability. Non-drying alkyd resins are sometimes used with melamine resins for heat-resistant white enamels.

Alkyd resins can be dispersed in water to form emulsions from which water paints are formulated. Compared with solvent paints or enamels, alkyd emulsion paints have these advantages: easier application, relative freedom from odor, no fire or health hazards from solvents, much faster drying, and less dirt collection. Compared with latex-base water paints, they usually give better coverage and a flatter finish.

**Alkyd Molding Compounds\*** When suitable polyester resins (alkyds), capable of cross-linking, are properly compounded with fillers, pigments, and catalysts, thermosetting molding compounds result that have rather unique properties. They are fast curing and may be made to flow around delicate inserts in intricate shapes. Fast closing presses are required and, depending upon the thickness of the part, cure times of 10 to 50 sec. are possible. Molding temperatures are usually in the range of 300 to 315°F, with molding pressures varying from 800 to 1500 psi.

Moldings exhibit excellent dimensional stability and electrical characteristics. Their arc resistance and elevated temperature service (up to 400°F) are of particular interest. Moisture and solvent resistances are good.

The molding compounds may be filled with a mineral filler or reinforced with fibrous glass. The mineral-filled products are available in

---

\* This section by W. O. Erickson and V. W. Ginsler of Barrett Division, Allied Chemical & Dye Corp. is included here by courtesy of Modern Plastics Encyclopedia Issue, 1956. It contains some duplication with the preceding article but is included for its additional information.

both putty and granular forms. The putty form is particularly useful in encapsulating small electrical resistors and capacitors. The granular types are free-flowing and adaptable to automatic molding operations. Numerous electronic components, such as tuner boards, tube bases, and connectors, are in production. The granular types are also finding their way into automotive ignition applications.

The fibrous glass-reinforced materials are usually in mat form and are characterized by their high strength. These materials have found widespread use in applications where a combination of high strength and good electrical properties is important. Thus, these materials are used in such applications as insulating brackets and bases, rocker rings, circuit breaker cases, and coil forms.

The alkyd compounds are more reactive by nature than other thermosets and therefore more sensitive to handling and storage conditions.

TABLE 2.2.  PROPERTIES OF A TYPICAL ALKYD MOLDING COMPOUND

(Average Values)

| Properties | Alkyds |
|---|---|
| Specific gravity | 2.22-2.24 |
| Tensile strength, psi | 3000-4000 |
| Compressive strength, psi | 16000-20000 |
| Continuous heat resistance, °F | 300-350 |
| Heat distortion temperature, 264 psi, °F | 350-400 |
| Dielectric strength, step-by-step, v. per mil | 300-350 |
| Machining qualities | good |
| Effect of sunlight | — |
| Per cent water absorption, 24 hr. | 0.08-0.10 |
| Resistance to strong acids | poor |
| Resistance to weak acids | good |
| Resistance to strong alkalies | poor |
| Resistance to weak alkalies | fair |
| Clarity | opaque |

## Allyl Resins

These form a class of polyester resins of which allyl diglycol carbonate, usually referred to as an allyl, is the best known. It is a colorless organic monomeric liquid of low viscosity and low volatility. When a catalyst such as benzoyl peroxide is dissolved in the monomer and heat is applied, the liquid gradually thickens to form a soft gel. With further heating this gel hardens into an insoluble, infusible, clear, colorless solid. The plastic therefore falls in the thermosetting group. One of its leading applications is optically clear sheets. Its properties in sheet form include clarity, low color, high abrasion resistance and solvent and temperature resistance.

A typical sheet material, known as allymer CR-39, has a surface comparable to polished plate glass in luster, smoothness, and chemical resistance. It is superior to plate glass in impact resistance and has but half the weight of glass. Its optical clarity makes it useful as photographic filters. It has less than 50 mils distortion at 265°F. Acrylics generally are fluid at that temperature. The burning rate of the allyls is about one-quarter that of cast acrylic. The abrasion resistance is much greater than that of methyl methacrylate.

### Butyrate (Cellulose Acetate Butyrate)*

By reacting purified cellulose with acetic and butyric anhydrides in the presence of sulfuric acid as catalyst and glacial acetic acid as solvent, an interesting thermoplastic material is produced. It has exceptional toughness, good impact strength, and is lighter in weight than cellulose acetate. Other properties include low heat conductivity, high dielectric strength, and good outdoor weathering and aging. Because of the latter it is used for gunstocks and fishermen's floats and tackle. Other applications include automobile tail-light lenses and wallboard molding. The latter is interesting because the material lends itself readily to dry extrusion which permits production in any length. Retaining strips for wallboard may even be nailed in cold weather without splitting, which is a big asset in the building trade.

The ratio of acetic and butyric components may be varied considerably to produce a flexibility ranging from hard to soft, and even to liquids. The latter are used for photographic film, lacquers, protective coating solutions, and protective strip coatings.

A proprietary butyrate known as Tenite Butyrate has about 13 per cent acetyl and 37 per cent butyryl. It has lower water absorption than cellulose acetate and better compatibility with water-resistant and non-volatile plasticizers.

**Plasticizers for the Butyrates.** Formulating or plasticizing cellulose acetate butyrate powder prior to marketing it as a molding powder is a

---

* Prepared in cooperation with B. P. Rouse, Jr., Tennessee Eastman Company, Division of Eastman Kodak Company, Kingsport, Tennessee.

simple process, since a variety of plasticizers of excellent compatibility has been developed for use with this material. Many of these plasticizers act as solvents for the cellulose ester and become an integral part of the plastic composition. As a result, the more compatible plasticizers have little or no tendency to exude, bleed, or evaporate under extreme service conditions. Plasticizers of the less volatile types, such as the butyl and higher phthalate esters and esters of adipic, azelaic, and sebacic acids produce butyrate plastics having superior dimensional stability, exceptional toughness, and good impact strength.

A noncompatible type plasticizer may be used to produce plastics which are suitable for a large number of applications. These are generally used in larger quantities and give plastics of a higher impact strength but lower surface hardness. In many cases the dimensional stability of such plastics is adequate.

The plasticizers are added to the cellulose acetate butyrate powder in carefully controlled amounts, usually by a mixing process under regulated heat and pressure for varying periods of time. Although solvent processes can be used they are not common for compounding this type of cellulosic plastic.

**Color Range of the Butyrates.** In recent years the basic color of butyrate plastics has been improved to the extent that brilliant, water-clear transparent materials are available for many applications. In general, these materials can be colored to any shade, any translucency, or any opacity. Colors are reasonably stable when subjected to elevated temperatures, ultraviolet light, or infrared rays. By the incorporation of ultraviolet light inhibitors greatly improved color and physical properties have been achieved. It should be pointed out that all colors are not equally stable. Some red dyes and pigments, for example, withstand the direct rays of the sun with less color change than others. Greens and blues must be pretested carefully before they are used in colored plastic compositions. It is customary for the manufacturer to carry on a broad testing program which includes accelerated testing in the laboratories as well as extensive outdoor testing in various localities.

The search for more stable coloring dyes and pigments never ceases. Suppliers of dyes and pigments, as well as manufacturers of plastics, are constantly trying to secure additional information on color fastness, heat resistance, weathering, and other color properties by making accelerated tests, such as the Weather-Ometer and Fade-Ometer, and by conducting outdoor tests at various testing stations throughout the country under a variety of climatic conditions. This wealth of information should be examined in cases where an article is to be subjected to unusual conditions, as such precautions can save irreparable mistakes. The best tests, of course, are conducted under actual conditions, although accelerated tests may reveal outstanding weaknesses.

Almost any special color effects—mottles, pearls, metallics, or tinsels —are obtainable and by blending two or more colors in predetermined proportions, walnut, ebony, satinwood, mahogany, tortoise shell, and marble effects can be obtained. The combinations are limited only by the scope of imagination. The variegations can be controlled by varying the flow differential of the components of the formulation.

**Physical Properties of the Butyrates.** Cellulose acetate butyrate plastics have superior dimensional stability and lower water absorption as compared with cellulose acetate plastics. Their toughness (as shown by their excellent resistance to impact) and other mechanical strength properties permit them to be used in a wide variety of applications. The lower specific gravity of the butyrate plastics, approximately 1.2 as compared with 1.3 for the cellulose acetate plastics, permits more moldings per pound of plastic. An indication of the range of physical properties which can be obtained in this material is given in Table 2.3.

Although cellulose acetate butyrate plastics cost more per pound than cellulose acetate, their lighter weight, toughness, dimensional stability, and ease of molding frequently overshadow the original cost and influence the molder in choosing them for many applications.

**Butyrate Lacquers.** Cellulose acetate butyrate has long been familiar to the lacquer trade in several different types. With the proper selection of solvents some of these can be used as the base for a novel coating material known as "gel dipping lacquer." This lacquer has the unique properties of being fairly mobile at temperatures above 120°F and of setting rapidly to a clear firm gel when cooled at ordinary room temperature (70 to 75°F). This permits the application of relatively thick coatings (up to .010 inch of dried lacquer) without wrinkling or running. The surface properties and appearance of the resulting coating are comparable to articles molded from cellulose acetate butyrate molding compositions. The properties of the coating can be varied considerably by changing the type and amount of plasticizer in the formulation.

Coating compositions can be made from low-viscosity high-butyryl content cellulose acetate butyrate by the proper incorporation of plasticizers. Such combinations usually include plasticizers, resins, and waxes which have a resulting solid-liquid transition at 230 to 250°F and achieve a coatable viscosity of 2,000 to 100,000 centipoises at 320°F. Upon cooling the melt solidifies into a relatively hard non-tacky transparent and flexible solid. Such compositions can be used for a variety of protective coatings.

A new product for the coating industry known as "Half-Second

Butyrate" is now being marketed. This is a low-viscosity type product which will permit concentrations of spray viscosities of 20 per cent solids. Half-Second Butyrate produces solutions of high clarity and excellent shelf-stability. Films of high strength and excellent flexibility can be obtained from formulations containing it. Formulations using Half-Second Butyrate have been tested for use in paper lacquers, heat-sealing adhesives, plastic lacquers, wood lacquers, metal lacquers, and melt coatings for both cloth and paper. Good adhesion, high resistance to water spotting, and remarkable stability to ultraviolet light are among the properties which permit its use in such a wide variety of applications.

TABLE 2.3. PHYSICAL PROPERTIES OF BUTYRATES

(Cellulose Acetate Butyrate)

(Average Values)

| Properties | Cellulose Acetate Butyrate |
|---|---|
| Specific gravity | 1.20 |
| Tensile strength, psi | 5000 |
| Compressive strength, psi | 4000 |
| Continuous heat resistance, °F | 190 |
| Heat distortion temperature, °F | 160 |
| Dielectric strength, v. per mil | 325 |
| Machining qualities | good |
| Effect of sunlight | slight |
| Per cent water absorption, 24 hr. | 1.4 |
| Resistance to strong acids | poor |
| Resistance to weak acids | good |
| Resistance to strong alkalies | poor |
| Resistance to weak alkalies | fair |
| Clarity | transparent to opaque |

## Casein Plastics*

Casein plastics are prepared from the protein of milk. Skim milk is treated with rennin which coagulates the protein. The coagulant is then dried and the resultant material is casein.

---

* Prepared in cooperation with American Plastics Corporation.

Casein particles may be transformed into a homogeneous plastic mass by adding moisture and applying heat and pressure. This is accomplished in an extruding machine. The extruded plastic is treated with formaldehyde and acquires horn-like properties.

The casein industry originated in Germany about 1910, in England during World War I, and later in America. Originally, only sheets and rods were produced. Its major use then, as today, was for the manufacture of buttons. Considerable time was lost until the plastic was cured by formaldehyde after extrusion. However, both time and material were saved by slicing the rod to the desired diameter and thickness as it was extruded. The curing then takes but a fraction of the time required for a full rod.

The cured plastic will burn, but will not support combustion. It is cream-colored and slightly opaque. It can be prepared transparent or in an unlimited number of opaque, translucent, or transparent colors. Mottled effects with two or more colors, irridescent effects with metal powders, or synthetic pearl are standard procedure.

TABLE 2.4. PHYSICAL PROPERTIES OF CASEIN

(Average Values)

| Properties | Casein |
| --- | --- |
| Specific gravity | 1.35 |
| Tensile strength, psi | 7600 |
| Compressive strength, psi | high |
| Continuous heat resistance, °F | 180 |
| Heat distortion temperature, °F | 200 |
| Dielectric strength, v. per mil* | 400* |
| Machining qualities | — |
| Effect of sunlight | colors fade |
| Per cent water absorption, 24 hr. | 10 or more |
| Resistance to strong acids | poor |
| Resistance to weak acids | good |
| Resistance to strong alkalies | poor |
| Resistance to weak alkalies | poor |
| Clarity | translucent or opaque |

* This is for dry material and has little significance as material takes up atmospheric moisture and is seldom dry.

Some typical uses for casein plastics include, besides buttons, buckles, slides, knitting needles, various fancy goods, knife handles, pens, pencils, etc. However, almost the entire output is consumed by the button industry.

The cured plastic is easily machined; it may be sawed, turned, sanded, drilled and ground. Polishing is accomplished in several ways, but is generally done chemically. The completely finished plastic is placed in hot sodium hypochlorite solution for several minutes, removed, and dried. A high glossy finish is obtained. Polished pieces may be dyed by placing them in a hot bath using acid dyes, but as the dye penetrates the surface to a very slight depth, no mechanical polishing should be attempted after the operation.

Casein is not resistant to water, and a sample immersed in it will gain weight and increase in volume. Electrically, dry casein plastic is a good insulator, but upon exposure to damp air it absorbs water which breaks down its insulating properties.

## Cellophane*

While cellophane is not a true plastic it is a close borderline material and should be mentioned briefly. It is made by treating highly purified cellulose with sodium hydroxide. The result is alkali cellulose. By adding carbon bisulfide this is changed to cellulose zanthate, which is thinned, filtered and allowed to stand in tanks to rid it of entrapped air bubbles. It is then ready to be formed into film. This may be done by depositing a thin coating on a fabric belt which carries the coating or film into a bath of ammonium sulfate where it is coagulated and hardened. After washing and some further treatment the regenerated cellulose emerges as a clear, transparent, and self-sustaining film or sheet which if dried would be brittle. To overcome this it is passed through a glycerol bath of which it absorbs about 7 per cent to gain flexibility. Finally, it is treated with plasticizers, resins, and waxes to become the well known commercial cellophane which is used as a protective wrapping material. It may be coated with an appropriate lacquer to make it moisture-proof or heat-sealable. Because of its low cost and wide range of properties it is the most widely used film today.

## Cellulose Nitrate

This member of the cellulosic family, also known as nitrocellulose or pyroxylin, is not generally molded. It cannot be injection molded because of its sensitivity to high temperature and in compression molding its easy

---

* This section prepared in cooperation with Boonton Molding Company.

plasticity under heat makes it necessary to chill the mold before removing the article. As a result of this the plastic is usually formed in blocks from which sheets are sliced. The blocks are formed by mixing cellulose nitrate in a dough mixer with camphor and alcohol and then heating and pressing the resultant jelly-like mass into solid blocks, or the mass may be extruded into rods and tubes. When the nitrogen content is reduced to about 11 per cent the material becomes soluble in an ether-alcohol mixture and may then be used in preparing Celluloid.

Cellulose nitrate is one of the cheapest plastics but its use is curtailed by its flammability. It is used for fountain pens, optical frames, drawing instruments, and tool handles. (See Chapter 4 for other uses.)

TABLE 2.5. PHYSICAL PROPERTIES OF CELLULOSE NITRATE
(Average Values)

| Properties | Cellulose Nitrate |
|---|---|
| Specific gravity | 1.37 |
| Tensile strength, psi | 7500 |
| Compressive strength, psi | 25000 |
| Continuous heat resistance, °F | 125 |
| Heat distortion temperature, °F | 145 |
| Dielectric strength, v. per mil | 450 |
| Machining qualities | excellent |
| Effect of sunlight | gets brittle, discolors |
| Per cent absorption, 24 hr. | 1.5 |
| Resistance to strong acids | poor |
| Resistance to weak acids | fair |
| Resistance to strong alkalies | poor |
| Resistance to weak alkalies | good |
| Clarity | transparent to opaque |

## Cellulose Propionate

This thermoplastic, the newest member of the cellulosic family, is classified chemically as an ester together with cellulose acetate and cellulose acetate butyrate. Similar in type to these materials, the flake is plasticized and will readily accept dyes and pigments to produce a complete range of colors.

As opposed to cellulose acetate butyrate, a mixed ester, cellulose propionate is a straight ester and as such, has slightly different physical properties and flow characteristics. It has very good impact strength and dimensional stability and is free of objectionable odor, but its over-all importance is its excellent balance of properties. It molds readily into intricate sections and the parts are characterized by freedom from welds and flow marks and a lustrous finish.

(Courtesy Celanese Corp. of America)

Figure 2.3. Construction of automobile arm rests molded of cellulose propionate. They have so lustrous a finish just as they come from the mold that they require no further buffing.

Cellulose propionate generally has the chemical properties of cellulosics with good resistance to hydrocarbons and mineral oils; it is noteworthy for its excellent ink resistance.

As might be expected, its principal applications fall into the industrial field for such parts as telephones, appliance housings, automotive arm rests, knobs, pens and pencils, football and crash helmets, business machine keys, radio cabinets, etc. The only presently available propionate is called Forticel; it is produced by Celanese Corporation of America. It is more stable than straight acetate, has no odor, weathers well, and is noted for its sparkling finish.

TABLE 2.6. TYPICAL PHYSICAL PROPERTIES OF FORTICEL

(Cellulose Propionate)

| | |
|---|---|
| Flow temperature, °F | 325-350 |
| Specific gravity | 1.18-1.21 |
| Tensile properties | |
| Yield, psi | 3380-5020 |
| Break, psi | 3470-5240 |
| Elongation, % | 56-66 |
| Flexural properties | |
| Flexural strength, psi at break | 6400-8500 |
| Rockwell hardness, R scale | 62-94 |
| Heat distortion, °F | 138-158 |
| Water absorption | |
| % Moisture gain | 1.5-1.8 |
| % Water absorption | 1.6-1.8 |

## Cold-Molded Compounds*

An interesting and important group of borderline plastics materials are known as cold-molded compounds because they are molded cold and baked after removal from the molds. These materials can be grouped in three classes: those using bitumen binders, those using cement binders, and those using resin binders. The most widely used are the bitumen binders consisting of asphalt or gilsonite, drying oils, dryer, coloring matter, and occasionally a small percentage of natural gums combined with asbestos fiber, with the latter about 80 per cent of the resulting compound.

The impact and tensile strength are about half those of phenolic materials and the cost of material and dies is considerably less than for hot-molded phenolics. When strength is required and weight and volume are not important, cross-sections can be increased considerably and costs still kept low.

The use of Portland cement as a binder gives pieces capable of withstanding temperatures as high as 1,000 to 2,000° F. These are used as

---

* Prepared in cooperation with Boonton Molding Company.

bases for electric heating coils in stoves. The cement binder parts are moisture absorbing to a large degree, ranging from 2 to 16 per cent. Phenolic binders can be mixed cold in liquid form with the fillers and preformed cold. They are then baked in ovens and cured. The lack of pressure during the curing operation reduces the strength of the finished article below the standard phenolic resin material, although it is much stronger than the asphalt binder.

In brief, the three types can be characterized as follows:

*Bitumen binders:* Least expensive; used principally in parts requiring a high degree of plastic flow in molding.

*Cement binders:* Good physical strength; high heat and arc resistance when suitably treated. Cost relatively high.

*Resin binders:* Physically stronger but not as heat resisting as bitumen binders.

TABLE 2.7. PROPERTIES OF COLD-MOLDED COMPOUNDS

|  | Organic | Inorganic |
|---|---|---|
| Specific gravity | 1.87-2.15 | 1.80-1.90 |
| Compressive strength, psi | 6,000-15,000 | 16,000 |
| Flexural strength, psi | 3,700-9,300 | 2,000-5,000 |
| Impact strength, ft. lbs. in notch | 0.4 | 0.4 |
| Hardness, Rockwell | M35-M65 | M35-M65 |
| Resistance to heat, °F (continuous) | 500 | 1,300 |
| Volume resistivity, ohm-cm | $1.3 \times 10^{12}$ | — |
| Dielectric strength, short time, volts | 85 | — |
| Dielectric strength, step by step, volts | 50-75 | 50-75 |
| Dielectric constant, 60 cycles | 15.0 | — |
| Dielectric constant, $10^6$ cycles | 6.0 | — |
| Power factor, 60 cycles | 0.20 | — |
| Power factor, $10^6$ cycles | 0.07 | — |
| Water absorption, 24 hr., % | 0.6-2.0 | 0.5-15.0 |
| Weak acids | Slight | Slight |
| Strong acids | Decomposes | Decomposes |
| Weak alkalies | None | None |
| Strong alkalies | Decomposes | None |
| Organic solvents | Attacked by some | None |
| Machinability | Poor | Poor |
| Clarity | Opaque | Opaque |
| Color possibilities | Dark only | Gray and Black |
| Burning rate | Nil | Nil |

Trade Names—Aico, Amerine, Garit, Gummon, Tegit, Thermoplax, Hemit.

The molds used are of the volumetric-pressure type consisting of a box fitted with an upper and a lower plunger for compressing the powder and ejecting the piece after forming. The box may be of cast iron, cast steel, or a forged block usually fitted with hardened steel liners. The plungers are of hardened tool steel.

Such a mold may be set up in a power punch press, a toggle press, or a quick acting hydraulic press. Since there is no curing time involved, one cavity will produce a large number of parts per hour. The phenolic molds require a large number of cavities to equal this production because of the delay in curing. This explains a large difference in mold costs.

The cold-molded materials mentioned above are processed by filling the open molds, either volumetrically or by pre-weighing the charge, and closing the molds under pressures varying from 5 to 500 tons psi. After the pieces are ejected from the mold they are baked in ovens at temperatures ranging from 100 to 400° F for 10 to 40 hours, depending on the particular compound used, the size and shape of the pieces, and the purpose for which they are intended.

Practically all cold-molded manufacturers compound their own raw material as opposed to the general practice in plastics molding of buying the material ready-mixed from large suppliers.

## Coumarone-Indene Resins*

The coumarone-indene resins are essentially hydrocarbon in nature since the indene far exceeds the coumarone present in the types found in this country. The name is more of historical than chemical significance. Their thermoplastic nature is believed to be due to their comparatively low molecular weight which is generally less than 1000, and to their suspected linear structure, although ring formation is also a possibility.

Raw materials for this group of resins are obtained from the coking of coal. The light oil fraction of the distillate boiling between 300 and 428° F may be used. For the more refined grades of resins, however, a narrower cut from this fraction is preferred. This fraction is further treated in various ways depending on the color limits of the proposed end use of the resinous product. Polymerization is carried out under controlled conditions using strong acids, such as sulfuric acid or alkyl sulfuric acids or acidic salts, such as the chlorides of aluminum, zinc, tin, boron, and others, as catalysts. The color, molecular weight, and softening point of the product depend greatly on how carefully the polymerization conditions are controlled as well as on the pretreatment of the raw materials.

* Prepared in cooperation with Dr. W. J. Wald, Manager, Technical Service Dept., Neville Chemical Co., Pittsburgh, Pa.

Commercially they vary from fairly viscous liquids to hard thermoplastic resins softening somewhat above 300° F by the Ball-and-Shouldered-Ring Method. The light-colored, higher softening grades are known as Nevindenes and the darker grades as Paradenes.

Coumarone-indene resins are available in colors ranging from a very pale straw to a deep red-brown and are graded commercially principally on this basis. The specific gravity ranges from 1.1 to 1.2, depending on the grade.

These resins find application either alone or as one of the components in floor tile binders, aluminum paint vehicles, metal primers, concrete curing compounds, pipe oils, waterproofing compounds, and impregnants, among others. They have also found extensive use in rubber compounding, general paint and varnish formulation, adhesives, chewing gum, printing inks, phonograph records, and sealing compounds.

Their inert hydrocarbon nature makes them particularly suitable where acid, alkali, salt or water resistance, good electrical properties, and reasonable cost are required. Their limited elasticity and slight yellow color have restricted their use. However, the former can be greatly improved, as is often the case, by proper selection of plasticizers.

The coumarone-indene resins have been modified, as in the case of the Nevillacs, through the introduction of a phenol into the polymer. Such resins have entirely different solubilities and compatibilities. For example, they become readily soluble in alcohols, as well as hydrocarbons. These modified products have been particularly useful in adhesives, especially those based on vinyl resins. They have also been effective with some of the special synthetic rubbers such as the butadiene-acrylonitrile type, and in the control of gelling and skinning in some otherwise difficult to handle varnishes.

Recently the hydrogenated coumarone-indene resins have come into prominence and pilot plant production has been started.

## Epoxy Resins*

The epoxy resins are among the newest of the large-volume plastics. Introduced in the early 1950's they achieved recognition quickly in industrial and appliance coatings, where they combine good adhesion with resistance to caustic and chemicals. More recently, they have come into usage as metal-bonding adhesives, potting and encapsulating compounds, and jigs, prototypes, and dies for the forming of sheet metals. Good wetting and adhesion to metals and glass fiber, ability to cure

* This section prepared in cooperation with Irving Skeist, President, Skeist Laboratories, 89 Lincoln Park, Newark, N. J. (Later: Skeist & Schwarz Laboratories, Inc.)

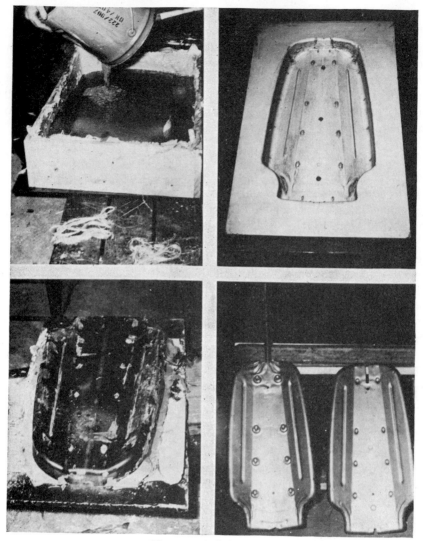

(*Courtesy Bakelite Co.*)

Figure 2.4.  The epoxies make emergency tools.

A company had contracted to supply about 100 prototype seat backs to an automobile manufacturer for its pre-production samples before regular production began.
Samples were needed before completion of regular tooling. In order to insure that
the customer received his samples on time, the company built interim tools from
compounds based on Bakelite epoxy resins. The method used demonstrates how easily
such tools can overcome production bottlenecks. Work starts with a wooden pattern
furnished by the customer. It is placed in a box and the entire exposed surface is
coated with a release agent. Several layers of glass fabric, bonded with the epoxy

resin, are placed over the wooden model. The resins cure without heat or pressure. After laminating, the remaining area in the box is filled with a mixture of the laminating resin and buckshot (top left). The finished die (top right) is a very strong, dimensionally stable reproduction of the pattern. After the die is made, another compound is cast in a plaster mold taken from the original wooden pattern. After removal from the mold (bottom left), this cast becomes the resilient punch for use with the die previously made. This punch is strong enough to form the metal without fracturing.

---

without application of external heat, low shrinkage during cure, good electrical characteristics, and excellent dimensional stability are some of the characteristics that have helped the growth of epoxies.

Two broad classes are available—solid resins, which are modified with other resins and unsaturated fatty acids to make coating materials; and liquid resins, which are hardened with curing agents for adhesives, potting, and for plastic tooling compounds. The solid resins are priced at approximately 60 cents a pound and the liquid resins at about 80 cents a pound. These prices are high, but the epoxies have prospered nevertheless.

Epoxy coatings are generally applied as solutions of the modified resins in hydrocarbon solvents. Upon evaporation of the solvent, the coating is baked to bring about the oxidation, polymerization, and condensation reactions that give the desired hardness and chemical resistance.

Epoxy-melamine resins are applied as primer coats for washing machines, combining excellent adhesion to metal with outstanding alkali resistance. They are weather and acid-resistant, non-staining, and flexible. Even sulfuric acid and its vapors do not affect the epoxies. Yellowing at elevated temperature is their only serious drawback.

The *liquid* resins are preferred for adhesives and plastics end uses. The viscous liquids are "cured"—converted to hard solids—by reaction with amine or acid anhydride hardeners. No pressure is needed. Some of the amine hardening agents begin to take effect on the resin at room temperature, so that it is possible to make very large castings without using an oven. As the resin hardens, heat is evolved. Shrinkage is slight, perhaps less than one per cent.

The unmodified epoxies cure to hard, inflexible resins. For greater toughness and flexibility, the epoxy is blended with liquid polyamides (Versamids) or polysulfides (Thiokol) prior to curing. The improved toughness is needed to give adhesives with higher peel strength, whereas the flexibility is important in the potting of delicate electronic components which may expand and contract in response to temperature fluctuations.

The straight resin, cured with liquid amines, is transparent; but modification with polysulfide or polyamide, as well as curing with solid hardeners, results in translucent or opaque castings.

The softening temperature is affected by modifiers and curing agents. The resin modifiers generally result in low softening temperatures, as do the aliphatic amine hardeners, but aromatic amine or acid anhydride hardeners give higher softening temperatures.

(Courtesy Bakelite Co.)

Figure 2.5. Epoxy resin being poured in the production of a tool. It takes about half an hour to line up and pour the resin. Anyone familiar with tooling processes can learn the use of epoxies in a short time. The compound will harden overnight.

As adhesives, the epoxies provide metal-to-metal bonds of superior strength. Adhesive bonding spreads the stresses, permitting the bonding of thin aluminum skins to give a stronger structure than can be obtained by riveting or welding. In the electronics industry, subassemblies are potted or encapsulated in epoxies to keep out moisture and corrosive fumes, thus prolonging their useful life.

Mixed with fillers, to lower the cost and increase hardness, epoxies are used in the manufacture of massive dies for forming sheet metal. Cast against a model, the epoxies reproduce complex shapes quickly, faithfully, and at a fraction of the cost of machining metal tools. Dimensional stability is excellent. For runs up to 50,000 pieces, epoxies are replacing Kirksite and other tool materials.

Fiber-glass reinforced epoxies are more resistant to water, jet fuels, and temperature-cycling than their polyester counterparts. Epoxy pipe and tubing retain their strength even in thin sections. Water pipe, probes for aircraft fuel tanks, coil forms and electrical conduit are among the growing uses.

Epoxies are produced by the reaction between epichlorohydrin and bisphenol, or similarly by the condensation of phenol, acetone, and epichlorohydrin. The properties may be varied greatly by the introduction of different organic radicals. For instance, esterification with acids from natural drying oils will give epoxy resins well suited to the formulation of paints and varnishes. Certain liquid epoxies cured with amine hardening agents will produce materials well adapted for making industrial tools. Other modifications result in some of the best adhesives of the plastics industry. In general, the epoxies have low shrinkage, high dimensional stability and good wetting characteristics. They have greater flexibility than the phenolics and greater chemical resistance than the alkyds.

Castings will cure at room temperature to produce good physical properties but with a relatively low heat-softening point (180 to 200° F). However, with a cure at 250 to 300° F it is possible to raise the heat-softening point to 300° F or more. Types include adhesives, coatings for industrial tools, potting compounds, prosthetics and foams.

TABLE 2.7. PROPERTIES OF EPOXIES

| Properties | Epoxy Resin Unmodified | Epoxy Resin Polysulfide—modified |
|---|---|---|
| Specific gravity | 1.15 | 1.20 |
| Tensile strength, psi | 10,000 | 5,000 |
| Elongation, % | low | 10 |
| Impact strength, Izod notched, ft. lb./in. | 1 | 5 |
| Heat distortion temperature, °F | 150-400 | 100-200 |
| Resistance to organic solvents | good | good |
| Resistance to acids | good | good |
| Resistance to alkalies | excellent | excellent |

## Ethyl Cellulose*

This plastic is made from the ethyl ether of cellulose and is therefore chemically distinct from the other cellulosics which are esters. It is a

* Prepared in cooperation with M. H. P. Morand, Dow Chemical Co.

tough, strong plastic with properties similar to the other cellulose derivatives; however, it is lighter, having a specific gravity of about 1.10 versus values of 1.2 to 1.4 for the other cellulosics. Resistance to alkali is a particular chemical property of ethyl cellulose that differentiates it from the cellulose esters.

Commercial ethyl celluloses are classified by the viscosities of 5 per cent solutions in alcohol-aromatic hydrocarbon mixtures. They are also classified by the degree to which cellulose has been etherified. Molding powders are generally formulated from compositions containing plasticizers plus 46 per cent ethoxyl ethyl cellulose. Ethyl cellulose with a 47 to 49 per cent ethoxyl content is widely used for coatings compositions.

Ethocel is the trade name for ethyl cellulose produced by the Dow Chemical Company. The Hercules Powder Company also produces ethyl cellulose under the trade name Hercocel E.

Engineers often develop applications for molded and extruded parts from ethyl cellulose which utilize its excellent toughness over a wide range of temperatures in combination with other properties such as good dimensional stability and freedom from odor. Examples of these are deep-freeze breaker strips, end caps for luggage, and a variety of military applications. Ethyl cellulose plastic has been used specifically in the construction of military rockets. In addition to its outstanding physical properties, this application takes advantage of the ability of certain ethyl cellulose formulations to be used in contact with propellants containing nitroglycerine. Other applications include wire insulation, hot-melt cloth coating, radio housings, extruded kitchen trim, and toys.

Ethyl cellulose enjoys several applications within the coatings field, practically all of which take advantage of its solubility in a variety of inexpensive solvents. Lacquers, specialty lacquers, and hot-melt paper coatings have been used regularly for a number of years. Two coating applications deserve particular attention. The first of these is "strippable coatings" for packaging precision metal parts. These can be made transparent so that the packaged part is readily identified and untouched until the coating is peeled off at the time of use.

Ethyl cellulose gel lacquers are particularly useful coatings. A gel lacquer is applied to the object by dipping it into a warm, relatively concentrated solution (*ca* 70° C) of ethyl cellulose. The solvents of the gel lacquer are adjusted so the solution gels at room temperature. This allows a coating to form on the cool surface of the object being dipped. Oven drying removes the solvent, leaving a relatively thick, tough coating. Notable examples of coatings applied in this manner are those for toughening bowling pins and for the manufacture of various electrical parts.

TABLE 2.8. PHYSICAL PROPERTIES OF ETHYL CELLULOSE

(Average Values)

| Properties | Ethyl Cellulose |
|---|---|
| Specific gravity | 1.10-1.12 |
| Tensile strength, psi | 6000-10000 |
| Compressive strength, psi | 3000-8000 |
| Elongation, % | 5-40 |
| Continuous heat resistance, °F | 125-190 |
| Heat distortion temperature, °F | 200-250 |
| Dielectric strength, v. per mil | 500 |
| Machining quality | excellent |
| Effect of sunlight | soon degrades outdoors |
| Per cent water absorption, 24 hr | 0.9-1.7 |
| Resistance to strong acids | poor |
| Resistance to weak acids | good |
| Resistance to strong alkalies | excellent |
| Resistance to weak alkalies | excellent |
| Clarity | transparent |

## Fluorocarbons

A group of extremely inert plastics is variously known as fluorothenes, fluorocarbons, and fluorochemical plastics. They are chemically characterized by having a large percentage of the hydrogen directly attached to carbon replaced by fluorine. One part of the group consists of the polymers of trifluorochloroethylene and includes Bakelite's fluorothene and Kellogg's Kel-F. These are available as resins and dispersions which have high thermal stability and excellent resistance to chemical attack. Oils, greases, and waxes are also produced. Among the unusual properties are the following:

(1) zero moisture absorption
(2) temperature range from −320 to +390° F
(3) high compressive strength
(4) non-wettability
(5) excellent electrical resistance
(6) high inertness

Another part of the general fluorocarbon group, more specifically known as tetrafluoroethylene, has the trade name Teflon. Its properties, as shown in Table 2.9, are somewhat similar to those of fluorothene and Kel-F, namely:

  (1) high inertness
  (2) excellent dielectric properties
  (3) heat-resistance
  (4) toughness
  (5) low coefficient of friction

Considered as a whole the fluorocarbon materials are thermoplastic, inert, and expensive. Molding powders are available—also sheets, tubes, and tapes. Some typical uses are gaskets, valve seats, insulation of wire (especially for aircraft), bags for storage of liquids, and drum liners. For other uses see Chapter 4.

At present two commercial types are available as stated:

  (1) polytetrafluoroethylene
        (a) Teflon — Du Pont
  (2) polychlorotrifluoroethylene
        (a) Kel-F — M. W. Kellogg
        (b) Bakelite fluorothene — Bakelite Company

These are all included in the thermoplastic group of resins even though one, Teflon, does not melt and flow. Teflon has unusual heat resistance with a possible service temperature from −450 to above 550° F. It has a waxy texture and is opaque with a milk white color. It is available in films, sheets, rods, and tubes and can be molded by special techniques. Aqueous solutions are used for wire coating and other finishes. Applications of Teflon include packing for pump shafts, spacers for coaxial cables, and insulation in electric motors. When Teflon has not been treated to alter its surface properties, it provides an almost frictionless surface. If treated, it can be cemented to almost any surface with conventional adhesives. As with other fluorocarbons it is supplied in three forms—molding powders, extrusion powders, which are combined with an organic extrusion aid, and water dispersions. The general-purpose molding powders are granules of 30 mesh size. These superficially resemble granulated paraffin. When fabricated into tape, sheets, rods, and wire coatings, the material is waxlike in appearance, and has the characteristic slippery feel. Its surface is so anti-stick that it is used to coat bakery rollers.

Kel-F has chemical resistance properties similar to Teflon. It is notable for its high impact strength at both high and low temperatures and for its resistance to thermal shock. It can be injection, compression, and extrusion molded.

Fluorothene is resistant to concentrated acids and alkalies up to 300° F, but it is swelled by some chlorinated hydrocarbons. Otherwise its properties fall in line with the other fluorocarbons. In general, the properties of Kel-F and fluorothene are the same. Both have extrudability and injection moldability in conventional equipment. Low permeability of films is a feature of all fluorocarbons. Laminates of fluorothene to glass and asbestos are available for tank linings and for other areas where cementing to surfaces is required.

An elastomer based on Kel-F is available, combining elastomeric properties with the excellent resistance to heat and corrosive chemicals characteristic of the fluorocarbons.

### Teflon Tetrafluoroethylene Resin*

This resin, first produced in a pilot plant at Arlington, New Jersey, in 1943, is now being made in full-scale facilities at the Du Pont plastics plant near Parkersburg, West Virginia. There tetrafluoroethylene gas is changed into the solid form by a polymerization process which causes the small gaseous molecules to combine into the giant ones which form the solid. Molded or extruded in thin sections, Teflon is translucent, but in thicker pieces, it is waxy and opaque in appearance. It can be colored by pigmentation, but normally it is white.

Teflon undergoes a solid-phase transition at 620° F, with a sharp drop in strength. It decomposes in the neighborhood of 750° F, to yield the gaseous monomer plus other gaseous fluorine derivatives. Small amounts of fluorine-containing gases are given off at temperatures above 500° F. Good ventilation must therefore be provided for extrusion and other mechanical operations in which these temperatures may be reached, as some of the gases are toxic.

The plastic has a combination of properties unobtainable in any other organic material now commercially available. Its resistance to chemicals and heat is better than most plastics now on the market. It is a highly efficient electrical insulation, even at high temperatures, and particularly at the high frequencies required for television and other electronic equipment. It is tough and flexible, and retains most properties at temperatures as low as −90° F. It will not absorb moisture, a property which adds greatly to its value as an electrical insulator, since its dielectric strength is not diminished by immersion in fresh or salt water. One of the most

---

* This section, prepared by Du Pont, is included here for its additional information even though some data are repeated from the section on fluorocarbons.

valuable properties of Teflon for many industrial uses is its non-adhesiveness.

Teflon is resistant to attack by chemicals that would destroy gold or platinum. It can be boiled in aqua regia, hydrofluoric acid, or fuming nitric acid with no change in weight or properties. The plastic also resists attack by organic materials and strong alkalies.

With a temperature range of −90 to 500° F, Teflon is successfully used for gaskets, valve packings, piping, and other applications in the chemical industry.

The excellent electrical properties of Teflon resin, coupled with its heat resistance and excellent mechanical properties, make it adaptable for many applications in the electrical industry which for years has been harassed by the problem of getting more power from equipment without burning up the insulation. Teflon makes it possible to design smaller and more compact electrical components having higher capacities than existing units.

TABLE 2.9.  PROPERTIES OF TETRAFLUOROETHYLENE AND POLYETHYLENE RESINS
(Average Values)*

| Properties | Tetrafluoroethylene (Teflon) | Polyethylene |
|---|---|---|
| Specific gravity | 2.15 | 0.92 |
| Tensile strength, psi | 2500 | 1750† |
| Compressive strength, psi | 1700 | low |
| Continuous heat resistance, °F | 500 | 220 |
| Heat distortion temperature, °F (66 psi) | 250 | 121 |
| Dielectric strength, v. per mil | 500 | 460 |
| Machining qualities | excellent | fair to good |
| Effect of sunlight | none | some crazing |
| Per cent water absorption, 24 hr | 0.005 | 0.014 |
| Resistance to strong acids | excellent** | poor to fair |
| Resistance to weak acids | excellent | excellent |
| Resistance to strong alkalies | excellent | excellent |
| Resistance to weak alkalies | excellent | excellent |
| Clarity | opaque | opaque to translucent |

* Based on Du Pont's tabulation.
** Completely inert to all chemicals normally encountered in industry.
† Du Pont lists 4,750 as tensile strength of its molded polyethylene.

A characteristic of the insulating material is its excellent resistance to arc-over. On failing, it vaporizes instead of forming a carbonized path. The electrical losses over a frequency range of 60 cycles to 300 megacycles are substantially constant, and lower than those of polyethylene and polystyrene.

Teflon is used in many industries where non-sticky surfaces are either essential or used to improve manufacturing operations. The surface of the plastic is actually slippery, a characteristic which also recommends its use in certain bearing applications.

Teflon is being used as a non-adhesive covering in automatic packaging machinery for smoother and more rapid heat-sealing of waxed paper and plastic films.

TABLE 2.10. PROPERTIES OF TRIFLUOROCHLOROETHYLENE RESINS

(Average Values)

| Properties | Resin |
| --- | --- |
| Specific gravity | 2.1 |
| Tensile strength, psi | 5700 |
| Compressive strength, psi | 30,000 to 50,000 |
| Continuous heat resistance, °F | 400 |
| Dielectric strength, v. per mil | 460 |
| Machining qualities | excellent |
| Effect of sunlight | none |
| Per cent water absorption, 24 hr | 0.001 |
| Resistance to strong acids | excellent |
| Resistance to weak acids | excellent |
| Resistance to strong alkalies | excellent |
| Resistance to weak alkalies | excellent |
| Clarity | transparent to translucent |

From a new form of Teflon known as "dispersions," researchers have developed a line of finishes which can be made to adhere to metal after fusion of the particles by baking at temperatures above the plastic's transition point of 620° F.

Teflon is available in the form of granular molding powder, dispersions, and extrusion compounds. The molding powder is used to manufacture a variety of products, such as gaskets, valve diaphragms, and expansion joints. The dispersions are extremely fine particles of the plastic suspended in water, giving the appearance of milk or cream. They may be employed in casting light-weight, unsupported films and for impregnating glass and other fabrics. They also constitute the raw material for finishes and enamels. Extrusion compounds are used in the production of tapes and wire insulation.

TABLE 2.11. COMPARATIVE CHARACTERISTICS CHART

| | Fluorocarbons | Nylon | Polyethylene | Acrylic |
|---|---|---|---|---|
| Chemical | Completely inert to all chemicals and solvents normally encountered in industry. Impervious to water. | Unaffected by common solvents, alkalies, dilute mineral acids and most organic acids. | Excellent chemical and water resistance. | Resistant to dilute alkalies, many strong acids and other chemicals. |
| Mechanical | Tough over a range of temperatures from —450 to 500°F. Non-adhesive. Low friction coefficient. Self-lubricating. | Tough and resilient at low temperatures. Requires little or no lubrication. Resists abrasion. | Tough and flexible over wide range of temperatures. | Rigid. Good dimensional stability. |
| Electrical | Excellent in electrical properties at all frequencies. | Good dielectric properties at commercial power frequencies. | Excellent dielectric properties over wide frequency and temperature range. | Good dielectric properties at all commercial power frequencies. |
| Structural | Tough and resilient. Resistant to impact. Impervious to weather. | Strong and durable. Good form stability. Light in weight. | Good strength and toughness Free from taste, odor and toxicity. When black pigmented, resists weather. Resists impact. Very light weight. | Resists weather. Shatter resistant. Good dimensional stability. Light in weight. Free from taste, odor and toxicity. |
| Decorative | Can be colored. Useful for color coatings to aid identification. | Good color stability. Attractive texture. | Easily colored. Attractive translucent texture. | Transparent. Available in range of colors. Transmits and "pipes" light. Unusual beauty. |

Courtesy Du Pont.

Teflon cannot be molded by conventional methods since it has no liquid flow stage. It is formed by a combination of compression and sintering processes that are somewhat analogous to those used in producing powdered metal parts. After forming into cylinders under high pressure it is baked at from 620 to 720°F which produces a homogeneous mass in a gel stage. The process is then completed by a further pressure operation.

### Furans

Used mostly for coatings, these thermosetting resins are available in a wide range of viscosities. They have excellent adhesive properties and cure to form a solid resin highly resistant to acids and alkalies. The low viscosity polymers are valuable for impregnating such materials as wood, plaster of Paris, and chemical stoneware. The furan resins are obtained by the condensation of furfuryl alcohol. Their good compatibility makes them useful as an additive for improving the chemical resistance of other thermosetting materials.

TABLE 2.12. PHYSICAL PROPERTIES OF FURAN

(Average Values)

| Properties | Furan |
|---|---|
| Specific gravity | 1.75 |
| Tensile strength, psi | 3800 |
| Compressive strength, psi | 12000 |
| Continuous heat resistance, °F | 290 |
| Heat distortion temperature, °F | 270 |
| Dielectric strength, v. per mil | 300 |
| Machining qualities | fair |
| Effect of sunlight | excellent resistance |
| Per cent water absorption, 24 hr | 0.16 |
| Resistance to strong acids | poor |
| Resistance to weak acids | good |
| Resistance to strong alkalies | good |
| Resistance to weak alkalies | excellent |
| Clarity | opaque |

## Melamine Resins*

During the past sixteen or seventeen years melamine-formaldehyde resins have become established as one of the most versatile resins available to industry. Thermosetting resinous compositions obtained from melamine are used in a wide variety of important industrial and decorative applications in molded form, as shock-resistant laminates for combat craft, and as decorative laminates for the household. Melamine resins can be used as durable boilproof adhesives; they are used in leather tanning, in textile processing, in the production of wet strength paper and durable, mar-resistant enamel finishes.

Melamine-formaldehyde and urea-formaldehyde resins are usually classified as aminoplastics. These two resins resemble each other somewhat but the melamine resins are superior in chemical and heat resistance, and in durability under exterior exposure.

In the production of molding compounds, melamine is first reacted with formaldehyde solution and the syrup obtained compounded with various fillers. The mixture obtained is dried under closely controlled conditions and further processed depending on the type of molding compound being produced. Dyes or pigments can usually be introduced at an appropriate stage during the operation to obtain colored molding materials.

Cured melamine-formaldehyde resins are entirely free from color and do not discolor at relatively high temperatures. When purified alpha-cellulose is used as the filler, together with pigments and/or dyes, molding compounds may be obtained in an almost infinite variety of colors, giving rugged moldings that hold their beauty and appearance under the most drastic service conditions. Unpigmented material gives translucent, pearl-white moldings.

High quality dinnerware is an outstanding product obtained from alpha-filled melamine molding compounds. Special effects may be incorporated into dinnerware by using a decorative melamine-resin-impregnated paper overlay. Other typical important uses are wash-resistant buttons, plastic coffeemakers, soda dispensers, cutlery handles and Aerosol containers.

Mineral-filled melamine molding compounds may be formulated for industrial applications requiring maximum arc and heat-resistance and dielectric strength. Glass fiber filled material is available, giving a combination of high impact strength, high heat-resistance, and good electrical properties.

* Prepared in cooperation with American Cyanamid Co.

Molding compounds employing wood flour as the filler are produced for general-purpose industrial molding, particularly transfer molding of parts with metallic inserts.

Melamine molding compounds are thermosetting and, during the molding operations, pass through the characteristic cycles of flow, set, and cure. They are usually molded at temperatures ranging from 310 to 350° F and at pressures from 1,500 to 6,000 psi for compression molding, to 20,000 psi for transfer molding.

(Courtesy American Cyanamid Co.)

Figure 2.6.  This hot tray is made of melamine and is available in decorator colors. The melamine resists heat and scratching.

In the production of laminates, glass cloth or other fabrics, or sheets of paper, are impregnated with melamine resin solution and dried to a controlled moisture content. Multiple plies of the impregnated sheets are laminated in a platen press and cured at temperatures of 275 to 310° F for 15 to 30 minutes at pressures of 1,000 to 1,200 psi.

The basic melamine-formaldehyde reaction product is not soluble in paint or enamel solvents. Further reaction with an alcohol such as butanol is required to develop the solubility required for use in a surface coating finish. In the production of an enamel the butylated resin is combined with an alkyd resin, usually in the range of 10 to 30 per cent melamine resin: 70 to 90 per cent alkyd resin.

Melamine resins are available, usually in powdered form dispersible in water, for use in the other applications previously listed.

For physical properties of the melamines see Table 2.13.

TABLE 2.13. COMPARATIVE PROPERTIES OF PHENOLICS, UREAS AND MELAMINES

| Properties | Phenolics[1] | Ureas[2] | Melamines[3] |
|---|---|---|---|
| Specific gravity | 1.32-1.45 | 1.47-1.52 | 1.47-1.52 |
| Tensile strength[5], psi | 7,500 | 5,500-7,000 | 7,000-8,000 |
| Compressive strength[5], psi | 20,000 | 30,000-38,000 | 40,000-45,000 |
| Molding property | excellent | excellent | excellent |
| Mold shrinkage, in. per in. | 0.006 | .006-.009 | 0.007-0.009 |
| Continuous heat resistance, °F | 325 | 170 | 210-230 |
| Heat distortion temperature, °F | 300-340 | 266 | 400 |
| Dielectric strength[4], v. per mil at 25°C | 315 | 350 | 310-330 |
| Machining quality | fair | fair | fair to good |
| Effect of sunlight | darkens | none | slight color change |
| Per cent water absorption, 24 hr | 0.3 to 1.0 | 0.4-0.8 | 0.1-0.6 |
| Resistance to strong acids | poor | poor | poor |
| Resistance to weak acids | good | good | excellent |
| Resistance to strong alkalies | poor | poor | poor |
| Resistance to weak alkalies | good | fair | excellent |
| Clarity | opaque | translucent-opaque | translucent-opaque |

1. Wood flour filler.    2-3. Alpha-cellulose filler.    4. Short time, ⅛ in. thick.    5. Average values used.

The term "continuous heat resistance" has a different interpretation with different materials. With the melamines and ureas it refers to the maximum temperature at which those materials can be held indefinitely with no change in appearance or color. The phenolics are dark in color to start with so that an attempt to compare them with the lighter materials may be misleading.

## Phenolics

Called rather affectionately by old-timers "the workhorse of the plastics industry" the phenolics now are about up with polystyrene in production poundage. For many years during the early days of the industry they stood at the top of the list. They are produced by the reaction of the carbonyl oxygen of formaldehyde with active hydrogens of phenol, cresols, or xylenols. Water is eliminated in the reaction so it is of the condensation type.

The phenolics, at first known as "Bakelite," were the first commercially important plastic. They are thermosetting materials and pass through three more or less distinct stages in reaching their final cure. These are known as A, B, and C stages, as explained elsewhere. By modifying the catalyst and using excess phenol in the reaction a thermoplastic material may be produced, called novolak. When this material is mixed with hexamethylenetetramine it can be cured to a thermosetting form.

*(Courtesy Bakelite Co.)*

Figure 2.7. Part of the equipment used in producing phenolic resins. The raw materials are weighed accurately in the weigh room above (not shown) and they are then piped to the kettles or stills shown where the reactions take place.

The properties of the various phenolic materials may be modified both by altering the starting components and by using various fillers and plasticizers.

In general, the phenolics are insoluble in most solvents, have good strength and good resistance to moisture and to elevated temperatures. Some grades readily withstand 400°F. They have dimensional stability through a wide range of temperatures, are nonflammable, and have excellent compression molding properties, that is, they hold inserts without cracking and preforms may be heated to speed up curing in the mold. They also are among the lowest priced of the commercial plastics. Phenolic molding compounds usually are dark in color because of inherent poor color stability. They are resistant to most solvents and acids, except oxidizing acids and caustic solutions.

The dark phenolics are extensively used for radio and business machine housings, telephone handsets, washing machine agitators and countless bottle caps, knobs and handles. They may be cast as well as molded and decorative and industrial articles are made by casting in thin sheets. Other uses include: adhesives for sandpaper and plywood; treating foundry sand (shell molding) as ion exchange resins; and as liquid resins for impregnating.

TABLE 2.14. SUMMARY OF PHENOLIC PROPERTIES*

| Important Qualities | Familiar Uses |
|---|---|
| Good balance of strength, hardness, rigidity | furniture drawers |
| Very good electrical insulator | electric switch boxes |
| Good rigid heat insulator | electric iron handles |
| High resistance to moisture | washing machine agitators |
| Good resistance to solvents and common chemicals | film developer trays |
| Opaque colors | appliance parts |

* Bakelite.

General-purpose phenolic molding compounds generally use wood flour as a filler. This may increase the strength by as much as 100 per cent. In fact, it is so extensively used not only with phenolics but with other plastics that the total annual wood flour consumption in the plastics industry exceeds 35,000,000 pounds. Many other fillers, such as asbestos, mica, macerated fabric and cotton and nylon flock, are used in special grades of phenolics.

## Polyamides

These form a group of resins of which the chief commercial type is nylon. The term nylon does not, however, refer to a particular product but rather to a family of chemically related products which may be fabricated in many ways. The nylon fibers in textiles are the best known but molding powders and coating materials are increasing in use. Several commercial nylons, varying in physical properties, are available, including nylon 66 and nylon 6. The trade name Zytel applies to a family of nylon molding powders which include these two types. In molded or extruded form nylon is translucent and cream white but it may be colored with pigments or dyes to any of several shades. It is tough over a wide range of temperatures, has high strength in thin sections, excellent abrasion resistance, and intermittent heat resistance up to 350°F. Its frictional properties make it a good bearing material. It can be steam-sterilized. Its specific gravity is 1.14 which is low for plastics, being exceeded only by polystyrene, 1.05, and polyethylene, 0.92. In addition, nylon has good resistance to solvents and chemicals and good dielectric properties as well as the property of self-extinguishing flame.

TABLE 2.15. PROPERTIES OF NYLON AND ACRYLIC RESINS

(Average Values)

| Properties | Nylon | Acrylic |
|---|---|---|
| Specific gravity | 1.12 | 1.185 |
| Tensile strength, psi | 13,000 | 9,000 |
| Compressive strength, psi | 11,000 | 14,000 |
| Continuous heat resistance, °F | 290 | 190 |
| Heat distortion temperature, °F (66 psi) | 300 | 175 |
| Dielectric strength, v. per mil | 400 | 400 |
| Machining qualities | excellent | excellent |
| Per cent water absorption, 24 hr | 1.1 | 0.27 |
| Effect of sunlight | slight discoloration | very slight |
| Resistance to strong acids | poor | good |
| Resistance to weak acids | good | good |
| Resistance to strong alkalies | good | good |
| Resistance to weak alkalies | excellent | excellent |
| Clarity | opaque or translucent | transparent (92% light transmission) |

Typical uses include sterilizable utensils, brush backs and bristles, gears, slide fasteners and, of course, textile applications.

The development of a new type of nylon artery graft, which has added years of useful activity to the lives of hundreds whose arteries have become damaged, has been announced by Monsanto Chemical Company. Development of the nylon artery makes it possible for even the smallest rural clinic to keep an adequate stock of grafts on hand for emergencies.

The consumption of nylon molding powders has increased ninefold since 1950 and is expected to reach the annual rate of about 25,000,000 pounds by 1958. Nylon textile yarn production in 1957 is estimated at 375,000,000 pounds. Polycaprolactam is a term frequently used for nylon 6.

### Polyester Resins*

The esterification reaction between polyhydric alcohols and polybasic acids produces a large class of materials known as polyester or alkyd resins. These resins exhibit a wide range of properties and are utilized in highly diversified commercial applications. The wide range of properties results largely from the type and proportions of chemical components used in manufacture.

When a saturated dihydric alcohol (i.e., one containing no double bonds) is reacted with a saturated dibasic acid under controlled conditions, water is evolved and chain molecules having terminal hydroxyl or carboxyl groups result. These molecules are the saturated polyesters. They can undergo further inter-molecular condensations but cannot be cross-linked.

When a dihydric alcohol and a dibasic acid, either or both of which contain a doubly-bonded pair of carbon atoms, are reacted, an unsaturated polyester is obtained. The double bonds render the unsaturated polyester capable of subsequent cross-linking. The unsaturated polyesters usually are blended with a reactive monomer (such as styrene) and reacted under the influence of special catalyst systems. The polyester and the monomer copolymerize to form a thermoset.

There is considerable confusion in references to the type of polyesters involved in various applications. By chemical definition, the reaction product derived from a polyhydric alcohol and a polybasic acid, whether or not the reaction product is modified by special alcohol or acid components, is still properly called a polyester. For practical purposes, however, an oil-modified polyester (i.e., a fatty acid-modified polyester) is always referred to as an alkyd or alkyd coating resin. To add to the complication, because the alkyd rather than the polyester designation was chosen to

---

* This section by W. O. Erickson and V. W. Ginsler of Barrett Division, Allied Chemical & Dye Corp. is included here by courtesy of Modern Plastics Encyclopedia Issue, 1956.

refer to certain proprietary molding compounds introduced some years ago, the practical usage of alkyd molding compounds has now been established. Certain saturated polyesters have become useful plasticizers and are often referred to as polymeric plasticizers. Other special polyesters are formed into film and textile products. A polyester product is a principal ingredient of polyurethane foam resins.

(*Courtesy Celanese Corp. of America*)

Figure 2.8. This swimming pool, shown in the process of construction, is produced in modular sections of polyester resin reinforced with glass cloth and mat. The sections in general are produced on male molds by hand lay-up procedure. They are provided with flanges which are bolted together and which, after application of additional resin, form leak-proof joints.

The polymerizable polyesters are a relatively new class of resins that first appeared commercially during World War II. They are noted especially for ease of handling, good physical properties, and speed of cure. Initial applications were in combination with fibrous glass in radomes, body armor, and miscellaneous nonstructural aircraft parts.

After World War II, civilian applications grew slowly. Gradually, lower resin costs, better technical know-how, and improved production techniques have resulted in an increasing number of applications.

Polyester resin volume in 1955 was very nearly 48 million pounds, approximately a 75 per cent increase over the 27 million pounds sold in 1954. This class of resins is now used for matched-metal molding, premix materials, laminates and hand lay-up applications, casting, and encapsulation.

A polyester, as the term is used here, refers to an unsaturated polyester base resin dissolved in a polymerizable monomer. The base resin component can be prepared from innumerable chemical combinations. It is this base component that usually is modified to obtain the various properties of the finished polyester.

Figure 2.9. Bakelite polyester resins used in reinforced plastics, supply the strength, resilience and resistance to impact and abrasion needed in outdoor playground equipment.

Essentially, dibasic acids and dihydric alcohols are heated to sufficiently high temperatures to react, split out water, and form ester linkages. As the reaction proceeds, many ester linkages are formed in one linear molecule. It is essential that at least a certain portion of the dibasic acids or the dihydric alcohols be unsaturated, i.e., contain double bonds, to assist in copolymerization. It is through the connecting of these double bonds with those of the monomer that curing takes place.

The dihydric alcohols most commonly used are glycols of ethylene, propylene, 1,3- and 2,3-butylene, diethylene, and dipropylene. Unsaturated dihydric alcohols are not commercially available. The dibasic acids, therefore, must supply the necessary unsaturation or double bonds to the polyester base resin. The unsaturated dibasic acid is usually maleic anhydride or fumaric acid. The most common saturated dibasic-acid components are phthalic anhydric and adipic and azelaic acids.

The polymerizable monomer can be styrene, vinyl-toluene, diallyl phthalate, methyl methacrylate, or triallyl cyanurate.

Under the influence of heat and/or peroxide catalyst, the monomer and unsaturated polyester base copolymerize. No gas or liquid is evolved during the cure. The curing reaction is exothermic and the heat evolved aids in speeding it. The particular nature of this polymerization provides the vital factors of speed and simplicity so important in field applications of polyesters.

**Fabricating Methods.** The main fields of application for the polymerizable polyesters are hand lay-up, preform or mat molding, premix molding, and casting.

The hand lay-up method is used to make large shaped articles such as boats and radomes. Fibrous glass mat or cloth supplies the necessary reinforcement. Either a male or female mold can be used. The fibrous glass polyester laminates are laid up against the mold. Sometimes a bag of impervious material is placed over the laminate and either vacuum or pressure used to hold it in place during cure. Curing can be at room or elevated temperature. Production is relatively slow.

Preform or mat molding utilizes heated, matched-metal molds. The mat or preform is placed into the heated mold, the catalyzed polyester is poured in, and closing the mold forces the resin throughout the reinforcement. Conventional molding cycles are 2 to 4 min. at 220 to 260°F and 50 to 200 psi.

Premix molding provides a rapid method of making less critical parts at considerably lower cost than by mat or preform molding. It makes possible the molding of parts with varying wall thicknesses, intricate contours, and molded-in inserts. In this method, resin, reinforcement, filler, and catalyst are mixed in a dough-type mixer. The resulting material varies from a putty to straw-like mass, depending on the composition. Typical molding cycles are ¾ to 2 min. at 270 to 300°F and 500 to 1500 psi.

In the casting field, little if any reinforcing agent is used. Castings are made from both clear and filled resin by pouring the catalyzed resin into a mold. Curing can take place at room or elevated temperature.

**Properties.** The important general properties typical of all polymerizable polyesters are : (1) Ease of handling. Polyesters in the uncured state are easily handled liquids. They cure to a solid material with no liquid or gases evolved. (2) Rapid cure for thermosetting resins. (3) Ease of coloring. Polyesters are light-colored liquids which can readily be pigmented to any desired color. (4) Excellent dimensional stability. (5) Good electrical properties. (6) Good physical properties.

Specialty type polyesters designed for specific applications can have one or a combination of the following additional properties:

(1) Good weathering and light stability. (2) Heat resistance. The use of monomers, such as triallyl cyanurate, in conjunction with highly unsaturated polyester bases, raises the operating temperature of polyester-fibrous glass laminates to 500°F. (3) Flame resistance. (4) Corrosion resistance.

**End Uses.** Polyester resins are so widely used that only a listing of the major fields can be given here.

Architectural sheet is a major outlet for polyesters and takes advantage of their ease of handling, good weathering, ease of coloring, and good physical properties. These sheets, used principally as skylights, industrial glazing, and awnings are made in light transmissions varying from 5 to 80 per cent.

Premix materials constitute one of the fastest growing segments of the polyester field at present. Major end uses are electrical equipment parts, refrigerator striker plates, automotive heater ducts, automotive air conditioner parts, and automotive garnish moldings (window frames).

The automotive heater housing application is an excellent example of a higher cost material (premix) replacing a lower cost material (steel) and resulting in a more efficient heater at a lower over-all cost. The original metal design required 15 separate metal stampings and many smaller parts. These parts have been replaced by 3 premix moldings.

Matched-metal moldings are represented by cafeteria trays, tote boxes, chairs, laundry tubs, washing machine tubs, automotive parts, lamp shades, bows, sleds, luggage and boats.

Hand lay-up applications, which were the first large-scale application of polyester resins, are still major production items. Radomes up to 36 ft. in length are being produced, boats up to 24 ft. long are in volume production, and tanks of various types are being made for the storage of certain corrosive liquids, for electroplating baths, and for similar uses.

Castings are being produced for aircraft glazing. Filled castings are being used in electrical components, such as cable terminals and terminal blocks. Decorative castings are the newest, largest, and most rapidly growing segment of this field. Polyester buttons are being produced in quantity.

Included among other polyester products are the following:

*Plasticizers:* A number of polyester plasticizers are available commercially. In general they are saturated resins of controlled molecular weight. They are more viscous and, because of their low volatility, are more permanent than other esters used for plasticizers, and they may be used in both organic coatings and plastics.

*Fiber and Film:* A special type of saturated polyester prepared from ethylene glycol and terephthalic acid has found application in the textile fiber field and as film. Clothing fabric woven with fibers (Dacron) of this polyester has good wear resistance and laundering characteristics. The film (Mylar) features well known tensile strength and tear resistance and is finding ready application in electrical and packaging applications.

*Polyurethane Resins:* Other saturated polyesters with lower molecular weights and differing compositions are entering the rapidly expanding field of polyurethane resins. The polyesters are used in conjunction with diisocyanate compounds to form foams, elastomers, and coatings.

Saturated polyesters and diisocyanates of appropriate composition can also be reacted to form polyurethane elastomers. These are capable of being cross-linked, by reaction with suitable agents, to form extremely tough and wear-resistant rubber products.*

A polyester-base insulating varnish has been developed which it is claimed will replace the more expensive silicone varnishes on some small electric motors. This varnish is quoted at $3.50 a gallon against $15.00 for silicone motor varnishes. Polyester magnet-wire enamels also are used in the manufacture of small motors.

A polyester-acrylic resin made into a translucent glass-fiber panel with the trade name Paraplex** withstood a two-year outdoor test without changing in appearance, whereas a conventional polyester glass-fiber panel under a similar test became opaque and discolored.

Polyester film finds a market in the packaging of precooked frozen meats and other food. The food is prepared merely by placing the unopened bag in boiling water for the desired time.

When Brunswick engineers sought the best material for the rake board of an automatic bowling alley pinsetter they tested many plastics and selected polyester resin and fiber glass. Its winning qualities were its light weight, smooth surface, toughness, and wear-resistance.

A fire-resistant type of polyester resin is produced by Durez Plastics Division, Hooker Electrochemical Company. The difference between this and conventional polyesters lies in the substitution of a chemical known as het† acid in place of phthalic anhydride. Applications include corrugated and flat translucent panels for daylighting in factories and schools.

---

* Concludes Barrett Division section.
** Rohm & Haas.
† Chlorendic acid.

Price of polyester conventional resins          33¢ to 38¢ per lb.
Price of fire resistant types                   43¢ to 48¢ per lb.

Glass-fiber reinforced polyester resins are now supplied in rope form, which lends itself to automatic molding. The plastics rope is drawn into a chopper where a guillotine blade slices a piece off to the required length and the piece then drops into the proper cavity of the mold.

TABLE 2.16. TYPICAL PROPERTIES OF CAST, UNFILLED, RIGID POLYESTERS
(Determined on castings ⅛ in. thick)

| | |
|---|---|
| Barcol hardness | 48 |
| Specific gravity | 1.22 |
| Ultimate tensile strength, psi | 10,600 |
| Ultimate compressive strength, psi | 22,500 |
| Ultimate flexural strength, psi | 16,700 |
| Heat distortion temperature, °F | 194 |
| Water absorption, 24 hr, % | 0.21 |
| Flammability, in./min. | 0.87 |
| Dielectric constant at 60 cycles | 3.43 |
| Dielectric constant at $10^6$ cycles | 3.00 |
| Power factor at 60 cycles | 0.012 |
| Power factor at $10^6$ cycles | 0.015 |
| Dielectric strength | |
| Short time test at 77°F | 344 |
| Short time test at 212°F | 312 |
| Step-by-step test at 77°F | 308 |
| Step-by-step test at 212°F | 259 |

Reinforced polyester panels with built-in metal mesh have been announced by the Resolite Corp., Zelienople, Pennsylvania. These glass-fiber reinforced panels feature aluminum or steel mesh embedded in the plastics. They have high impact strength and suggest such uses as protective skylights, windows or similar applications. Sheets are available in both a standard and a special fire-retardant type. They can be obtained clear and in five colors—ice blue, pale green, yellow, sky blue, and coral. Average light transmission value is 50 per cent.

TABLE 2.17. PROPERTIES OF TYPICAL RIGID POLYESTER LAMINATES

(Determined on laminates ⅛ in. thick)

|  | Mat Laminate [a] | Cloth Laminate [b] |
|---|---|---|
| Resin content, % | 63.9 | 38.0 |
| Specific gravity | 1.49 | 1.80 |
| Barcol hardness | 51 | 69 |
| Ultimate tensile strength, psi | 16,900 | 45,000 |
| Ultimate compressive strength, psi | 27,000 | 35,400 |
| Water absorption, 24 hr, % | 0.18 | 0.18 |
| Ultimate flexural strength | | |
| at 73.5°F, psi | 37,500 | 58,700 |
| at 160°F, psi | 23,800 | 51,700 |
| after 2 hr boil, psi | 21,600 | 53,100 |
| Modulus of elasticity | | |
| at 73.5°F, psi | $1.45 \times 10^6$ | $3.0 \times 10^6$ |
| at 160°F, psi | $0.78 \times 10^6$ | $2.3 \times 10^6$ |
| after 2 hr boil, psi | $1.11 \times 10^6$ | $2.7 \times 10^6$ |

[a] Mat laminate: 3 plies of 2-oz., chrome-finished glass mat, cured 3 min. at 235°F. between metal platens at a pressure of 0 to 15 psi.

[b] Cloth laminate: 12 plies of 181-style glass fabric, silicone-finished and cured 3 min. at 235°F. between cauls at a pressure of 0 to 15 psi.

Mylar is Du Pont's trade mark for a durable, exceedingly tough modified polyester film. It is available in thicknesses ranging from 0.00025 to 0.0075 inch and is usually supplied in roll form. Its uses include electrical insulation for transformers, capacitors and generators besides many non-electrical applications such as a printed covering for acoustical tile.

Terephthalate polyesters should be mentioned here although their importance to date has been mostly in fibers. Of these probably Dacron fibers and fabrics are best known.

When properly stressed in production these materials form the toughest of all fibers. Dacron is made from methyl terephthalate and ethylene glycol. It is available as continuous filament yarn and as staple. Its tensile strength for the high tenacity variety is reported as 106,000 to 109,000 psi with an elongation of 11 to 13 per cent. It has a specific gravity of 1.38 and a melting point of 480°F. It has good resistance to most mineral acids but only moderate resistance to alkalies. At present its chief uses are for apparel, curtains, belts, and fire hose.

TABLE 2.18. TYPICAL PHYSICAL PROPERTIES OF UNFILLED, CAST BLENDS OF RIGID AND FLEXIBLE POLYESTER RESINS FOR VARYING RESIN CONTENT

| Resin Content | | Heat Distortion Temperature (264 psi) | Tensile Strength | Elongation | Flexural Strength | Modulus of Elasticity in Flexure |
|---|---|---|---|---|---|---|
| Rigid | Flexible | | | | | |
| % | % | °F | $10^3$ psi | % | $10^3$ psi | $10^5$ psi |
| 100 | 0 | 194 | 10.6 | 1.8 | 16.7 | 6.9 |
| 90 | 10 | 183 | 11.2 | 2.3 | 17.3 | 6.8 |
| 80 | 20 | 174 | 10.1 | 2.8 | 17.5 | 5.6 |
| 70 | 30 | 163 | 9.1 | 3.7 | 18.3 | 5.4 |
| 60 | 40 | 150 | 8.5 | 4.8 | 15.1 | 3.9 |
| 50 | 50 | 138 | 5.8 | 8.2 | 11.2 | 2.7 |
| 40 | 60 | 125 | 4.2 | 22.1 | — | — |
| 30 | 70 | 116 | 3.3 | 32.2 | — | — |
| 20 | 80 | 100 | 2.7 | 41.2 | — | — |
| 10 | 90 | — | 2.3 | 54.2 | — | — |
| 0 | 100 | — | 1.4 | 65.3 | — | — |

Polyester molding powders may be reinforced with short glass fibers to produce moldings with unusual properties. Such powders can be handled or processed on conventional injection, compression or transfer molding equipment. They have better heat performance and better strength than the unreinforced powders. They can be held to closer tolerances and the finished part resists dimensional change due to moisture and weathering.

Reinforced polyesters have been used for valves in the pulp and paper industry, for parts for a marine clutch control, and for the cooling fan built in as part of an electric motor, to name but a few applications.

TABLE 2.19. A POLYESTER METAL-FILLED MOLDING COMPOUND

(Average Values)

| Properties | Polyester |
|---|---|
| Specific gravity | 2.2 |
| Tensile strength, psi | 3,500 |
| Compressive strength, psi | 18,000 |
| Continuous heat resistance, °F | 320 |
| Heat distortion temperature, °F | 400 |
| Dielectric strength, v. per mil | 400 |
| Machining qualities | good |
| Effect of sunlight | slight |
| Per cent water absorption, 24 hr | 0.11-0.5 |
| Resistance to strong acids | poor |
| Resistance to weak acids | good |
| Resistance to strong alkalies | poor |
| Resistance to weak alkalies | fair |
| Color range | not good |

**Citrate Polyesters.**\* Citric acid, the only pure tricarboxylic acid available in quantity at a moderate cost, has long been of interest in the polyester and alkyd fields. The glycerol esters have been most frequently mentioned. When citric acid and glycerol in approximately equivalent proportions are esterified at 320 to 390°F a hard thermoset resin results. Carriers may be impregnated with the partially esterified mixture, or with the reactants themselves in solution, and subsequently baked. The risk of premature gelation may be avoided by employing a molar ratio of glycerol to citric acid of 3:1 in the esterification. This reaction may safely be carried to a low acid number and the resulting triester applied in water or aqueous alcohol as a coating. Subsequent baking at 320°F leads to a water-resistant finish said to be equal or superior to linseed oil coatings in a number of respects. Polyesters of citric acid and glycerol also have been described as useful adhesives and cloth-coatings. It is further reported that citric acid, heated with an unsaturated fatty acid

---

\* Prepared in cooperation with C. Knuth, Chas. Pfizer & Co., Inc., Brooklyn, N. Y.

and a trace of mineral acid, is converted to the unsaturated tricarboxylic acid, aconitic; if a terpene is present the aconitic acid condenses with it. Alkyds useful in varnishes and gasket materials have been prepared by esterifying citric acid with such polyols as castor oil, pentaerythritol, and trimethylol propane.

Unsaturated polyesters suitable for casting and laminating are prepared by esterification of citric acid with allyl alcohol and a glycol. Four moles of citric acid are esterified with 3 moles of a glycol and then with 6 moles of allyl alcohol. The resulting neutral syrups can be homopolymerized to transparent, rigid products with peroxide catalysts. Polymerization rates are lower than those obtained with the glycol maleates but higher than with other allyl resins tested. The polyesters are compatible with methyl methacrylate and vinyl acetate but not with styrene.

### Polyethylene

The fifth plastic type in production for 1956 was polyethylene, but in the minds of most students of the plastics market this is the plastics with the brightest future. The total production of polyethylene in 1950 was under 50,000,000 pounds but in 1956 its production had increased almost tenfold to 450,000,000 pounds, and some estimates place its 1960 production at close to 1,000,000,000 pounds.

The polyethylene resins have outstanding electrical properties and excellent water resistance. They also have good resistance to most organic chemicals. They are the lightest of all the plastics with a specific gravity ranging from 0.91 to 0.96. In appearance they are translucent white and have a rather waxlike feel. As materials for fabrication they are about half way between rigid and nonrigid plastics, or half way between polystyrene and plasticized vinyls.

They can be molded, extruded, calendered and applied in films, either from solutions or by flame-spraying. They soften at about 230°F. In film form they have good tensile and tear strength and puncture resistance. As a result of these properties, combined with an absence of taste or odor, they are used extensively for packaging fresh produce, hardware, toys, and many other types of merchandise. Some typical uses for other forms of polyethylene are squeezable bottles, acid-resistant tank and pipe linings, wire insulation, molded containers, bristles, and textiles. One of the largest polyethylene moldings is a 22-gallon can. Other large moldings include dish pans, baby baths and laundry baskets.

Housewives, discouraged with the failure of some plastics, are regaining confidence through their experience with polyethylene, partly due to the sound design of many recent polyethylene dishes and kitchen utensils. It is claimed that more than half of the annual polyethylene used in housewares will be in pieces ranging from 3 to 12 pounds each. The average price of polyethylene molding powder is 39 cents per pound and the average per pound price of the finished household item is $2.04.

Figure 2.10. Polyethylene film is used as a strawberry mulch by the Ishibashi Brothers on their California ranch. The film is 0.00125 in. thick and 34 in. wide. It has half inch holes along the edges to allow irrigation water to reach the plant roots.

Polyethylene as originally developed in the United States by Bakelite and Du Pont was produced by a high-pressure method. Within recent years the Ziegler and Phillips low-pressure processes have been brought to this country by several United States chemical companies. One of these, Du Pont, states "Polyethylene produced by low-pressure techniques differs from high-pressure polyethylene; it has additional strength, stiffness and resistance to heat distortion and vapor transmission."

A material similar to polyethylene—an olefin polymer based on ethylene—is said to represent a new family and bears the trade name Fortiflex. It is a highly crystalline material with some physical properties similar to those-of conventional polyethylene and with some properties that are superior. It is denser, more rigid, harder, and has greater surface gloss—properties which are better for some applications and not as good for others. The Manufacturing Chemists' Association has published data showing Fortiflex to have heat resistance above 225°F and tensile strength more than double that of conventional polyethylene.

The development of Irrathene, irradiated polyethylene, was announced in 1954 by the General Electric Company of Schenectady, New York, and is now in commercial production. Irrathene electrical insulation is produced in the form of tapes and films which retain the excellent elec-

*(Courtesy Bakelite Co.)*

Figure 2.11. A new 22-gallon trash can molded of polyethylene imparts all of the properties of this material to what has long been one of the most unsightly of all household items. It is noiseless, break resistant, non-rusting, non-denting, lightweight, colorful and easy to clean. Colors are molded in so that they cannot be chipped or washed away. The lid can be unlocked with a simple twist of the wrist. The top diameter of the can is 20½ in. and the height is 27¾ in. Rust is no problem since polyethylene resists water, oil, grease, harsh alkalies and even sharp acids. Even after rough handling by the garbage collector, can springs back into shape without showing a dent, and the usual clatter is eliminated at the same time. The retail price is about $12.95.

trical properties of polyethylene over a wide temperature and frequency range. The material has a high dielectric strength and a low power factor. Non-melting and dimensionally stable at high temperatures it has been recommended for use as a Class A insulating material for a hot-spot rating of 225°F. However, in sealed systems or in the absence of oxygen the material is said to withstand temperatures up to nearly 400°F with little or no change in mechanical or electrical properties over prolonged exposure.

*(Courtesy Celanese Corp. of America)*

Figure 2.12. Drum liners of polyethylene are becoming increasingly popular. They are tear resistant, highly inert to most chemicals and low in moisture vapor transmission.

Some recent investigations have developed the fact that carbon black dispersed in polyethylene resin is effective in preventing degradation due to sunlight and weathering. Those who wish to know more about this interesting work and its results are referred to Acheson Dispersed Pigments Co.*

* 2250 E. Ontario St., Philadelphia 34, Pennsylvania.

Figure 2.13. A new type of outdoor bowling pin molded of polyethylene.

TABLE 2.20. PHYSICAL PROPERTIES OF POLYETHYLENE*
(Average Values)

| Properties | High Modulus Type | Low Modulus Type |
|---|---|---|
| Specific gravity | 0.93-0.95 | 0.92 |
| Tensile strength, psi | 4000 | 1700 |
| Compressive strength, psi | — | — |
| Continuous heat resistance, °F | 250 | 212 |
| Heat distortion temperature, °F | — | 120 |
| Dielectric strength, v. per mil | 600 | 460 |
| Machining qualities | good | fair |
| Effect of sunlight | surface crazing | surface crazing |
| Per cent water absorption, 24 hr | — | 0.01 |
| Resistance to strong acids | poor | poor |
| Resistance to weak acids | excellent | good |
| Resistance to strong alkalies | good | good |
| Resistance to weak alkalies | excellent | good |
| Clarity | translucent to opaque | translucent to opaque |

* See also Table 2.9.

**Polyethylene Fibers.** In the textile industry the polyethylene fibers most widely used are the staple fibers. These are produced by melting the molding powder, then extruding thin filaments through a spinneret, and solidifying these by cooling either in water or air. The result is a monofilament which is too plastic and easily stretched to be suitable for use as a textile yarn. It therefore must be drawn to orient its structure and to give it suitable mechanical properties. It is set by annealing, usually in a hot water bath. The staple is produced by chopping or cutting the monofilaments into short lengths. The fibers range from 0.005 to 0.05 inch in diameter.

Polyethylene yarns are also produced by combining a number of fine monofilaments, and twisting them sufficiently to hold them together in the form of a yarn.

A floss or mass of short fine fibers of random lengths may be produced by subjecting the filaments immediately after extrusion to a blast of compressed air. Such a floss may be laid out as a sheet on suitable rolls and bonded by heat to form a non-woven fabric.

The properties of polyethylene yarns are, of course, controlled to a large extent by the general properties of the basic material. Compared with other synthetic yarns they have above average extensibility and below average strength. Prolonged exposure to sunlight tends to decrease the tensile strength but this may be counteracted with suitable pigments. The low specific gravity gives the polyethylene yarns the greatest yield in yards per pound of any of the synthetic yarns. As an example a monofil 0.08 inch in diameter will average about 17,000 yards per pound.

Fabrics made from these yarns are used in curtains, upholstery, and as filter cloth in chemical plants.

TABLE 2.21. SUMMARY OF POLYETHYLENE QUALITIES AND USES*

| Important Qualities | Familiar Uses |
|---|---|
| Unbreakable and waxy | squeeze bottles |
| Ranges from rigid shapes to flexible film | tumblers, package film |
| Seals in water vapor but allows passage of oxygen | food bags |
| Very good electrical insulator | radar cable insulator |
| Highly resistant to most solvents and chemicals (hydrochloric acid, for example) | chemical carboys |
| Full range of satiny colors. Can be heat sealed. | packaging |

* Bakelite.

## Polystyrene

This widely used thermoplastic is characterized by low specific gravity, good resistance to water and chemicals, and by fine clarity. In addition, it has good dimensional stability, is readily moldable, is water white in color and has the highest insulation power of the more common thermoplastics. It is soluble in aromatic hydrocarbons but has very low water absorption; it has good mechanical strength. Its uses include impregnation of electric coils, lamination of fabrics, and bonding of abrasive wheels.

Because polystyrene is free from taste and odor and is easily molded, it is extensively used in housewares and for toys. Some of the more common uses are combs, flashlight cases, clock cases and novelties. Other uses include wall tile, refrigerator parts, and small radio housings.

TABLE 2.22. PHYSICAL PROPERTIES OF POLYSTYRENE

(Average Values)

| Properties | Polystyrene |
| --- | --- |
| Specific gravity | 1.06 |
| Tensile strength, psi | 6,500 |
| Compressive strength, psi | 13,000 |
| Rockwell hardness (M scale) | 80 |
| Dielectric strength, v. per mil | 600 |
| Heat distortion temperature, °F | 185 |
| Resistance to flame | fair |
| Resistance to water | good |
| Resistance to acids | fair |
| Effect of sunlight | fair (yellows outdoors) |
| Crazing resistance | fair |
| Abrasion resistance | good |
| Light transmission, % | 93 |

Its relatively low price and its ready adaptability to injection molding have brought production up near the top of the list. It has surpassed phenolics within the past few years and is now second only to the vinyls in total monthly output. It is one of the lighest of plastics with a specific gravity of 1.055. It can be injection molded to sharply defined detail.

Polystyrene molding materials are usually fabricated by high-speed, automatic injection molding, for which they are excellently adapted. Sprues, gates, and other sections removed from the molded pieces in the finishing operation can be reworked, thus reducing waste to a minimum.

The principal shortcomings of polystyrene are its brittleness, low heat resistance, and tendency to craze. Crazing often results from the use of metal inserts. Prolonged stress on thin sections should be avoided. To overcome such difficulties several modified varieties have been offered commercially. Impact resistance has been increased by modifying it with a rubbery constituent but it has been difficult to find an additive which will improve its heat resistance. Perhaps the most successful work has been in the field of substituted styrenes. Methylstyrene made by a new monomer synthesis by American Cyanamid research workers has produced molding compounds resistant to 212°F, with shrinkage less than 0.31 per cent.

A styrene-acrylonitrile copolymer is available from Bakelite Co. This resin resists staining by inks, carbon paper, oil, and cleaning fluid and is used for electric typewriter keys, bars, and knobs.

TABLE 2.23. SUMMARY OF POLYSTYRENE PROPERTIES*

| Important Qualities | Familiar Uses |
| --- | --- |
| Rigid, as strong at freezing as at room temperature with a good wearing surface | refrigerator storage bins |
| Does not absorb water | wall tile |
| Good electrical insulator | radio housing |
| Can be clear transparent | light diffuser |
| Full range of transparent, translucent opaque colors | jewelry, kitchenware, toys |

* Bakelite.

## Polyurethanes*

The polyurethanes (also called isocyanate resins) are perhaps the newest entry in the field of plastics in the United States. An outgrowth of research in Germany and in the United States during 1937-1945, they have approached commercial production here only within the last two years. Prior to that time both production of polyurethanes and applications of isocyanate resins were in the development stage. With the successful German development of elastic isocyanate foam of exceptional quality, however, full-scale isocyanate production became economically attractive. The resulting major reduction in the prices of these compounds imme-

* Prepared in cooperation with J. H. Saunders, Assistant Director of Research, Mobay Chemical Co.

diately broadened their scope of practical applications. The chief fields of use now include flexible and rigid foams and coatings, with adhesives and synthetic elastomers being in the development stage, but showing great promise. A host of other potential uses are being investigated.

**Foams.** During the last year urethane foams have achieved new importance with the rapid development of soft and flexible varieties. These flexible foams are offering competition to latex foam rubber and flexible vinyl foams. In addition, the development of rigid urethane foams has continued at an accelerated rate.

Generally, both types of urethane foams are prepared commercially from polyesters,* diisocyanates, and water. The mechanical characteristics of the foam depend largely on the choice of polymer. By varying the degree of branching one can prepare either flexible or rigid foams. The diisocyanate reacts with the polyester, converting that low molecular weight, liquid polymer, into a high molecular weight elastomer or plastic. At the same time the diisocyanate reacts with the water to generate carbon dioxide, which foams the resin. The density of the foam is controlled by the amount of water and the corresponding amount of diisocyanate used. Thus density and degree of flexibility or rigidity can be controlled independently.

In addition to these major ingredients other agents such as catalysts and emulsifiers may be added to control the rate of foaming and the cell structure of the foam.

One of the most significant factors in the field of urethane foams is the development of suitable machinery for the continuous production of foam of outstanding quality and uniformity of structure. Blocks of flexible foam up to 80 in. wide, 25 ft. long and 10 in. high are being produced. Spray-gun type and intermittent foaming equipment are also being developed.

An outstanding advantage of urethane foams is that they can be "foamed in place," without applying heat or pressure. The foam rises, completely filling irregular cavities, and bonds well to the walls of the container. The foaming reactions are exothermic and of sufficient driving force to complete curing of the foam. This is of special value in the use of rigid foams for structural and insulation purposes, where great savings in labor may be realized. It is also of value in foaming shaped articles in molds using flexible or rigid foams.

The urethane foams are exceedingly versatile in their applications. Foam properties available include soft, flexible, or tough, rigid types of great strength, as well as an infinite number having properties between these two extremes. All types are characterized by excellent resistance

---

* Or polyethers.

to oxidation, solvents, and temperature. Other properties are more specific, depending upon whether or not the foam is flexible or rigid.

Flexible foams having a predominantly open cell structure are available in a density range of 2 to 6 lb./cu. ft. The foam may be prepared in a variety of colors, and may easily be produced so that it will not support combustion. Mechanical properties are such that a 2.5 lb./cu. ft. urethane foam is superior to a medium density latex foam in load bearing characteristics and tensile strength.

This combination of properties makes flexible urethane foam excellent for cushions, upholstery, padding and rug underlay. The flame-resistant characteristics make it specially attractive for use in public buildings and for transportation vehicles. Its high tensile, tear, and abrasion resistance make it desirable for use as toys, sponges, and gaskets. Its open cell structure and good sound absorption, flame resistance, and ease of being spray-painted insure its use as an acoustic insulation medium.

Rigid urethane foams are available in a density range of 2 to 30 lb./cu. ft., and have predominantly closed cells. A variety of these are available having different mechanical properties. Compression and tensile strengths are outstanding. In addition, their adhesion to container walls and impact and vibration resistance are excellent. The dielectric properties, chemical resistance, and thermal conductivity properties are good. The maximum temperature for use is high—305°F for a standard 12 lb./cu. ft. foam.

These properties make the rigid foams attractive for applications requiring simplicity of processing equipment, good mechanical strength, temperature and vibration resistance, and closed cell structure. They have been used extensively in the aircraft industry for filling cavities in radomes, ailerons, rudders, elevators, wing tabs, and for insulating cabin ventilating systems. Other important uses include the construction of non-sinkable boats and pontoons. Applications in the field of insulation, as in houses and refrigerators, are being explored.

## The Vinyls

These comprise a large group of thermoplastic resins which taken as a whole, have the highest production rate in this country of any plastics; their present rate of increase in use is equalled only by the polyethylenes. All the vinyls have in common a vinyl linkage but here is another instance where plastics nomenclature is difficult to follow because not all resins with a vinyl linkage are included in this group. The styrenes and the acrylics both contain the vinyl linkage but in commercial practice are not considered as vinyls.

The following eight resins are generally considered as completing the group of commercial vinyls:

> polyvinyl acetal
> polyvinyl acetate
> polyvinyl alcohol
> polyvinyl butyral
> polyvinyl carbazole
> polyvinyl chloride
> polyvinyl chloride-acetate
> polyvinylidene chloride

The vinyls as a family are characterized by toughness and chemical inertness. In general, they have excellent electrical properties and are readily modified with plasticizers and other ingredients. Modifiers can be used to produce elastomeric materials and others ranging from rigid to putty soft.

As a group the vinyls offer a versatility not matched by any other family of plastics. They span the scale from rigid polyvinyl chloride pipe to flexible vinyl butyral used for safety glass sandwiches, to vinyl plastisol molded squeeze toys. For economy on a volume basis when requirements are not too strict they can be filled with chalk or clay, at 2 cents a lb., or blown into foams that are more than 90 per cent air. Many types of processors find use for the vinyls. These vary from large manufacturers of upholstery and shower curtains with million dollar calender-banbury installations to plastisol molders and electronic heat-sealers with facilities valued at less than $10,000.

A brief description of each of the vinyl types appears in the following pages.

TABLE 2.24. SUMMARY OF VINYL PROPERTIES*

| Important Qualities | Familiar Uses |
| --- | --- |
| May be flexible, semi-rigid, rigid | curtains, floor tile, light shields |
| Long-wearing: hard to break either in rigid or flexible form | phonograph records |
| Excellent electrical insulator | wire insulation |
| Resists penetration of water | wading pool |
| Can be clear transparent | packaging |
| Full range of transparent, translucent, opaque colors | safety glass interlayer, lamp shades, table mats |
| Can be heat sealed | rainwear |

* Bakelite.

**Polyvinyl Acetal Resins.** Obtained by partial hydrolysis of polyvinyl acetate the properties of these acetal resins depend upon the molecular weight of the starting polyvinyl acetate and the degree of hydrolysis. Values usually lie somewhere between the properties of the polyvinyl formals and those of the polyvinyl butyrals with which the acetals are related. If butyraldehyde is the starting material polyvinyl butyral is formed.

The uses for this group, which includes the acetals, the formals and the butyrals, are mostly in lacquers, coatings, and impregnations but these resins may also be used for moldings and for castings. They have poor water resistance but high softening temperatures.

**Polyvinyl Acetate.** This odorless and colorless thermoplastic resin is used mostly as a copolymer with polyvinyl chloride, but with special fillers it may be used for moldings and extrusions. Its specific gravity is 1.19 and it probably is best known as an ingredient of plastic wood. Other uses include lacquers and inks, protective films, floor tiles, and artificial leather. It forms a good adhesive and a size for paper.

TABLE 2.25. PHYSICAL PROPERTIES OF VINYL ACETATE

(Average Values)

| Properties | Vinyl Acetate |
|---|---|
| Specific gravity | 1.19 |
| Tensile strength, psi | 4700 |
| Compressive strength, psi | varies |
| Continuous heat resistance, °F | easily softened |
| Heat distortion temperature, °F | 100 |
| Dielectric strength, v. per mil | varies |
| Machining qualities | fair |
| Effect of sunlight | no effect |
| Per cent water absorption, 24 hr | 3 |
| Resistance to strong acids | poor |
| Resistance to weak acids | good |
| Resistance to strong alkalies | poor |
| Resistance to weak alkalies | excellent |
| Clarity | transparent |

**Polyvinyl Alcohols.** Some unusual properties are found in these thermoplastic resins. If completely hydrolyzed they will dissolve in water, a property used in fabric design and in lace production. Polyvinyl alcohol fibers are mixed with non-soluble fibers for the purpose of weaving and are then dissolved leaving the pattern or the lace intact.

These resins have good clarity, abrasion resistance, and strong adhesive properties. They have good resistance to oils and chemicals and good water solubility. Molding powders, water solutions, and cast and extruded sheets are available.

TABLE 2.26. PHYSICAL PROPERTIES OF VINYL ALCOHOL

(Average Values)

| Properties | Vinyl Alcohol |
|---|---|
| Specific gravity | 1.21-1.31 |
| Tensile strength, psi | 3000 |
| Compressive strength, psi | * |
| Continuous heat resistance, °F | * |
| Heat distortion temperature, °F | * |
| Dielectric strength, v. per mil | * |
| Machining qualities | fair |
| Effect of sunlight | none to slight |
| Per cent water absorption, 24 hr | 30 or more |
| Resistance to strong acids | poor |
| Resistance to weak acids | poor |
| Resistance to strong alkalies | poor |
| Resistance to weak alkalies | poor |
| Clarity | transparent to opaque |

* This material readily absorbs enough atmospheric moisture to make these values useless.

**Polyvinyl Butyral.** This resin, which has a hydroxyl content, has proved to be the best safety glass interlayer because of its clarity, toughness, and adhesiveness. It is also used for bullet-proof glass. The resins are available as molding powder but find relatively small application as moldings because of the availability and versatility of the other vinyls. The butyrals have good compatibility with plasticizers and can be modified by the addition of thermosetting materials, such as phenolics, to raise their water resistance and softening temperature. Added toughness, and thermal and abrasion resistance have been produced in this way.

TABLE 2.27. PHYSICAL PROPERTIES OF VINYL BUTYRAL

(Average Values)

| Properties | Vinyl Butyral |
|---|---|
| Specific gravity | 1.12 |
| Tensile strength, psi | 6000 |
| Compressive strength, psi | low |
| Continuous heat resistance, °F | 125 |
| Heat distortion temperature, °F | 120 |
| Dielectric strength, v. per mil | 375 |
| Machining qualities | good |
| Effect of sunlight | slight |
| Per cent water absorption, 24 hr | 2.0 |
| Resistance to strong acids | good |
| Resistance to weak acids | good |
| Resistance to strong alkalies | good |
| Resistance to weak alkalies | good |
| Clarity | transparent to opaque |

**Vinyl Carbazole Resin.**\* More compact electronic units operating at high frequencies and utilizing exceptionally high temperatures have largely been made possible by the development of new resinous materials. Among the most interesting of these plastics is polyvinyl carbazole which combines a high heat distortion point with the ability to maintain excellent electrical properties under exceptional operating conditions. A mica shortage was largely responsible for research leading to these new dielectric materials which can be used where mica is not suitable. They have the trade name Polectron and are produced commercially by General Aniline & Film Corp. by very specialized, high-pressure acetylation techniques. Their properties are summarized in Table 2.28.

The outstanding commercial application of Polectron *monomer* is as a dielectric impregnant for stationary electrical assemblies, such as rolled

---

\* Prepared in cooperation with General Aniline & Film Corp.

and stacked condensers. Its unique characteristics make it possible to first impregnate the condensers with molten monomer and subsequently to polymerize it by means of heat to give rigid assemblies.

Data obtained from laboratory evaluation of monomer-impregnated paper condensers show the following:

*Power Factor* at 1 kc. decreases from 0.4 to 0.7 per cent at room temperature to a minimum of 0.3 per cent at 80°C, then increases to about 1.4 per cent at 130°C.

*Capacitance* increases approximately 6 per cent from 30 to 120°C with the curve rising somewhat faster at higher temperatures.

*Insulation resistance* is considerably higher than that of most impregnated condensers, having a value of 2000 to 3200 megohms at 60°C. This value drops to 21 to 25 megohms at 120°C.

TABLE 2.28. PHYSICAL PROPERTIES OF VINYL CARBAZOLE
(Average Values)

| Properties | Vinyl Carbazole |
| --- | --- |
| Specific gravity | 1.20 |
| Tensile strength, psi | varies |
| Compressive strength, psi | low |
| Continuous heat resistance, °F | 260 |
| Heat distortion temperature, °F | 225 |
| Dielectric strength, v. per mil | 800 |
| Machining qualities | fair |
| Effect of sunlight | slight |
| Per cent water absorption, 24 hr | 0.1 |
| Resistance to strong acids | fair |
| Resistance to weak acids | good |
| Resistance to strong alkalies | fair |
| Resistance to weak alkalies | good |
| Clarity | opaque |

Polectron *monomer* is a skin irritant but the polymer has a weak effect. Oral toxicity of the monomer is also relatively high. However, special precautions regarding ventilation and protective clothing will eliminate or greatly decrease hazards of handling.

Polectron *polymer* is useful in a wide variety of molding or fibering purposes. It is an effective impregnant for paper, cotton, silk, glass and other fibrous materials, resulting in products capable of withstanding high ambient temperatures. It can either be compression or injection molded, the latter generally giving better physical strength. In general the molding temperature is dependent upon the degree of plasticization which, in turn, directly affects the heat distortion point of the molded piece. In the laboratory, a molding cycle of 10 minutes heating and 10 minutes molding time at 390 to 480°F under a pressure of 1000 to 4000 psi with subsequent cooling at 250 to 300°F has been satisfactory, though the ejected piece tends to be brittle when temperatures above 440°F are used. The addition of a non-polar plasticizer such as a diphenyl, terphenyl, amyl naphthalene, phenanthrene, or electrical-grade resin such as polystyrene, permits the use of a lower molding temperature.

Polectron polymer may be injection molded at 425-550°F at pressures varying from 10,000 to 35,000 psi. As a fibrous structure may develop to a varying degree during this process, the temperatures here as well as in compression molding of fibrous compositions must be carefully controlled. If they are too high a complete relaxation of the fibers occurs with a marked loss in mechanical strength. If they are too low, a porous material with poor water resistance results.

**Other Vinyls.** Several vinyls other than those described here are available although the applications are as yet unimportant. Vinyl pyrrolidone is used some in pharmaceutical work and has been used in special cases as a blood plasma extender. Vinyl alkyl has been tried as an adhesive and has some promise as a binder in the leather industry.

**Polyvinyl Chloride (PVC).**  This widely used thermoplastic resin is similar to polyvinyl chloride-acetate but the copolymer is easier to fabricate. Polyvinyl chloride is colorless and tough, and has excellent acid and alkali resistance. However it is incompatible with most resins outside the vinyl group and when unplasticized, is hard to work. It is relatively brittle at freezing temperatures, but flexibility can be secured by the use of plasticizers. Its properties can be altered considerably by changing the method of polymerization. Small amounts of stabilizers must be added during manufacture to prevent slow decomposition. Polyvinyl-chloride textile fibers and brush bristles find moderate use because of their resistance to gasoline and alcohol.

Some proprietary rigid polyvinyl chloride compounds are claimed to have the best chemical resistance of the commonly used thermoplastic resins. One such compound has a specific gravity of 1.42, a tensile strength of 7000 psi, and a heat distortion temperature of 175°F. It is easily extruded and the end products have excellent resistance to outdoor weather.

TABLE 2.29.  PHYSICAL PROPERTIES OF POLYVINYL CHLORIDE

(Average Values)

| Properties | Polyvinyl Chloride |
|---|---|
| Specific gravity | 1.35 |
| Tensile strength, psi | 8,000 |
| Compressive strength, psi | 10,000 |
| Continuous heat resistance, °F | 212 |
| Heat distortion temperature, °F | 150 |
| Dielectric strength, v. per mil | 650 |
| Machining qualities | good |
| Effect of sunlight | none |
| Per cent water absorption, 24 hr | 0.05 |
| Resistance to strong acids | good |
| Resistance to weak acids | excellent |
| Resistance to strong alkalies | excellent |
| Resistance to weak alkalies | excellent |
| Clarity | transparent to opaque |

**Polyvinyl Chloride—Vinyl Acetate.** Because of their good workability these copolymers are the most popular of the vinyls. Compounded with a good plasticizer such as dioctyl phthalate they become rubberlike and can be given almost any desired degree of stiffness. The rigid forms have excellent dimensional stability, low mold shrinkage, good electrical properties, freedom from taste and odor and are exceptionally resistant to acids, alkalies and many other chemicals.

The elastomeric types are used for upholstery coating, for shoe soles and uppers and for many other applications which are explained more fully in Chapter 5. The moldings find extensive application as phonograph records and closures. These copolymers can be calendered, molded, extruded, cast and solution-coated. Sheets and films are readily heat sealed. The usual proportions in the copolymers are vinyl chloride 90 per cent and vinyl acetate 10 per cent. However, for use in lacquers the vinyl acetate proportion is greatly increased.

TABLE 2.30. PHYSICAL PROPERTIES OF VINYL CHLORIDE-ACETATE
(Average Values)

| Properties | Vinyl Chloride-Acetate |
|---|---|
| Specific gravity | 1.3 |
| Tensile strength, psi | 3500 |
| Compressive strength, psi | 2000 |
| Continuous heat resistance, °F | 160 |
| Heat distortion temperature, °F | varies |
| Dielectric strength, v. per mil | 400 |
| Machining qualities | good |
| Effect of sunlight | darkens slightly |
| Per cent water absorption, 24 hr | 0.2 |
| Resistance to strong acids | good |
| Resistance to weak acids | excellent |
| Resistance to strong alkalies | good |
| Resistance to weak alkalies | excellent |
| Clarity | transparent to opaque |

## Polyvinylidene Chloride (saran)

Closely associated with the vinyl plastics are the vinylidene chlorides which have been given the generic term saran. They are available with softening points ranging from 150 to 350°F. They are resistant to most acids and alkalies (except ammonium hydroxide) and are unaffected by most solvents.

The sarans, noted for their low water absorption and dimensional stability, have been used for underground piping and pipe fittings in areas where electrical factors make metal piping short lived. Saran fibers and monofilaments are readily extruded and the fibers find uses in curtain and drapery fabrics, rugs, carpets and awnings. The monofilaments find their largest application in window screens and brush bristles. Other uses for the sarans include fishing leaders, instrument belting, dog leashes and some parts for automobiles.

Films of saran are tough, easily heat-sealed, and highly water resistant— properties which make them well-suited for packaging. In this field saran competes with polyethylene. Saran molding powders are available for molding, extrusion, and casting.

TABLE 2.31. PHYSICAL PROPERTIES OF VINYLIDENE CHLORIDE (SARAN)
(Average Values)

| Properties | Vinylidene Chloride |
|---|---|
| Specific gravity | 1.68 |
| Tensile strength, psi | 4000 |
| Compressive strength, psi | 2500 |
| Continuous heat resistance, °F | 180 |
| Heat distortion temperature, °F | 140 |
| Dielectric strength, v. per mil | 350 |
| Machining qualities | good |
| Effect of sunlight | slight |
| Per cent water absorption, 24 hr | 1.5 |
| Resistance to strong acids | excellent |
| Resistance to weak acids | excellent |
| Resistance to strong alkalies | excellent |
| Resistance to weak alkalies | excellent |
| Clarity | translucent to opaque |

## Silicones*

The silicones are a relatively new class of engineering materials. Characterized by an unusual combination of properties, they have proved to be the solution to many problems in design, production and maintenance. They have increased the reliability and operating temperature span of production equipment and have reduced the maintenance required to keep production lines operating on schedule. Today, three companies produce silicones for industry, namely, Dow Corning Corporation, General Electric Company and Union Carbide and Carbon Corporation.

Chemically, silicones are semi-inorganic polymers. Their stability is attributed to their unique molecular structure of alternate silicon and oxygen atoms. In contrast to organic materials based on a carbon-to-carbon linkage, the silicones, due to the bond energy of their silicon to oxygen backbone, are held together with a force half again as strong. As a result, they show excellent resistance to the effects of heat, oxidation, and weathering. Furthermore, their unusual chemical structure and composition make them water repellent, incompatible with most organic polymers, notably indifferent to temperature variation, and resistant to electrical breakdown.

---

* Prepared in cooperation with T. A. Kauppi, Manager of Product Engineering, Dow Corning Corp., Midland, Mich.

In the plastics industry, the following physical forms of silicones are used: release agents, adhesives, laminating resins, electrical insulation, protective coating vehicles, anti-seize agents, molding compounds, and additives.

**Silicone Molding Compound.** High strength, heat-stable molded parts for mechanical or electrical applications made with silicone molding compound include aircraft brake assemblies; molded parts for jet engines, aircraft ignition systems, and guided missiles; terminal boards; connector plugs; switches; motor slot wedges and insulators.

Silicone molding compound is a high-impact, glass-fiber filled, thermosetting material that can be formed by either compression or transfer molding techniques. Properties of molded parts are influenced by mold design and size, and by preforming and molding methods. In general, the heat distortion temperature is above 900°F; flexural strength is in the range of 14,000 psi at room temperature, 5000 psi at 400°F; arc resistance is in the range of 175 seconds, and water absorption is about 0.1 per cent.

**Silicone Laminating Resins.** Silicone laminating resins are used primarily to bond glass cloth to produce heat-stable, structural and electrical laminates. They are also effectively used to bond asbestos cloth and finely divided powders such as silica, mica, and carbon. The resins available include those designed for both low-pressure and high-pressure laminating techniques.

In general, silicone glass cloth laminates have a high order of heat stability, excellent dielectric properties over a wide frequency range, superior arc resistance, and low water absorption. They retain a higher strength-to-weight ratio at high temperatures than do many light metals.

**Foamed Silicone Resins.** Silicone resins are available which may either be foamed in place to produce light-weight rigid structures, or foamed in blocks which are then cut to the desired shape and size for other uses.

They are outstanding in the field of foamed resins, as they have a distortion temperature of over 700°F. Thus, the flame of a gas burner may be turned on a foamed silicone resin without loss of the foam structure, without burning the resin, and with but slight loss of physical strength.

These resins are sold as ready-to-use powders. When properly foamed, the pores are uniform in size and distribution and they are unicellular. Such foams have a water absorption in the range of 2 to 3 per cent after 24 hours immersion. Thermal conductivity is in the range of 0.3 Btu/hr/ sq ft/°F/ in. of thickness. Densities range from 12 to 16 lb/cu ft.

**Silicone Adhesives.** Contrary to the usual "adhesive" characteristic exhibited by most silicones, a few are designed to serve as pressure-sensitive materials. As such, these silicones remain pliable and retain good adhesive strength from $-80$ to $500°F$. In addition, they possess excellent dielectric properties and good resistance to moisture, weathering, and aging. Pressure-sensitive silicone adhesives adhere well to plastics, metal, glass, and paper. Designed primarily for producing pressure-sensitive tapes, they are also used to adhere a variety of materials to fabricated plastic parts and components.

**Silicone Interlayer for Laminated Glass.** Silastic Type K Interlayer* serves as the center layer in "safety glass" windshields for supersonic aircraft. Laminated windshields made with this material retain full strength and clarity at temperatures ranging from $-65$ to over $350°F$. Up to $160°F$ they have somewhat less shatter-resistance than the conventional laminate, but the strength of the conventional plastic interlayer falls off so sharply above this that at $200°F$, the new silicone is more than twice as strong.

In the uncured stage, the silicone rubber interlayer is a soft, plastic, and extremely tacky sheet, calendered between layers of polyethylene-coated paper. Readily flowable under pressure, it requires no bonding adhesive.

When laminated and cured under pressure in either flat or curved "glazings," this sheet forms a tough, rubbery interlayer with excellent optical properties. Haze and distortion are minimized, and a high order of transmittance is obtained over the entire spectrum.

**Silicone Electrical Insulation.** The properties of silicones have made possible a new class of electrical insulation (Class H) designated for hottest spot temperature operation of $180°C$.

With a life expectancy in the range of 10 to 100 times that of the next best class of insulation under the same operating conditions, Class H (silicone) insulation is used to (1) increase the life and reliability of electric machines; (2) provide a 25 to 50 per cent service factor that permits more efficient use of motors and power; (3) increase the power per pound ratio of electric machines. The various forms of silicones find direct application in the manufacture of electrical or electronic equipment, and in the production of electrical insulating compounds.

The silicones used in electrical applications include liquid dielectrics, dielectric compounds, wire enamels and varnishes, cloth coating varnishes, dipping and impregnating varnishes, and potting compounds.

Electrical insulating components made with various forms of silicones include: silicone varnished glass cloth and tape; silicone bonded mica and mica-glass combinations; silicone-asbestos-glass and saturated asbestos components; silicone varnished glass tying cord; silicone bonded glass-served magnet wire; silicone enameled magnet wire; silicone-glass lam-

---

* Produced by Dow Corning Corporation.

inates; silicone insulated wire and cable; pressure sensitive glass tape; and silicone rubber coated fabric and tape.

**Silicone Protective Coating Vehicles.** Paints and enamels formulated with silicone resins span the gap between vitreous enamels and organic protective coatings. They include baking enamels, air-dry finishes, and maintenance paints formulated to give maximum protection to metal surfaces exposed to heat, weathering, and corrosion.

Also available are modified silicone resins for formulating paints, enamels, and varnishes; resins designed for cold blending with organic resins; and solid, solvent-free resins for the preparation of silk screen enamels or other special coatings.

**Silicone Release Agents.** Silicone release agents are available in several forms including: "straight" fluids and their emulsion or solvent solutions, greaselike compounds, and semi-permanent mold coating treatments.

In general, silicone release agents provide clean easy release, reduce scrap, do not break down to form a carbonaceous deposit, and cut mold cleaning to a minimum.

Silicones are used effectively in releasing virtually every type of plastic, and are also widely used in the rubber, plywood and metal industries.

A note of precaution is injected in the literature on the use of silicone release agents on parts to be painted or plated. In some cases, sufficient silicone may transfer to the part being molded, causing difficulty in painting or plating. It is recommended, therefore, that if painting or other finish is desirable, the use of silicone release agents be thoroughly tested, including finishing of the part.

**Silicone Anti-seize Agents.** Non-melting, oxidation resistant, greaselike silicones are effectively used on stud and head bolts of continuous extruders, on hold down bolts, and on nozzles and inserts of injection molding machines for plastics. The use of silicones in such applications eliminates seizure of studs and bolts, simplifies changing nozzles and inserts, and substantially reduces teardown time.

**Silicone Additives.** Certain silicones are added to paints, at very low concentrations, to prevent floating, to increase mar resistance and slip, and to improve pigment wetting. Others effectively reduce cratering and improve flow-out and wetting characteristics. By addition of the proper silicone, it is possible to create hammer finishes with a variety of organic paint resins.

As additives to plastics, certain silicones are used to increase water repellency, prevent hazing, and improve adhesion.

The simplest silicone resins are formed by the almost simultaneous hydrolysis and condensation (by dehydration) of various mixtures of methyl chlorosilanes.

A fast curing silicone resin copolymer which provides a hard, glossy heat-resistant finish on such items as heaters and stoves, and which bakes in 30 min. at 400°F is offered by the General Electric Company and Dow Corning Corp.

TABLE 2.32. COMPARISON OF GLASS FIBER FILLED SILICONES
AND GLASS FIBER FILLED POLYESTERS

(Average Values)

| Properties | Silicones | Polyesters |
|---|---|---|
| Specific gravity | 1.8 | 2.2 |
| Tensile strength, psi | 5,000 | 3,500 |
| Compressive strength, psi | 14,000 | 18,000 |
| Continuous heat resistance, °F | 450 | 320 |
| Heat distortion temperature, °F | 900 | 400 |
| Dielectric strength, v. per mil | 200-400 | 400 |
| Machining qualities | good | good |
| Effect of sunlight | none to slight | slight |
| Per cent water absorption, 24 hr | 0.1 | 0.11-0.5 |
| Resistance to strong acids | good | poor |
| Resistance to weak acids | excellent | good |
| Resistance to strong alkalies | fair | poor |
| Resistance to weak alkalies | good | poor |
| Clarity | opaque | opaque |

## Urea Formaldehyde

Ordinarily referred to simply as ureas, these thermosetting materials, developed in 1929, were one of the early plastics. Their characteristics are similar to the melamines to which they are related, both being amino plastics. The ureas are odorless, tasteless, and non-toxic. Like the melamines, they are unaffected by detergents or ordinary cleaning fluids, or by alcohol, oils, and greases. The specific gravity varies with the nature of the fillers used but is about 1.5 for both ureas and melamines. Other physical properties between the two are similar except that the melamines have better heat and chemical resistance.

Typical uses for the ureas are buttons, tableware, light reflectors, radio housings, and equipment such as scales. They are also used as textile finishes and as adhesives. The ureas should not be used for applications involving continuous weathering or exposure to extreme changes of humidity.

The properties of ureas are given in Table 2.13.

# 3. FORMS OF PLASTICS

The usefulness of a plastic material depends to a large extent upon the form in which it is used. The forms which are possible vary from fibers so fine as to be almost invisible, to ponderous moldings and reinforced structural members. In general, each type of plastic has certain limitations as to the forms into which it can be produced. Thus a relatively few plastics are suitable for drawing into fibers and some are only moldable with difficulty. This chapter serves as an intermediate link between the properties of plastics and the applications of plastics. The items described are not all strictly forms of plastics. They may be parts, such as fillers and plasticizers, or borderline materials such as plywood. But all are closely associated with plastics, and as a group it is hoped they will furnish a general idea of the nature of the diverse components which, in a sense, are the building blocks of the plastics industry. It has been difficult to avoid some duplication with Chapter 5 (Applications) and with Chapter 6 (Processing). The following forms will be described here:

| | |
|---|---|
| Adhesives and bonding agents | Laminated film |
| Coatings | Laminates, low-pressure |
| Alkyd coating resins | Liquids and pastes |
| Extruded forms | Machined parts |
| Fibers | Moldings |
| Fillers | Molding powders |
| Films and sheets | Plasticizers |
| Foams | Plywood |
| Laminates | |

## Adhesives and Bonding Agents*

Adhesives are substances capable of holding materials together by surface attachment. Bonding often includes the use of a material (usually

---

* This section adapted in part from John Delmonti's section in Reinhold's "Encyclopedia of Chemistry."

a resin) to hold grains or particles together as in a grinding wheel or fibers in a non-woven fabric. The terms adhesives and bonding agents are used interchangeably and often rather loosely. Several basic mechanisms explain this bonding action. In some instances there is evidence that chemical bonds are established involving electron sharing, though more usually mechanical considerations prevail. High bond strength depends upon high cohesive strength in the adhesive film—in particular it depends on the innate properties of the material. Thus, the evolution of adhesives has paralleled the development of film-forming materials. Films are formed by evaporation of volatiles, by diffusion of volatiles into porous surfaces, and by polymerization.

Adhesives are available to industrial users in the following physical forms: powders which may be melted or dissolved, solutions of film-forming materials, dispersions of film formers (rubber latices), films (supported or unsupported), meltable stocks or rods, and separate packages of resin compounds and curing agents.

The use of plastic adhesives for fastening metal-to-metal is increasing and some manufacturers predict an extensive future for this process. One of the most important materials in this field is epoxy resin. Versamid-epoxy adhesives, as produced by General Mills, are claimed to bond almost any material to any other; they are being successfully used to replace soldering in repairing metal parts. These and other epoxy adhesives are also used in production operations, e.g., insulated tumblers are made by joining nested moldings to give trapped air insulation between their walls. Acetate toys of complicated shape are produced more economically by cementing together simple moldings.

Cycleweld is the trade name for a group of thermosetting adhesives produced by Chrysler Corp. They may be applied by spray, brush, or roller. Successive thin coats are generally applied, with brief intervening drying periods. Final drying is at an elevated temperature (180°F).

Another proprietary adhesive, Redux, made by Rohm and Haas, consists of a phenolic liquid used in combination with a powder, the liquid being spread by brush and the powder dusted on later. Curing is with pressure at elevated temperature.

An epoxy adhesive made by Miracle Adhesives Corp., New Philadelphia, Ohio, requires no mixing and is said to have a pot life of 30 days and a shear strength when properly applied of over 3000 psi.

In bonding metal-to-wood it is customary to apply a metal-type resin adhesive to the metal surface and a wood type adhesive to the wood surface and then to join the two surfaces with heat and pressure. Metal-clad plywood is made in this way. The phenolics, ureas, vinyls, and casein are typical of the materials used for wood adhesives. Plywood can be made in a continuous operation by feeding, from spools, phenolic impregnated tissue between layers of veneer. Resorcinol has been particularly successful in bonding wood products.

Glass fibers may be bonded with polyesters and other resins to form laminates, or reinforced plastics. These are covered later in this chapter under the heading "Laminates."

In many cases, two parts can be joined simply by applying a suitable cement to the surfaces of the materials and pressing them together until the cement sets. This method is often accelerated by the application of heat. In some cases, notably films joined for packaging, this simple process has been highly mechanized, operating on a continuous and semi-automatic basis.

When materials lend themselves to heat-sealing or heat-bonding, this method is usually preferred. The vinyls fall in this category; heat-sealing with or without solvents is the general practice when they are being used. Elaborate semi-automatic electrical heat-sealing equipment is available. But even so the method is difficult to apply and to control; it does not give as strong a bond as electronic sealing, in which heat is generated within the film being sealed instead of merely being applied to the surface. Pressure is applied at the same time as the heat. Two types of equipment are based on this principle—the bar sealer and the continuous sealer. Equipment for the continuous process resembles a sewing machine and is usually known as an electronic sewing machine. Several variants of such a machine are available. For more information about the heat-sealing process see Chapter 6.

Polyethylenes can often be bonded economically by heat-sealing. Nylon can be bonded to nylon with adhesive compounds based on phenolic resins or with an 85 per cent solution of alcohol in water. A large number of plastic bonding adhesives are available for the various types of moldings and extrusions. For the most part, these are proprietary compounds based on casein, phenolics, ureas, synthetic rubbers, and some thermoplastic resins. The following are typical bonding applications:

> Battery separators
> Brake linings and clutch facings
> Coated abrasives
> Evaporation control
> Forming dies and patterns
> Grinding wheels
> Investment castings

Organic and inorganic fiber bondings
Sand molds and cores
Sealing solutions
Shell molds and cores
Thermal and acoustical insulation
Tools, dies, jigs, and fixtures

## Coatings

Approximately one-fourth of all resins are consumed as coating materials. The alkyds are the most widely used but nearly any one of the many different plastics may be put in solution and applied by brushing, spraying, roller coating, or dipping. The trend in coating is toward greater use of synthetic resins and less use of oils and natural resins.

The principal coating resins today are alkyds, ethyl cellulose, melamine polystyrenes, acrylics, and silicones. These may be used alone but more commonly they are cross-blended with each other or processed with oils, waxes, or natural resins. Less common but important coating resins include the coumarone-indenes, phenolics, ureas, and allyls. These will probably find increased use in future applications.

Coatings which consist of a colloidal rather than a true solution are known as "dispersion resins" and these, due to their relatively large particle size, do not penetrate fibrous materials as much as other resins do. They are applied where surface irregularities are to be overcome. A few typical such applications are the following: boats, office equipment, traffic paints, and metal window frames.

Cellulose nitrate lacquers are extensively used even though precautions must be taken to avoid open flames. Their major market is for finishing furniture. In addition to the usual lacquers which are resistant to high temperatures, silicone coating materials may be safely used at 600°F or more. Used primarily for stove finishes, they are being used in increasing amounts in the electrical field and for applications where advantage can be taken of their excellent chemical resistance. Modified silicone-aluminum coatings are good for temperatures close to 1000°F.

Cellulose acetate is not as widely used for coatings as cellulose nitrate and ethyl cellulose. More promising are the mixed cellulose esters such as cellulose acetate-butyrate and cellulose acetate-propionate.

Urea-alkyd resins are used for baking finishes that are resistant to discoloration for extensive periods. Industrial applications include bathroom fixtures, refrigerators, and laundry equipment. Phenol-alkyd type resins are used as undercoats for automotive finishes.

Vinyl chloride-vinyl acetate finishes are finding increased application in the coating field. They are used to paint swimming pools and the hulls of submarines. They are odorless, colorless, and nonflammable.

The resin-forming constituent in an organic coating, which is the type considered here, is called a "binder." Several hundred binders from the plastics group are now commercially available. Coatings have many functions—some are decorative, some are preservative (as for wood) and others prevent metal corrosion. The latter must have good resistance to any corrosion-promoting chemicals. Important here are polyethylene, polytetrafluoroethylene, and the vinyls, known as the "barrier-type" coatings. Another type, also used to protect against corrosion, functions by assisting polarization at the metal surface. Certain of the constituents adhere tightly to the metal surface and make it less wettable by water and electrolytes.

The coating industry with its many ramifications is a huge industry— larger even than the total plastics industry in dollar value. The resins alone in the over-all coating industry amount to about $250,000,000 a year.

As alkyds find their chief application in coatings, the following special section on alkyd coating resins is included here. For more about the alkyds see Chapter 2.

### Alkyd Coating Resins*

Polyester resins used in organic coatings are usually known as alkyds. They are distinguishable from other polyesters in that they contain fatty monobasic acids as "oil modifications" and are usually furnished in solvents. Because of popular usage, these polyester resins will be referred to as alkyds throughout the discussion of coating resins.

The predominant group of alkyd resins used in the manufacture of surface coatings employs phthalic anhydride as the main polybasic-acid constituent and such polyhydric alcohols as glycerol or pentaerythritol. Other polyhydric alcohols, such as glycols, di- or tripentaerythritol, sorbitol, or trimethylolethane, can be used to emphasize special resin properties. In addition to the polybasic acid and polyhydric alcohol components, alkyd resins for protective coatings are modified with oxidizing or non-oxidizing fatty acids derived from vegetable and, in some cases, marine oils.

Oil-modified alkyd resins of the air-drying type cure by oxidation of

---

* This section by W. O. Erickson and V. W. Ginsler of Barrett Division, Allied Chemical & Dye Corp. is included here by courtesy of Modern Plastics Encyclopedia, issue, 1956.

their drying oil constituent. In the case of the baking type, in which the oil modification may be oxidizing or non-oxidizing, the alkyds cure by co-condensation with alkylated amino resins in the presence of heat.

Quantitatively and qualitatively, the oil modification of alkyd resins produces profound effects on the properties of these products. Alkyds generally contain from 30 to 70 per cent of oil and, depending on their specific range of oil content, are classified approximately as follows:

| Classification | Oil Content (%) |
|---|---|
| Short-oil | 30-46 |
| Medium-oil | 46-56 |
| Long-oil | 56-70 |

**Short-oil Alkyds.** Short-oil alkyds contain fewer of the aliphatic, solvent-tolerant, fatty-acid chains in their molecular structure, and, hence, are prone to be incompatible in aliphatic solvents. They are supplied as solutions in aromatics, such as xylene or toluene. Modified with non-oxidizing oils, such as coconut or castor oil, they are used as plasticizers in cellulose nitrate lacquer formulations to contribute the necessary properties of adhesion, flexibility, durability, and color retention to modern automotive and other fast-drying industrial lacquer finishes. Short-oil, non-oxidizing alkyds are also used extensively with urea and melamine resins in baking enamels; they yield exceptionally hard, tough finishes for refrigerators, washing machines, home freezers, and other appliances.

Short-oil, oxidizing alkayds based on soya, dehydrated castor or cotton-seed oils have a broad application in all types of industrial baking finishes. In conjunction with acid-catalyzed urea resins they have also found successful application in forced-dry, wood-furniture finishes that are superior in abrasion resistance, impact strength, and durability to oleoresinous varnishes or cellulose nitrate lacquers.

**Medium- and Long-oil Types.** Medium- and long-oil alkyds that are soluble in mineral spirits are modified most frequently with oxidizing oils. They are used in brushing-type, air-drying finishes. Many government specifications call for alkyds of this group and most of the familiar household paint products, such as alkyd, flat wall-paint, 4-hour high-gloss enamel, and porch, floor, and deck paints, are presently manufactured from either medium- or long-oil alkyd resins.

Recent availability of "odorless" and "low-odor" mineral spirits has permitted development of medium- and long-oil alkyd resin solutions in these solvents for interior alkyd-based flat paints and gloss enamels that are free from obnoxious odors. These products have shown a gain in usage in a market that two or three years ago seemed to be headed toward complete domination by water-thinned latex paints. Long-oil and extra long-oil alkyds at 100 per cent solids are also increasing in usage as modifiers for various water-dispersed latices and as components of exterior house paints.

**Modified Alkyds.** Oil-modified alkyd resins may be further modified by processing them with other materials to emphasize special properties. Common modifiers are rosin, phenolic resins, styrene, and silicones. Such additional modification, however, is usually a compromise in which some properties are gained and others lost.

Highly thixotropic alkyds have been developed by modification with polyamide resin. Paint products produced from polyamide-modified alkyds are unusual in appearance in that they are jelly-like, but are quickly reduced to ordinary consistency by mechanical agitation.

**Non-phthalic Alkyds.** Rosin or terpenes, and maleic anhydride or fumaric acid undergo a Diels-Alder reaction, forming a tribasic acid. This reaction product can be esterified with glycerol or fatty acid glycerides to produce alkyd resins that exhibit properties superior to those of the varnishes manufactured by simply cooking maleic-modified ester gum with oils. Although these alkyds cannot be considered equivalent quality substitutes for phthalic alkyds, they have special applications.

The use of alkyd resins in surface coatings has increased considerably faster during the past 25 years than their corresponding use in paint production. Alkyd resin production (solids basis) reached 241 million pounds in 1946; approximately 450 million pounds were produced in 1955. There are three main reasons for this substantial growth—versatility, uniformity, and economy.

*Versatility:* Alkyds, in general, are better coatings than oleoresinous varnishes and are adaptable to a wide variety of air-drying and baking finishes for wood, metal, plaster, paper, and plastics. In addition, alkyds function as plasticizers for cellulose nitrate.

*Uniformity:* The growth of alkyd resin production has fostered development of a new scientific attitude in the paint and varnish industry. The chemical controls required for successful alkyd production have replaced the individual judgment of the varnish maker, resulting in greater uniformity from batch to batch.

*Economy:* Alkyd resins are low in cost and their raw materials are abundant. The efficiency of handling packaged, ready-to-use vehicles of high quality and wide scope represents a greater stride in progress than any previously made in the history of paint making.

The following are important materials and applications in surface coating:

*Materials:*

Alkyds
Chlorinated naphthalenes
Epoxy resins
Modified phenolic resins and solutions
Phenolic resins and solutions
Polyethylene
Polystyrene emulsions
Vinyl acetate resins and emulsions
Vinyl butyral resins
Vinyl chloride and copolymer resins
Vinyl ether resins
Zyrox resins

*Applications:*

Adhesives
Dipped and slush molded goods
Household finishes
Marine finishes
Metal coatings
Organosols and plastisols
Packaging and storage applications
Paper, foil, and cloth coatings
Protective coatings
Sponge and foam products
Varnishes and lacquers

## Extruded Forms

Plastics material available in continuous lengths often is extruded. Familiar extruded items include garden hose, rods and tubes, and architectural shapes. The acetates and butyrates extrude easily and are extensively used for the T and H profiles which builders use to fasten wallboard. One attractive feature is that they can be nailed in place much as wood forms can. The butyrates have a little better resistance to cold than the acetates and thus can be nailed in cold weather without cracking. Butyrate tubing has proved superior to iron pipe and even to tile for processing syrup and vinegar and for many other industrial chemical applications.

Polyethylene tubing is used extensively for dispensing beer, and for many other commercial applications. Vinyl tubing is well adapted for use in medical equipment.

Films and sheets are extruded in several ways. Long straight dies are sometimes used but the common practice is to extrude the tubes and then slit and spread these to form films or sheets. Nearly all thermoplastic materials can be extruded; the thermosetting plastics, in general, cannot be extruded. Recently a special noncontinuous method has been developed for extruding sewer pipe of phenolic. Monofilaments are extruded in small diameters. These are classified as fibers and as such are described elsewhere.

Figure 3.1. Typical extruded sections for use with wallboard.

Ethyl cellulose is extruded as fluted tubes for tool handles. Beads are machined from small-bore acrylic tubing. Oil-resistant tubing is extruded from plasticized polyvinyl alcohol. The use of extruded architectural shapes has increased amazingly during recent years. Shapes formerly thought impossible are now handled with ease by experienced extruders. These include scuff pads for luggage, sealing strips for glass windows, fluoroscent light reflectors (often with complicated profiles), and table and counter moldings.

The result of extrusion may be strips, tubes, rods, monofilaments, sheeting or profile sections. Strips of various widths and thicknesses find applications ranging from blanking stock for spectacle frames to decorative grillwork for furniture. Extruded tubing is used in applications ranging in size from tiny catheter tubes to oilfield pipe and is available in many shapes other than circular. Rod is used for knitting needles and carpenter tool handles. Both rods and tubes can be machined automatically to produce innumerable small parts. Films and sheets may be heated and then shaped by blowing with air pressure or formed by vacuum. Many extruded materials can be cemented with solvents, sealed electronically, embossed, or laminated.

The physical properties required in the finished extruded product should be the governing factors in the selection of materials fed to the hopper.

Figure 3.2. Lightweight extruded polyethylene pipe is used to supply water to summer cabins and year-round homes in a new development. The flexibility and lightweight of polyethylene make it easy to handle. One man can carry a 400-foot roll of polyethylene pipe with a ¾-inch inside diameter. Such a roll weighs about 52 pounds. A comparable length of conventional pipe would weigh at least 10 times as much. A two-man team quickly unrolls the flexible pipe in ditches scooped out by a grader.

## Fibers

The synthetic fiber industry has grown rapidly since the introduction of nylon which now has an established place both in textiles and in plastics. The broad classification of "man-made-fibers" is broken down into synthetic and non-synthetic fibers. The non-synthetic group is further divided into regenerated fibers such as viscous rayon and derivative fibers such as acetate rayon. The large synthetic group includes all the fiber-making resins among the 32 resins listed in Chapter 2. Some of the important fiber plastics (resins) are polyamides (nylon), acrylics (Orlon), saran, and polyesters (Dacron).

Continuous filament nylon has almost replaced silk for women's hosiery. It also is used for underwear and other applications in the textile field. Two nylons are available as fibers. The familiar material, Nylon 66, is formed by condensation polymerization of the salt resulting from the reaction of hexamethylene diamine with adipic. Nylon 6 which is important in Europe is being produced commercially in this country. It is an isomer of Nylon 66 but has a lower melting point (about 430°F).

Two types of fibers are derived from acrylonitrile—acrylic fiber (Orlon) and vinylidene chloride fiber (saran). A copolymer of acrylonitrile and vinyl chloride produces an interesting fiber known as dynel which is used for many industrial fabrics and, more recently, for men's apparel.

The lightest is a polyethylene fiber with specific gravity of 0.92. Nylon is the next lightest with 1.14 specific gravity. Woven fabrics of polyethylene are used for automobile upholstery and for many specialty applications where the chemical inertness is important. In addition to continuous filament fibers several of the resins are made into staple fibers either by cutting or by a special technique employing strong air blasts directed against the material as it emerges from the spinnerets. This is explained elsewhere. Staple Orlon is readily woven or knitted. It has good resistance to outdoor exposure but is flammable after melting, whereas dynel, because of its high chlorine content, is not.

Dacron is available both as continuous fiber and as staple. Its melting point is about 500°F, and its moisture absorption is about 0.4 per cent. It has good strength and resilience wet or dry. Teflon fiber, now available, retains the outstanding physical properties of the base material—tetrafluoroethylene.

The production of all true synthetic fibers has reached about 100 million pounds a year which is less than one-tenth the annual production of rayon.

A process for making fine-fiber webs from plastics resins such as vinyl, acrylic, nylon, and polyester has been announced by American Viscose Corp. The plastics or similar materials are melted or dissolved in volatile solvents and sprayed into an air stream to form super-fine fibers. During spraying, the microfibers may be mixed with rayon or other fibers and the mixture deposited on a moving belt in random distribution, thus forming a web. The microfibers have a permanent electric charge, irregular lengths, and diameters ranging from 0.5 to 10 microns. The webs formed are highly absorbent and may be used as filters or in non-woven fabrics, or as insulation layers for sleeping bags and winter clothing.

Table 3.1. Some Man-made Fiber Comparisons

| | Rayon | Acetate | Nylon | Orlon | Dacron |
|---|---|---|---|---|---|
| Description | Regenerated cellulose. | Modified cellulose. | Made from hexamethylenediamine and adipic acid. | Made from polyacrylonitrile. | Made from ethylene glycol and dimethyl-terephthalate. |
| Production | Spun through spinneret into coagulating bath. | Spun through spinnerets hardened by warm air. | Spun through spinnerets solidified by filtered cool air. | Spun similar to acetate. | Spun similar to nylon. |
| Application | Makes true crepes. Used in dresses, suitings, carpets, and draperies. Used in blends. | Fabrics of soft hand and fine appearance—satins, jerseys, and organdies. Usually in blends. | Hosiery, socks, dresses, underwear, shirts, sails, draperies, typewriter ribbons. | Sport shirts, dresses, suits, socks, work clothes, filtration fabrics. | Skirts, socks, ties, dresses, suits, fire hose, curtains, sails. |
| Characteristics | Soft hand, inexpensive, good drapeability and absorbency, hand washable and dry cleanable. | Lustrous appearance; resists moths; good colors; draping qualities; unique effects. | Durable, tear resistance, shape retention, quick drying, resists moths, mildew and perspiration. | Bulk with light weight; wrinkle recovery; crease retention; resists sunlight and many chemicals. | Wet and dry crease retention; resists shrink and stretch; cleans readily; good draping qualities. |
| Washing | Mild soap in warm water; rinse in warm water; iron when nearly dry. | Wash color fabrics separately; mild soap warm water; iron on wrong side with warm iron. | Hand washing best; squeeze suds through fabric; separate white from colors; warm water. | Soap or synthetic detergents; follow instructions of manufacturer; otherwise treat as cotton. | Same as for nylon. |

TABLE 3.2. COMPARISON OF PROPERTIES OF SOME SYNTHETIC TEXTILE FIBERS
(Average Values)

| Properties | Polyamides (Nylon) | Polyesters (Dacron, etc.) | Polyacrylonitrile (Orlon, etc.) | Polyvinyl chloride, vinyl acetate (Vinyon, etc.) | Polyvinylidene chloride (Saran, etc.) | Tetrafluoroethylene (Teflon, etc.) | Polyacrylonitrile vinyl chloride (Dynel, etc.) |
|---|---|---|---|---|---|---|---|
| Specific gravity | 1.14 | 1.38 | 1.17 | 1.35 | 1.72 | 2.3 | 1.31 |
| Average tensile strength gr. per denier | 6.8 | 4.2 | 5.2 | 4.0 | 2.0 | 1.7 | 3.0 |
| Wet per cent of strength | 87 | 100 | 95 | 100 | 100 | 100 | 100 (50 above 200°F) |
| Elongation at 65% R.H. in per cent | 19 | 26 | 16 | 18 | 27 | 13 | 30 |
| Resistance to heat | sticks at 455°F | sticks at 455°F | sticks at 455°F | shrinks at 150 melts at 250 | shrinks at 160 softens at 250 | excellent, stable to 500°F | good but shrinks at 240°F |
| Resistance to aging | excellent | excellent | excellent | excellent | fair | excellent | very good |
| Effect of sunlight (prolonged) | slight | some loss of strength | almost none | none | slight darkening | slight effect | slight loss of strength |
| Effect of moths | not attacked | not attacked | not attacked | not attacked | not attacked | not attacked | not attacked |
| Effect of mildew | not attacked | not attacked | not attacked | not attacked | not attacked | not attacked | not attacked |
| Resistance to acids and alkalies | good | good | fair to good | excellent | excellent | excellent | good |
| Dyes used | acetate and acid | acetate azoic and vat | acetate basic and vat | dispersed with aid pigment | solution colored | acetate with difficulty | acetate, acid, direct |

## Fillers

Fillers are added to give a plastic specific mechanical and electrical properties and to increase its resistance to various service conditions. Although they often reduce the per pound price, they are seldom used for this specific objective. The percentage of filler is usually between 20 and 50 by weight. Some common fillers and their functions are as follows:

*For bulk:*

| | |
|---|---|
| wood flour | jute |
| asbestos | cotton flock |
| sawdust | wood pulp |
| mica | |

*For reinforcement:*

| | |
|---|---|
| glass fibers | asbestos |
| cotton fibers | wood flour |

*For hardness:*

| | |
|---|---|
| metallic carbides | quartz |
| silicone carbide | mica |

*For thermal or chemical resistance:*

| | |
|---|---|
| asbestos | sand |
| graphite | metallic oxides |
| diatomaceous earth | powdered metals |
| quartz | |

*For appearance:*

| | |
|---|---|
| metallic oxides | powdered metals |
| organic pigments | phosphorescent calcium sulfide |

Mold lubricants are sometimes added to facilitate release from the die after a piece is molded. A typical material is calcium stearate.

Materials similar to the fillers just described are often used with laminated and reinforced plastics but they are usually introduced in the form of fabric or mats and are not generally called fillers.

## Films and Sheets

An expanding list of plastics capable of producing films and sheets is available to the fabricator and designer. A few of the most frequently used materials are listed below:

acrylics
cellophane
cellulose acetate

ethyl cellulose
polyethylene
polyester
polystyrene
polyvinyl alcohol
polyvinyl chloride
vinyl chloride-vinyl acetate
vinylidene chloride

Films may be divided into three general markets: packaging; industrial (scotch tape, garden mulch, balloons, etc.); and soft goods (raincoats, umbrellas, and shower curtains).

The first three film materials in order of present production are cellophane, polyethylene, and vinyl copolymers. Of these the use of polyethylene as a film material is increasing more rapidly than the other two. For a more complete discussion of film applications see Chapter 5.

TABLE 3.3. FILM PRODUCTION PER YEAR*

| Plastic | Pounds |
| --- | --- |
| Cellophane | 250,000.000 |
| Polyethylene | 66,000,000 |
| Vinyl chloride and copolymers | 58,000,000 |
| Cellulose acetate | 20,000,000 |
| Cellulose nitrate | 15,000,000 |
| Ethyl cellulose | 1,000,000 |
| Polyvinyl alcohol | 500,000 |

* Average values for 1954, 1955 and 1956.

"Sheeting" is the term applied to continuous material; "sheet" is applied to relatively small pieces of sheeting cut to specific lengths. The term "film" actually refers to thin sheeting, and is an optional term which the American Society for Testing Materials (ASTM) recommends for thicknesses not greater than 0.010 inch. In commercial practice 3 mils (0.003 in.) is usually the upper limit for thickness of film. This is especially true of packaging materials.

Sheeting is made by one of several different methods. The film-forming mass may be cast onto a large wheel or onto an endless metal belt, the thickness of the material being determined by the position of a doctor knife held adjacent to the casting wheel or belt. Casting on a paper carrier is a new process which will be discussed later.

Sheeting may also be produced by calendering, as explained in Chapter 6, but a more common method is by extrusion. One method, introduced by the Tennessee Eastman Company, is to extrude a thin tube and then to slit one side of the tube and lay it out over a suitable spreading device to form a flat film. Sheeting and film are produced from nearly all types of plastics. Chapter 5 discusses some typical applications for sheets made from the following materials:

| | |
|---|---|
| Cellulose acetate | Nylon |
| Cellulose acetate butyrate | Polyethylene |
| Cellulose propionate | Polystyrene |
| Ethyl cellulose | Polyvinyl butyral |
| Fluorothenes | Vinyls (polyvinyl chloride and |
| Methyl methacrylate | polyvinyl chloride acetate) |

A comparison of the properties of three of the principal transparent sheeting materials is given in Chapter 2. It will be seen from this that the acrylics are the lightest but also, next to polyester film, the strongest in tension. The acetate sheets can be produced with excellent clarity but their usefulness in some applications is limited because of their high water absorption which is about 3.3 per cent in 24 hours as against 0.2 per cent for the allyls.

The physical properties given in Chapter 2 are indicative of the properties of the film.

Vinyl sheets are available in translucent, transparent, or opaque forms and in an extensive range of colors. They come in varying thicknesses ranging from film which is 3 mils or less to as much as 1 inch. Thicker parts usually are called "slab stock." Sheets may have a press finish or a calender finish and may be rigid or flexible.

All types of vinyl sheets may be cut, stamped, or sheared with standard tools. The flexible types can be bonded to each other or to other materials by heat-sealing methods. Rigid sheets are available from 0.005 to 0.025 in. thick, either cut, with a matté finish, or in continuous rolls having a calender finish. Both flexible and rigid sheets can be formed and shaped with heat. The rigid sheets can be formed around mandrels into complicated, three-dimensional shapes, and they can be machined, much as metal sheets can be formed on standard metal-working equipment. They can be vacuum formed.

Cellulose acetate film is produced in continuous lengths and in thicknesses of 0.001 in. or less up to 0.01 in. or more. The thickness is limited to about 0.01 in. because of the slow drying rate. However, thick sheets may be produced by skiving them from pressed blocks. Standard sheets are 20 x 50 in. and can be given a high polish between plates in a press operation. The gage of film is often expressed in thousandths of an inch multiplied by 100,000. Thus a film 0.002 in. thick would have a gage number of 200. In addition to cellulose acetate film and sheeting, films and sheets are produced from cellulose acetate butyrate, ethyl cellulose, and cellulose acetate propionate.

The polyamides are excellent film and sheet-forming materials. By adding plasticizers, properties may be produced in nylon films varying from rigid to elastic.

A flexible foamed plastics sheet insulation, called Armaflex, is manufactured by the Armstrong Cork Co., Lancaster, Pennsylvania. It is adaptable to curved or irregular surfaces with little or no fitting and cutting, and withstands temperatures as high as 160°F. Thickness can be built up by applying successive layers. The foamed plastics sheets are available in thicknesses of ⅛ to ¾ inch. Applied with the proper adhesive, the sheets do not require mechanical supports. Their flexibility makes them suitable for insulating large tanks, irregularly shaped vessels, oversize pipes, and refrigeration and air-conditioning equipment.

A new material, known as Rhinolyte, consists of nylon mesh, laminated between two sheets of vinyl. Electronically welded, this light weight material is strong and completely waterproof. It is used for tarpaulins by the construction, agricultural, transportation and other industries. A 20 x 20 ft. heavy-duty tarpaulin weighs only about 37 pounds. It is also reportedly flexible to minus 50°F, and resists chemicals, tearing, and abrasion.

**Acrylic sheets.** These are usually formed by casting and the process is more difficult than with CR-39 or polystyrene. In curing, which is usually done at from 265 to 300°F, a critical point is reached when excessive heat is given off by the material itself. Ovens with rapidly moving air are provided to eliminate this excessive heat. Casting is usually done between plate glass sheets. The glass sheets are mounted one above the other with spacers around the edge to keep them apart the distance desired for the thickness of the casting. Because of shrinkage the spacers should either be made of elastomers such as plasticized polyvinyl chloride or of metal covered with paper. In the latter case, they must be removed at the right point in the curing cycle to permit shrinkage without having the casting drawn away from the glass sheets which constitute the mold. In casting, the mold is horizontally inclined and a special funnel is used to feed the liquid material in between the glass plates. Sometimes the liquid is prepolymerized to a syrupy condition so as to speed up curing. Even so, the curing time is slow and ranges from one day to one week.

Acrylic sheets are standard for transparent enclosures on aircraft. Edge-lighted sheets are used as radar plotting boards. Other uses include outdoor sign material, industrial window glazing, and safety shields over moving machine parts.

TABLE 3.4. TYPICAL SHEETING APPLICATIONS*

*Cellulose acetate*

| | |
|---|---|
| carpet sweeper windows | packaging |
| containers | photographic film base |
| instruction sheets | table mats |
| instrument faces | toys |
| mechanical shielding | windows in pocket folds |

*Cellulose acetate butyrate*

| | |
|---|---|
| automobile tail lights | mechanical shielding |
| containers | rigid safety guards |
| instruction sheets | |

*Cellulose propionate*

| | |
|---|---|
| drawing instruments | food protectors |

*Ethyl cellulose*

| | |
|---|---|
| deep-drawn containers | goggles |
| electrical tape | sales displays |
| food packaging | |

*Fluorothenes*

| | |
|---|---|
| electrical insulation | high-frequency dielectrics |

*Methyl methacrylate*

| | |
|---|---|
| aircraft enclosures | watch crystals |
| dials | windows |
| display boxes | |

*Nylon*

| | |
|---|---|
| conveyor belts | seat material |
| furniture strips | vacuum packages |

*Polyethylene*

| | |
|---|---|
| electrical insulation tapes | packaging |
| garment bags | refrigerator items |
| liners for closures | |

*Polystyrene*

| | |
|---|---|
| cable wrapping | electrical insulation |
| cosmetic packages | shades in fluorescent lighting |
| decorative objects | table mats |

*Polyvinyl butyral*

safety glass interlayer

*Vinyls (polyvinyl chloride and polyvinyl chloride acetate)*

| | |
|---|---|
| acid tank lining | rainwear |
| boats | suspenders |
| book binding | umbrellas |
| curtains | upholstery |
| luggage | wading pools for children |
| phonograph record preforms | |

* See also Chapter 5.

TABLE 3.5. CELLULOSE ACETATE FILM AREAS

| Thickness, in. | Gage | Sq. in. per lb. |
|---|---|---|
| 0.00088 | 88 | 25,000 |
| 0.001 | 100 | 22,000 |
| 0.0012 | 120 | 18,300 |
| 0.0014 | 140 | 15,700 |
| 0.002 | 200 | 11,000 |
| 0.003 | 300 | 7,300 |

## Foams

Many liquid resins will form foams with the proper introduction of a gas. The use of foams in industry is increasing as pointed out in Chapter 5. In general, foams may be divided into two main groups—rigid and flexible. The leaders in the flexible group are the vinyl type and the polyurethanes. By varying the production technique, the polyurethanes may be used for both flexible and rigid foams but the rigid group has not enjoyed the same activity due to difficulties in handling. Rigid foamed polystyrene has had extensive use in the building industry. It may be either foamed in place or produced in the form of sheets or rectangular slabs. Slabs, 3 or 4 in. thick and 4 x 8 ft. in dimension are used for closet walls and other non-supporting partitions by coating them with cement plaster.

Expandable polystyrene is finding many new interesting uses of which the following are a few examples: insulation, where closed cell structure is an advantage; sandwich construction, where controllable density and low thermal conductivity (K value) are favorable for insulated panels; packaging, where toughness is stressed; and toys and displays, where ability to be molded to intricate shapes is important.

## Laminates

Most any material—cloth, paper, or woven glass fibers—may be impregnated with a resin, laid up in layers and then cured by heat and pressure to form a laminate. The terms "high-pressure" and "low-pressure" laminates are commonly used but the distinction between the two types is not clear. When a pressure of 1200 psi or more is used the product generally is called a "high-pressure laminate." Textolite and Formica are typical of the well known high-pressure laminates.

TABLE 3.6. COMPARISON OF PLASTIC FOAMS*

| Foam | Type | Density Range, Lb/Cu Ft | Cell Structure | Relative Cost | Properties | Applications |
|---|---|---|---|---|---|---|
| Cellulose acetate | Rigid; thermoplastic. | 6.0-8.0 | Unicellular | High | Good mechanical strength and temperature stability. | Insulation, flotation, structural. |
| Epoxy | Rigid; thermoset. | 2.0-25.0 | Unicellular | High | Good electrical properties. Difficult to process. | Radome fillers; electrical embedments. Foamed in place. |
| Polyurethane (Isocyanate) | Rigid or flexible; thermoset. | 1.5-35.0 | Unicellular and interconnecting | High | Good tensile strength and chemical and rot resistance. Poor light resistance. Toxic formulation control. Toxic process. | Cushioning; padding; general replacement for foam rubber. Foamed in place. |
| Phenolic | Rigid; thermoset. | 0.1-20.0 | Unicellular and partly interconnecting | High | Very poor to very good mechanical strength. Good temperature stability. | Insulation; structural; radome fillers; packaging; oil evaporation covers. Foamed in place. |
| Polyethylene | Flexible; thermoplastic. | 10.0-20.0 | Unicellular | High | Good electrical properties. | Electrical wire coverings. |
| Polystyrene | Rigid; thermoplastic. | 2.0-10.0 | Unicellular | Low to moderate | Good moisture resistance. Poor thermal and chemical resistance. | Packaging; floatation; decoration. |
| Rubber (Latex) | Flexible; vulcanized. | 2.0-25.0 | Unicellular and interconnecting | Moderate to high | Poor tensile strength. Flammable. Very poor light and chemical resistance. | Cushioning; padding; mattresses; fillers; floatation; carpet underlays; shoe soles. |
| Silicone | Rigid or flexible; thermoset. | 6.5-20.0 | Unicellular | High | Good high temperature resistance. | High-temperature insulation. |
| Urea | Rigid; thermoset. | 0.5-20.0 | Unicellular | High | Poor mechanical strength. | Insulation; oil evaporation covers. |
| Vinyl | Rigid or flexible; thermoplastic and thermoset. | 2.0-45.0 | Unicellular and interconnecting | Moderate to high | Good tensile strength. Nonflammable. Good chemical and rot resistance. Excellent process and formulation control. | General replacement for foam rubber; floatation; cushioning; shoe soling; heat sealing; insulation; sponges; packaging; decorative; toys; crash padding; floor mats; acoustical. |

(Courtesy of Plastics Technology)

The production of such laminates consists of stacking up the desired number of resin impregnated sheets on a press and then applying heat and pressure to bond the layers and cure the resin. Because a press and relatively high pressures are required, such laminates are limited to flat sheets and simple shapes, and they are generally impregnated with phenolic or other thermosetting resins. Rods and tubes and simple cross-sections are readily handled but more complicated shapes and continuous lengths fall in the province of low-pressure laminates. Plywood is a laminate but because of its special nature it is considered and described as a separate product. The presses used for high-pressure laminates do not have to be flat. Shallow curves are handled easily, making it possible to produce chair seats and the dished inner doors on refrigerators by the high-pressure technique. Small parts may be punched or machined from laminated sheets.

Fillers (i.e., the sheet stock before resin impregnation) have about as much effect on the final laminate properties as the resins. For instance, a phenolic resin-impregnated laminate with various fillers may have the following values for tensile strength:

| Filler | Tensile Strength, psi |
| --- | --- |
| Fabric (cotton) | 9,000 |
| Paper | 6,000 |
| Asbestos | 5,000 |
| Woven glass fibers | 10,000 |

When color is desired in a laminate ureas or melamines are used and for decorative effect a tap or cover sheet with special design may be applied. In general, high-pressure laminates have good electrical characteristics, good strength and heat resistance, dimensional stability, and good machinability.

Polyester laminate flat sheets can be made between platens on continuous equipment. Formed laminates can be produced in mating molds made of concrete, plaster or other low-cost material.

## Laminated Film

In order to combine the properties of different materials it has become general practice to use one film with another. Laminating a plastic film with metal foil and with other materials such as cloth and paper has also met with success. A laminate consisting of paper and aluminum foil and

TABLE 3.7. MATERIALS AND APPLICATIONS SUGGESTED BY BAKELITE'S
LAMINATING MATERIALS DIVISION

*Materials:*
Chlorinated naphthalenes
Cresol resins
Epoxy resins
Phenolic resins
Polyester resins
Polystyrene emulsions
Resorcinol resins
Silicone resins
Urea resins

*Applications:*
Dielectrics
Electrical castings
Glues and cements
    Lamp-basing resins and cements

Impregnates
    Densified wood
    Honeycomb core
    Reinforced plastics

Laminates
    Decorative
    Industrial
    Plywood
    Postformed
    Timber

Moldings
    Glass reinforced moldings
    Pulp products
    Wood aggregate products

Plastic solder

polyethylene is used for photographic film. Mylar-polyethylene laminates are used for packaging frozen foods. Mylar laminated to vinyl films makes good table tops. A three-ply laminate consisting of acetate, aluminum foil, and polyethylene is used where a high degree of moisture protection is needed. Acetate film may be printed for decorative purposes. Other film laminates of interest include felt and Mylar for airplane interiors, acetate and saran for packaging pharmaceuticals, and polyethylene with aluminum foil for packaging frozen food.

## Laminates, Low-Pressure

By using polyester resins and others which cure at low pressures, laminates can be made to almost any desired length. Flexible resins are available for applications such as awning material; low-pressure rigid resins with glass cloth as the fabric layer are used in the production of parts such as structural members for airplanes. An overlapping of terms exists between low-pressure laminates and reinforced plastics. The latter term is usually reserved for thicker and more curved sections such as those used for automobile fenders. Also, the nature of the fabric or filler tends to determine the term used. A glass cloth, low-pressure laminate, as a rule, is a reinforced plastic whereas a flat paper and resin laminate will be called a laminate only if high pressure (above 250 psi) is required; it will be called a low-pressure laminate if curable at low pressures.

## Liquids and Pastes

A water suspension of fine particles of a rubberlike plastic is known as a "latex" and is used to produce coated, cast, and other products. When the dispersion is in a liquid plasticizer instead of water it is called an "organosol" or a "plastisol." An organosol is defined as a colloidal dispersion of a synthetic resin in a plasticizer with or without other materials. It is used for molding, casting films, coating and printed with resins, often without volatile solvents or high temperatures. When the proportion of plasticizer to resin is altered it is possible to produce paste-like materials which have special uses. An epoxy resin paste, for instance, is used to repair defective castings. A thixotropic paste or putty is spread over defects and allowed to harden, leaving a raised surface to be machined later to proper dimensions. In some work, pastes are superior to resin solutions in that they do not have a volatile component which would have to be evaporated. See Table 1.4 for detailed definitions.

## Machined Parts

Plastic rods, tubes, and sheets form the raw material from which most machined parts are made. Tubes and rods are usually machined on shapers and automatic screw machines; sheets are machined on stamping and forming presses and planers. Thermoplastic sheets may be vacuum formed on automatic machines as described in Chapter 6. They may also be heated and shaped against forms. Thermosetting sheets may be post-formed into simple bends or drawn into simple contoured shapes. Post-forming, however, generally is limited to a cloth-based special type of phenolic laminated sheet. Moldings are machined for greater dimensional precision. In general the same machining technique as used on metals is applicable to plastics.

## Moldings

A large portion of all plastics reaching the consumer does so in the form of moldings. These are made on presses—compression, injection, transfer or extrusion—as described in Chapter 6. The term "molding" has been broadened to cover extrusion although the end products of an extrusion press have little resemblance to the products of other molding presses. Extruded items include strips, tubes, and wire coatings while molded items usually are complex shaped units of which a telephone receiver is typical.

The raw material for both molded items and extrusions is molding powder, although a special grade is often specified for extrusions. Moldings are often designed with metal inserts, and in some cases these determine whether compression or injection presses are to be used. It is simpler to handle the flow of the melted plastic around inserts in compression presses. In general, thermosetting materials are molded on compression presses and thermoplastic materials on injection presses. There are about 1300 molders and 260 extruders in the United States.

## Molding Powder

This term is so familiar in the plastics industry that a description might seem unnecessary. Nevertheless there are many types of molding powder and the physical form is significant as well as the chemical composition. The material actually may be a powder (i.e., composed of fine grains) or it may consist of small cubes or other shapes ranging in size up to one-eighth inch or more. To produce variegated effects the powder (particles or granulations) may be supplied in several colors to be mixed by the molder.

Various effects may also be secured by using different batches, each with a different degree of flow. Wavy effects are produced by using powder components of a different hardness but of the same color.

A popular form of molding powder for extrusion consists of small cylinders, perhaps 3/16 in. in diameter and 5/16 in. long. These are made by extruding thin rods and then running them through a properly timed chopper. In this way scrap may be reused—perhaps mixed with some virgin material.

## Plasticizers

Most resins are plasticized by heat, solvents, or plasticizers. The latter, while not strictly a form of plastic, are nevertheless, an important component of the industry. Solvents are also important but being more familiar and common to other industries they are omitted here. Solvents often disappear in processing and so are not present in the end product. Plasticizers, on the other hand, are relatively non-volatile compounds which impart some permanent characteristics to the end products of which they form a part.

As a rule, plasticizers are low-melting solids or high-boiling organic liquids. Their use is increasing as also is their variety. Literally thousands of plasticizers are available. They are used to improve flexibility or toughness or to better the flow of a plastic. Some resins, polyvinyl chloride, for example, may be compounded with a plasticizer at an elevated temperature. Without plasticizers most resins could not be processed into films, sheets, and fibers. Two types of plasticizer—chemical and oil types—are used in plastics.

| Some common chemical plasticizers | Some common oil plasticizers |
| --- | --- |
| tributyl phosphate | castor oil |
| dibutyl phthalate | treated tung oil |
| butyl stearate | brown soya oil |

## Plywood

This is a specialized type of laminate which deserves individual comment. Custom has gradually given the term a specific meaning. It refers to a type of wood ply construction, which has an odd number of plies, of which any two adjacent plies must have the grain direction at right angles. Construction must be balanced, that is, there must be as many plies on one side of a core piece (if it has a core piece) as on the other.

Different bonding materials are used which give a variation in over-all properties. Phenolic is the customary bond for outdoor grades of plywood, and sometimes surfacing with a phenolic resin impregnated paper increases weather resistance. Metal clad plywood is also available. Many other designs have been used, one of which has a core of honeycomb material to give thickness and stability. The core is then faced with standard plies.

Bonding agents for plywood have been improved to such an extent in recent years that the previous objections to veneers have all but disap-

TABLE 3.8. AVAILABILITY OF FORMS*

| Material | Forms Available |
|---|---|
| Acrylics | rigid sheets, rods and tubes, molding powder, solutions, adhesives and elastomers |
| Alkyds | molding powder and liquid resin |
| Melamine and urea | molding powder or granules, foamed material and solutions |
| Casein | rigid sheets, rods and tubes, powder and liquid |
| Acetates | granules, pellets, sheet, film, rods, tubes, strips, and coated cord |
| Butyrates | pellets, granules, film and coatings |
| Ethyl cellulose | granules, flake, sheet, film, rods, tubes and foil |
| Cellulose nitrate | rods, tubes, sheets |
| Fluorocarbons | powder and granules, sheets, rods and tubes |
| Polyamides | molding powder, sheets, rods, tubes and filaments |
| Phenolics | woodflour molding compound or with a chopped fabric, asbestos or other filler, preforms, and sheets for post-forming |
| Polyethylene | powder, sheets, film, filaments, rods and tubes |
| Polyesters | cast sheets, rods, tubes and liquids |
| Polystyrene | molding powder, granules, sheets, rods and shapes, foamed blocks, liquids and adhesives |
| Silicones | molding compounds, resins, coatings, greases, fluids and as silicone rubber |
| Polyvinyl acetal | molding powder, sheets, rods and tubes |
| Polyvinyl acetate | granules and film-forming emulsions |
| Polyvinyl alcohol | molding powder, sheets, films, tubes and rods |
| Polyvinyl carbazole | molding powder and films |
| Polyvinyl chloride | resins and latices |
| Polyvinyl chloride-acetate | molding powders, organosols, sheets, rods and tubes |
| Polyvinylidene chloride (saran) | molding powder, sheets, tubes and rods |

* Prepared in cooperation with The Society of the Plastics Industry.

peared. Now rare woods are available in an economical form by bonding a face veneer to a low-cost plywood.

Even though bonded with synthetic resins, plywood is not generally considered a plastic form. Yet for some inexplicable reason similar forms of fabric laminates and of reinforced plastics are included as definitely part of the plastics industry. A most active section of The Society of the Plastics Industry is known as the Reinforced Plastics Section. It does not cover plywood.

A method of preprocessing the finish on plywood has met with some success. It consists of applying a coating of thermosetting resins before passing the plywood through rollers. Another finishing technique consists of rapid heating and cooling the plywood to cause the lignin to soften and thus bind the cellulose fibers. This gives greater rigidity and solidness and an improved appearance. In this process high heat is applied almost instantaneously, for perhaps 1/20 of a second. This does not ignite the wood, as the release of pressure cools the wood instantly.

# 4. PRODUCTION AND PRICES

Most statistics of the plastics industry cover either production or prices. This chapter is an attempt to give the essential features of both. Table 4.1 gives the over-all plastics production figures for the last twenty years. The detailed Tariff Commission's figures covering production and sales of plastics and resin materials for 1956 are given in Table 4.2 and prices in resume and in detail are given in Tables 4.7 and 4.8, respectively.

Some production figures are listed in the company statements which appear in Chapter 8 and for convenience, these will be analyzed briefly here. Some comment was also included in Chapter 1.

The ten leading plastics materials companies had sales amounting to more than half the total for all plastics materials in the country, namely 1.1 billion dollars, and the five foremost of these ten had plastics sales totaling 889 million dollars. The profit on plastics sales for the ten amounted to about 120 million dollars or an average of a little over 10 per cent of sales. This figure is based partly on the assumption that the profit on plastic sales was at the same ratio as the profit on total sales. For instance, the consolidated companies in the Hooker Electrochemical group had total sales in 1956 of about $110,000,000 with a profit of $11,500,000, or 10.5 per cent. Its plastic sales were about 25 per cent of the total or $27,500,000 and for the purpose of this analysis it is assumed that the profit on this portion was the same as that on the total which gives the profit on plastic sales of this company as about $2,880,000. Not all the companies whose statements appear in Chapter 8 list the percentage of plastics sales to total sales but those that do show an average of 17 per cent as the proportion of plastics sales to total sales.

Of the larger manufacturers, The Dow Chemical Company shows the largest ratio of plastics sales to total sales—32 per cent. Its total sales (all products) were $565,300,000 in 1956 thus indicating plastics sales of $180,896,000.

Some idea of the sound base on which the plastics industry rests may be had from the size of many of the companies producing plastics materials. Of these, five companies have total annual sales above the $1,000,000,000 figure, and seven others are above the $500,000,000 mark. All told, eighteen of the manufacturers of plastics materials listed in Chapter 8 each have total annual sales above the $200,000,000 level.

### The 1956 Record

Plastics production nearly reached the four billion pound figure in 1956 by increasing about 5 per cent over 1955. This is noteworthy since only ten years ago production was less than one billion pounds.

The total production for all plastics and synthetic resin materials for 1956 was approximately 3,910,000,000 pounds, compared with 3,738,-916,000 pounds in 1955.

The 1956 growth comes on top of the 30 per cent increase in plastics production for 1955. For 1957 estimates place production approximately 5 per cent higher than for 1956.

The production record set in 1956 established the plastics industry, for the first time, as a two billion dollar industry. The value of its products in 1956 is estimated at approximately $2,056,450,000.00, compared with $1,869,458,000.00 in 1955.

The plastics industry as a whole operated at close to capacity during 1956, and there are indications that this will be increased at least 5 per cent in 1957, bringing the total capacity to approximately 4,200,000,000 pounds.

A preliminary analysis of some of the basic plastic raw materials shows increases in some and decreases in others, with no pronounced changes, except for polyethylene and polyesters. Approximate 1956 production figures for these several raw materials are: polyethylene, 541,128,000 pounds, up 30 per cent; polyesters, 71,800,000 pounds, up 30 per cent; vinyls, 729,500,000 pounds, up 10 per cent; polystyrenes, 636,000,000 pounds, up 4 per cent; phenolics and other tar acid resins, 503,000,000 pounds, about the same as 1955; ureas and melamines, 312,000,000 pounds, about the same as 1955; cellulosics, 140,000,000 pounds, down about 10 per cent.

Sales statistics covering molders, extruders, and mold makers, indicate that the molders and extruders as a group, enjoyed approximately a 6 per cent increase in business in 1956 over 1955.

Thermosetting molders are estimated to have had a 10 per cent increase in business in 1956, while the thermoplastic molders found their business off slightly.

The mold makers, as indicated by sales statistics, enjoyed an increase in business over the last few months of 1956, bringing their sales about 16 per cent above 1955. As it takes a mold three or four months before it gets into production, this is considered to be a favorable sign for increased output of molded parts in 1957.

TABLE 4.1.  TWENTY YEARS PRODUCTION** OF SYNTHETIC PLASTICS
AND RESIN MATERIALS*

| Year | Pounds |
|------|--------|
| 1936 | 132,913,000 |
| 1937 | 163,030,000 |
| 1938 | 130,359,000 |
| 1939 | 213,028,000 |
| 1940 | 276,814,000 |
| 1941 | 428,326,000 |
| 1942 | 426,731,000 |
| 1943 | 653,332,000 |
| 1944 | 784,137,000 |
| 1945 | 818,020,000 |
| 1946 | 994,277,000 |
| 1947 | 1,251,699,000 |
| 1948 | 1,480,876,000 |
| 1949 | 1,491,111,000 |
| 1950 | 2,150,518,000 |
| 1951 | 2,431,408,000 |
| 1952 | 2,333,924,000 |
| 1953 | 2,776,627,000 |
| 1954 | 2,827,803,000 |
| 1955 | 3,569,300,000 |
| 1956 | 3,910,000,000 |

* Based on United States Tariff Commission figures.
** Approximate figures.

TABLE 4.2.   UNITED STATES TARIFF COMMISSION'S REPORT ON PRODUCTION
AND SALES OF PLASTICS AND RESIN MATERIALS IN THE UNITED STATES,
PRELIMINARY 1956 AND JANUARY 1957

(In pounds. Dry basis unless otherwise specified)

| Item | Preliminary Total 1956 | | January 1957 | |
|---|---|---|---|---|
| | Production | Sales | Production | Sales |
| Cellulose plastics:[1] | | | | |
| Cellulose acetate and mixed ester: | | | | |
| Sheets, under 0.003 gage | 19,383,669 | 19,626,935 | 1,440,428 | 1,309,744 |
| Sheets, 0.003 gage and over | 16,656,118 | 16,533,245 | 1,438,472 | 1,217,714 |
| All other sheets, rods, and tubes | 7,282,394 | 7,048,656 | 612,021 | 513,768 |
| Molding and extrusion materials | 92,744,685 | 91,721,018 | 7,455,973 | 7,000,531 |
| Nitrocellulose sheets, rods, and tubes | 5,254,287 | 4,834,837 | 376,988 | 488,843 |
| Other cellulose plastics | 5,651,149 | 5,158,877 | 524,756 | 307,946 |
| Phenolic and other tar-acid resins: | | | | |
| Molding materials[1] | 214,728,646 | 190,456,640 | 17,558,707 | 16,674,519 |
| Bonding and adhesive resins for— | | | | |
| Laminating (except plywood) | 62,832,035 | 44,365,011 | 5,211,501 | 4,139,273 |
| Coated and bonded abrasives | 15,644,206 | 16,505,780 | 1,692,440 | 1,670,029 |
| Friction materials (brake linings, clutch facings, and similar materials) | [2] | [2] | [2] | [2] |
| Thermal insulation (fiber glass, rock wool) | 56,151,252 | 55,128,535 | 4,458,990 | 4,242,148 |
| Plywood | 44,187,162 | 35,612,601 | 3,755,541 | 2,834,587 |
| All other bonding and adhesive uses | 49,788,936 | 47,636,880 | 4,913,746 | 4,415,928 |
| Protective-coating resins, unmodified and modified except by resin | 29,502,644 | 25,762,863 | 2,709,587 | 2,414,651 |
| Resins for all other uses | 39,455,445 | 34,275,826 | 3,782,269 | 3,266,772 |
| Urea and melamine resins: | | | | |
| Textile-treating and textile-coating resins | 40,784,421 | 38,895,869 | 3,398,043 | 3,461,405 |
| Paper-treating and paper-coating resins | 24,774,608 | 23,277,343 | 2,545,736 | 2,318,543 |
| Bonding and adhesive resins for— | | | | |
| Plywood | 102,081,404 | 95,360,575 | 7,338,293 | 7,257,214 |
| All other bonding and adhesive uses, including laminating | 25,205,208 | 23,878,210 | 2,158,213 | 2,275,027 |

TABLE 4.2 (*Continued*)

| Item | Preliminary Total 1956 | | January 1957 | |
|------|------------|--------|------------|--------|
| | Production | Sales | Production | Sales |
| **Urea and melamine resins:** (*Continued*) | | | | |
| Protective-coating resins, straight and modified | 37,249,525 | 27,816,969 | 3,488,263 | 2,630,538 |
| Resins for all other uses, including molding | 87,166,793 | 84,477,750 | 7,657,056 | 7,874,611 |
| **Styrene resins:** | | | | |
| Molding materials[1] | 433,036,877 | 389,384,474 | 32,295,697 | 36,093,284 |
| Protective-coating resins, straight and modified | 91,135,040 | 87,386,556 | 7,428,840 | 6,900,748 |
| Resins for all other uses | 104,415,845 | 104,973,111 | 11,211,112 | 9,874,756 |
| **Vinyl and vinyl copolymer Resins, total[3]** | 752,410,321 | 717,592,426 | 67,096,334 | 64,724,638 |
| Polyvinyl chloride and copolymer resins (50 per cent or more polyvinyl chloride) for— | | | | |
| Film (resin content) | — | 78,064,204 | — | 8,094,174 |
| Sheeting (resin content) | — | 52,505,087 | — | 5,760,834 |
| Molding and extrusion (resin content) | — | 203,811,721 | — | 18,804,807 |
| Textile and paper treating and coating (resin content)[4] | — | 62,930,561 | — | 6,196,842 |
| Flooring (resin content) | — | 65,499,631 | — | 5,957,804 |
| Protective coatings (resin content) | — | 28,521,587 | — | 3,076,650 |
| All other uses (resin content) | — | 74,621,127 | — | 3,438,158 |
| All other vinyl resins for— | | | | |
| Adhesives (resin content) | — | 36,563,154 | — | 2,987,842 |
| All other uses (resin content) | — | 115,075,354 | — | 10,407,527 |
| **Alkyd resins:** | | | | |
| For protective coatings: | | | | |
| Phthalic anhydride types: | | | | |
| Unmodified | 270,375,085 | 124,490,503 | 22,912,895 | 9,881,407 |
| Modified with tar acids, rosin and/or other materials except styrene | 70,977,064 | 39,413,829 | 8,575,409 | 4,362,288 |
| Polybasic acid types (except phthalic): | | | | |
| Unmodified | 3,930,815 | 3,117,319 | 298,606 | 181,458 |
| Modified with tar acids, rosin, and/or other materials, except styrene | 11,710,150 | 5,184,359 | 1,558,241 | 571,320 |

TABLE 4.2 (*Continued*)

| Item | Preliminary Total 1956 | | January 1957 | |
|------|------------|-------|------------|-------|
|      | Production | Sales | Production | Sales |
| Alkyd resins: (*Continued*) | | | | |
| For all other uses (modified and unmodified resins) | 16,049,335 | 14,814,984 | 1,603,329 | 1,496,107 |
| Coumarone-indene and petroleum polymer resins | 245,585,916 | 241,845,584 | 17,643,660 | 18,431,928 |
| Polyester resins | 72,587,769 | 65,291,568 | 7,264,772 | 6,443,851 |
| Polyethylene resins | 556,919,133 | 509,398,977 | 52,356,773 | 53,187,799 |
| Miscellaneous synthetic plastics and resin materials: | | | | |
| Molding materials[1, 5] | 43,541,644 | 40,712,576 | 4,654,617 | 4,541,687 |
| Protective-coating resins[6] | 11,448,208 | 5,723,057 | 1,170,018 | 483,276 |
| Resins for all other uses[7] | 117,894,300 | 109,311,942 | 10,174,445 | 10,312,804 |

[1] Includes fillers, plasticizers, and extenders.

[2] Included with "All other bonding and adhesive uses."

[3] Production statistics by uses are not representative, as end use may not be known at the time of manufacture. Therefore, only statistics on total production are given.

[4] Includes data for spreader and calendering-type resins.

[5] Includes data for acrylic, nylon, silicone, and other molding materials.

[6] Includes data for epichlorohydrin, acrylic, silicone, and other protective-coating resins.

[7] Includes data for acrylic, rosin modifications, nylon, silicone, and other plastics and resins for miscellaneous uses.

NOTE: Epichlorohydrin listed in this table is a solvent for cellulose esters and some other resins. Rosin statistics have been omitted from this table.

TABLE 4.3. PLASTICS USED IN AUTOMOBILES

| Type | Annual Pounds—1955 |
|------|-------------------|
| Butyral sheeting (safety glass) | 17,000,000 |
| Cellulose acetate butyrate | 5,200,000 |
| Methacrylates | 7,400,000 |
| Nylon | 3,800,000 |
| Phenolics | 5,200,000 |
| Vinyls | 21,000,000 |
| Total | 59,600,000 |

This averages about 9 pounds per car which is very low. Most estimates range from 15 to more than 20 pounds per car. This table is thought to be approximately correct however for the types of plastics listed. It omits polyesters, urethanes, fluorocarbons, epoxies, and others, all of which are used in the average car.

TABLE 4.4. COMPANIES AND WORKERS IN PLASTICS

*Plastic Material Manufacturers*
52 chemical companies
20,000 workers

*Molders and Extruders*
1,450 plants
30,000 workers

*Fabricators*
1,500 plants
More than 5,000 workers

*Plastic Film and Sheeting Processors*
60 companies
20,000 workers

*High Pressure Laminators*
50 companies

*Reinforced Plastic Manufacturers*
120 companies

} 6,000 workers

*Coaters*
80 companies

This table gives a rough idea of the size of the plastics industry. There are other categories and the total number of workers in the industry is estimated at well over 100,000.

TABLE 4.5. TOTAL PRODUCTION OF PLASTICS IN 1956*

| Type | Production in Pounds** |
|---|---|
| Vinyls | 725,000,000 |
| Polystyrene | 625,000,000 |
| Polyethylene | 525,000,000 |
| Alkyds | 500,000,000 |
| Phenolics*** | 475,000,000 |
| Urea and melamine | 325,000,000 |
| Cellulosics | 150,000,000 |
| All others | 575,000,000 |
| Total | 3,900,000,000 |

* Based in part on U.S. Tariff Commission reports and in part on estimates of *Modern Plastics* and others.

** At the time of preparing this table the actual figures for 1956 production were not known. These estimates are higher than some but in March 1957 many authorities believed the 1956 total would exceed 4 billion pounds which figure has been used elsewhere in this book.

*** Including other tar-acid resins.

## Growth of Plastics

A recent magazine* carried the following headline: "Plastics Growing Five Times Faster than All Industry." This startling statement gives some idea of the pace with which plastics are finding new markets and replacing older materials in established markets. On a cubic foot basis, which takes advantage of the light weight of plastics, sales of plastics have drawn ahead of copper and all other nonferrous metals. The vinyls head the list of plastics in production but polyethylene is growing rapidly and the number of producers of polyethylene has jumped in a relatively few years from two to twelve or more. Still it will be some years before polyethylene threatens the vinyls for first place in total plastics production. This is partly because the vinyls form such a large and diversified family. As indicated in Chapter 2, there are at least eight subdivisions in this vinyl family, each having characteristics which set it apart from the others for certain applications. Vinyl chloride and the copolymer vinyl chloride-acetate sales jumped ahead by featuring upholstery and floor covering. The vinyls also are entering the coating field more aggressively, thus competing with the alkyds. Resins especially prepared for spray coating of metals show promise and a new process known as "spread-coating" is designed for use with vinyls.

Second on the plastics production list comes polystyrene which, to the surprise of many, continues as a leading molding material despite several disadvantages. It is more brittle than the cellulosics and yet it is replacing them in many applications. It is less resistant to chemical attack than polyethylene, ages more quickly than the acrylics, and is not as easily compounded as the vinyls, but it is low in cost and is readily molded on high-speed injection molding machines—factors which apparently outweigh all of polystyrene's shortcomings. The production of polystyrene for 1956 has been reported close to 525,000,000 pounds but the 1956 government total for the styrene family came to over 600,000,000 pounds. This discrepancy is partly because modifications such as styrene-butadiene copolymer are included under the general heading of polystyrene. The total for molding material under this heading was about the same in 1956 as in 1955. Some 20 per cent of the total is reported as entering the broad end-use field of refrigeration which has recently met new competition from other plastics. A butadiene-styrene rubber blend when extruded into sheets and then vacuum formed into refrigerator door panels still holds

---

* *Chemical Week.*

its own as a popular application. April 1956, with a reported sales total of over 40,000,000 pounds, was the largest styrene volume month on record.

Polyethylene, with a 1956 production of over half a billion pounds and with the steepest growth curve of any plastic, should certainly be watched. The film, used extensively for food packaging, has grown with the development of supermarkets. Other new applications include its use as linings for swimming pools, mulching covers for gardens, and rain protection for tennis courts. Some 1250 square yards of this film, heat-sealed and balloon shaped, were blown up to form a building structure, held up by air pressure and held down around the edges by a large nylon tube filled with water. This was an experimental building to house an appliance store, but if the idea catches on it could lead to a large additional use of polyethylene film. Polyethylene has replaced gutta percha in transatlantic cables. Conventional polyethylene is soft and low-melting but a new German development produces a material which is semi-rigid instead of flexible and this may lead to additional production. A process independent of the German development is reported by Phillips Chemical Co. with a new plant in the making at Pasadena.

The alkyds which are closely related to the unsaturated polyesters are the predominant resins used in coatings. Their curve of production has flattened out recently probably due to the increased application of other resins in the coating field. Some alkyd molding powder is produced with a limited market based on its high arc resistance. The inherent brittleness of the alkyd molded items will limit their increase in production. Nevertheless the total production of the alkyds remains among the top figures in the plastics industry. The 1956 total was approximately 500,000,000 pounds.

The phenolic production curve has been irregular during recent years. It dropped in 1952 and again in 1954; 1956 appeared to be down slightly below 1955 but most authorities believe that phenolics will have a good, steady, and slowly increasing demand in the years ahead. They still are tops in the electrical industry for such items as outlets, circuit breakers, switchgear, and motor components. Looking ahead, some new developments seem likely. A modification, resorcinol-formaldehyde, is increasing in demand for bonding aircraft propellors at room temperature. Foundry use of phenolics is on the increase and structural timber which uses waste wood is definitely a good application for phenolics as the bonding agent.

Phenolic bases for printed circuits showed an upward trend, with a good year in 1956 and another good year in prospect for 1957.

Monthly sales of phenolics held up well during the first part of 1956 with an average monthly production of close to 17,000,000 pounds. This is considered good although the capacity to produce phenolic molding powder is reported as 30 to 35,000,000 pounds a month. The monthly average of molding powder sales dropped during the last half of 1956 and the total for the year has been estimated at about 200,000,000 pounds. The total for all types of tar-acid resins for 1956 was estimated at 475,000,000 pounds, but went higher.

The ureas and melamine resins taken as a group (amino resins) come next with an estimated 1926 production of 325,000,000 pounds. Of this large poundage only about one-fourth is used as molding powder. The balance is distributed between coatings for paper and textiles which account for 70,000,000 pounds and as bonding resin for plywood and laminates. Dishware consumed about 30,000,000 pounds of melamine molding powder despite its higher cost in comparison with ureas.

The cellulosics as a group had sales in 1956 of about 150,000,000 pounds. This includes about 20,000,000 pounds of photofilm, not included in the usual government figures. Sales in 1955 were about 140,000,000 pounds and the 1956 increase is credited largely to a switch in the women's shoe industry from wood heels to acetate heels. The latter are said to be cheaper when finishing costs are included. One estimate gives 25 to 30,000,000 pounds of acetate as the total used for women's heels in 1956.

### Prices of Plastics

Because of the many variations in types of any one plastic, prices are difficult to list and any list must be considered as indicative of a general level only, unless a manufacturer's type is described. Table 4.6 presents an attempt to give simple and yet representative prices covering most of the common materials. Prices change, of course, and this list may be out of date by 1958 or before. The trend has been downward in most cases; in fact, the per pound average of all plastics prices has dropped from about 75¢ in 1927 to about 35¢ today, despite the introduction of several very high priced materials such as the fluorocarbons at $8.00.

In judging per pound prices for finished parts—moldings, for instance—there is an even wider variation than there is with molding powder. In this case not only are the possible variations in the type of molding powders included but in addition the variations in extent of finish, quantity required, design of molds, and specified tolerances also have to be considered. The molder should always be asked to procure the molds and assume responsibility for them so that he will not be able to shift responsibility for faulty work.

TABLE 4.6. APPROXIMATE PRICES*

For convenience the following abbreviated list of general-purpose prices is given here. Detailed figures are on following pages.

| | |
|---|---|
| Acetates | $0.33 |
| Acrylics | 0.75 |
| Butyrates | 0.50 |
| Epoxy resins | 0.90 |
| Fluorocarbons | 8.00 |
| Ethyl cellulose | 0.72 |
| Melamine | 0.47 |
| Phenolics | 0.20 |
| Polyamides (nylon) | 1.43 |
| Polyesters | 0.37 |
| Polyethylene | 0.41 |
| Polystyrene | 0.29 |
| Polyurethanes | 2.80 |
| Polyvinyl acetate | 0.42 |
| Polyvinyl alcohol | 0.80 |
| Polyvinyl chloride | 0.30 |
| Polyvinyl chloride-acetate | 0.40 |
| Polyvinylidene chloride (saran) | 0.39 |
| Silicones (glass-filled) | 2.50 |
| Ureas | 0.33 |

* These prices are averages based on several manufacturers' quotations.

TABLE 4.7. PRICES OF RESINS AND PLASTICS

The following are prices per pound of some of the commercial materials. They are for ordinary quantities as quoted by the manufacturers and have been adapted from lists appearing in *Chemical and Engineering News* for December 1956.

*Bakelite Phenolics:*

| | |
|---|---|
| Molding compounds, general-purpose, black and brown, 50-lb bags | 0.202 - 0.25¾ |
| General purpose, standard, colors, 50-lb bags | 0.23½ - 0.34 |
| Impact resistant, 50-lb bags | 0.25½ - 0.30¾ |
| Electrical insulating, drums | 0.27½ - 0 31½ |
| Heat resistant, 50-lb bags | 0.20½ - 0.25½ |
| Chemical resistant | 0.24½ - 0.31½ |
| Coatings resins and 100% phenolic, non-heat hardening, 400-lb container | 0.28¼ - 0 54¾ |
| 100% phenolic, heat hardening, 400-lb container | 0.36½ - 0.39½ |
| Phenolic "resin-baking" resins and solutions, 400-lb container | 0.35  - 0.42½ |

Table 4.7 (*Continued*)

*Bakelite Polyethylene:*

| | |
|---|---|
| Extrusion and molding, pellets, natural, 50-lb bags | 0.41 - 0.53½ |
| Colors, 50-lb bags | 0.37½ - 0.56½ |

*Bakelite Resins:*

| | |
|---|---|
| Polyester resins, standard, 500-lb drums | 0.31½ - 0.45 |
| Epoxy resins, standard, 375-500-lb drums | 0.48¼ - 0.80 |
| Epoxy hardeners, standard, 450-500-lb drums | 0.67 - 0.80 |
| Fluorothene resins and compounds; standard, 150-200-lb bags | 8.50 -10.00 |

*Bakelite Styrene Polymers and Copolymers:*

| | |
|---|---|
| Molding, general-purpose, crystal, 50-lb bags | 0.27½ |
| Standard colors | 0.31½ |
| Impact compounds; TMD-2155, natural and black, 50-lb bags | 0.38½ - 0.41½ |
| TMD-2155, standard colors, 50-lb bags | 0.42½ - 0.44½ |
| Extrusion materials; impact compound, black, 50-lb bags | 0.32 - 0.34 |
| Standard colors | 0.34½ - 0.38½ |

*Bakelite Vinyl Resins:*

| | |
|---|---|
| Molding compounds, natural and black (VND-9734), 50-lb bags | 0.28 |
| Molding compounds, colors (VND-9960, 9970, 9980), 50-lb bags | 0.33½ |
| Extrusion compounds, natural, black, white | 0.26½ - 0.47 |
| Vinyl acetate resin solution (A-70), 69-72% by weight in acetone, 55-gal. drums, gal. | 5.10 |
| Vinyl alcohol-acetate resin solution (T-24-9) and MA-28-18; 55-gal. drums, gal. | 2.02 - 2.76 |
| Vinyl ether polymers, 400-lb drum, lb | 0.18 - 0.85 |
| Vinyl chloride-acetate resins, 50-lb bags, lb | 0.27 - 0.44 |
| Vinyl chloride resins, 50-lb bags, lb | 0.27 - 0.30 |
| Modified vinyl chloride-acetate resins (VMCH, VAGH), 50-lb bags, lb | 0.41 - 0.55 |

*Borden Durite Phenolics:*

| | |
|---|---|
| General-purpose molding compounds, 50-lb bags, drums | 0.20½ - 0.25 |
| Impact resistant, drums | 0.27½ - 0.42 |
| Heat resistant, 50-lb bags | 0.20½ - 0.31¼ |

*Borden Lemol Polyvinyl Alcohol:*

| | |
|---|---|
| Partially hydrolyzed, f.o.b. Leominster, Mass. | 0.73 - 0.94 |

*Borden Polyvinyl Chloride:*

| | |
|---|---|
| VC-100, medium molecular weight straight polyvinyl chloride dry blending easy processing type | 0.27 |
| VC-113, vinyl chloride, vinyl acetate copolymer, phonograph records, vinyl asbestos flooring, etc. | 0.32 |

TABLE 4.7 (*Continued*)

*Celanese Cellulose Acetate:*

| | |
|---|---|
| Extrusion and injection, all transparent colors and extrusion materials | 0.50 |
| Injection, general colors, translucents, metallic pearls, opaques including black | 0.46 |
| Injection, special colors including black for injection | 0.39 |

*Celanese Forticel Cellulose Propionate:*

| | |
|---|---|
| Molding compounds, plain colors, transparents, translucents and opaques, including black, 20,000 lb or more, freight prepaid | 0.63 |
| less than 20,000 lb | 0.64 - 0.71 |

*Celanese Marco Polyesters:*

| | |
|---|---|
| Rigid, general-purpose (light stable), freight prepaid 40 drums and over | 0.33 - 0.36 |
| Rigid, general-purpose | 0.33 |

*Ciba Epoxy Resins:*

| | |
|---|---|
| Araldite 502, contact pressure laminating, high strength, non-ret. drums, truckload (23,000 lb and over), minimum transportation allowed | 0.80 |
| Araldite 6005-6010, unmodified amber liquid epoxy resin for casting and laminating, drums | 0.80 |

*Cyanamid Adhesive and Laminating Resins:*

| | |
|---|---|
| Urac 110, urea-formaldehyde, neat powder | 0.20½ - 0.22½ |
| Melurac 300, melamine-urea-formaldehyde, filled powder | 0.25 - 0.29 |
| Melurac 301, melamine-urea-formaldehyde, neat powder | 0.28 - 0.33 |
| Melurac 304, melamine-urea-formaldehyde, neat powder | 0.26½ - 0.28½ |
| Cymel 405, melamine-formaldehyde, laminating, powder | 0.40 - 0.42 |
| Cymel 428, melamine-formaldehyde, laminating, powder | 0.41 - 0.43 |
| Cyacor 151, urea-formaldehyde core binding resins, powder | 0.21½ - 0.23½ |

*Cyanamid Coating Resins:*

| | |
|---|---|
| Rezyl, non-drying, modified alkyds for lacquers | 0.22¼ - 0.51 |
| Cymel, melamine-formaldehyde | 0.32¾ - 0.40 |
| Beetle, condensation products of urea-formaldehyde | 0.19½ - 0.47¼ |
| Cycopol, resin polymers for fast air drying and baking surface coatings | 0.21¼ - 0.33 |

*Cyanamid Molding Compounds:*

| | |
|---|---|
| Cymel 1077, 1079, melamine-formaldehyde, all colors, alpha cellulose filled, 19,999-10,000 lb | 0.47 |
| 9999-1000 lb | 0.48 - 0.57 |
| Cymel 1077, 1079, ungranulated or powder | 0.43 - 0.55 |
| Cymel 3020, fabric filled, colors, 25-lb bags, single color, 30,000 lb or more, Bound Brook | 0.57 |
| 1000-29,999 lb | 0.59 - 0.62 |

TABLE 4.7 (*Continued*)

---

*Cyanamid Molding Compounds: (Continued)*

| | |
|---|---|
| Cymel 404T, 404R, unfilled, translucent, natural color, 200 and 250-lb containers, Wallingford | 0.85 |
| less than standard container | 0.95 |
| Cymel 3136, glass fiber filled, natural color, Bound Brook, 175 lb or more, net | 1.05 |
| less than 175 lb | 1.15 |
| Beetle molding compound, powder, standard container | 0.30 |
| less than standard container | 0.49 |
| Beetle molding compound, special colors, granulated, single color, 30,000 lb or more, same basis | 0.33 |
| 29,999-1000 lb | 0.34 - 0.45 |
| (Ungranulated Beetle powders 3¢ per lb less than granulated) | |

*Cyanamid Polyester Resins:*

| | |
|---|---|
| Laminac No. 4110, low-temp. cure, open assembly hand layup work, 55-gal. drums (500 lb net) | 0.33 - 0.34½ |
| No. 4116, general-purpose, low reactivity | 0.33 - 0.34½ |
| No. 4123, general-purpose for matched metal and hand layup work | 0.34 - 0.35½ |

*Dow Polyethylene:*

| | |
|---|---|
| Injection molding (700-M), rigidity, crack resistance; 20,000 lb and over, bags, Velasco or Midland, freight prepaid | 0.4) |
| Injection molding (900-M) uniformity, moldability; 20,000 lb and over, bags, Velasco, freight prepaid | 0.41 |
| Tubular film extrusion (500-E) 20,000 lb and over, bags, Velasco, freight prepaid | 0.41 |

*Dow Polystyrene:*

| | |
|---|---|
| Styron 666, general-purpose, crystal, unlimited color range; extrusion or molding; 50-lb bags, 20,000 lb and over, Midland, Mich., Allyn's Point, Conn., or Torrance, Calif., freight prepaid on 50 lb or more | 0.27½ |
| Styron 665, for extrusion; higher molecular weight than No. 666; 50-lb bags, 20,000 lb and over | 0.27½ |
| Styron 777, standard and special colors; medium impact material; 50-lb bags, 20,000 lb and over | 0.34 |
| Styron 475, natural and black, high-impact polystyrene with 10 times elongation of general-purpose resin, 50-lb bags, 20,000 lb and over | 0.32 |
| Styron 440; heat resistant impact formulation; radio cabinets; 50-lb bags, 20,000 lb and over | 0.32 |
| Styron standard and special colors of above, 50-lb bags, 20,000 lb and over | 0.34½ |
| Styron 480, natural and black, extra high impact strength; good heat resistance and surface gloss; 50-lb bags, 20,000 lb and over | 0.38½ |

TABLE 4.7 (*Continued*)

*Dow Resins:*

| | | |
|---|---|---|
| Polystyrene coating (PS-2, PS-3), 200-lb drums, carload or truckload, Midland, Mich., freight equalized | | 0.25 |
|     less than carload or truckload | | 0.30 |
|     less than standard drum | | 0.35 |
| Polyvinylidene chloride (Saran Resin F120), drums, carload or truckload, Midland, Mich. | | 0.58 |
|     less than carload or truckload | | 0.60 |
|     less than standard drum | | 0.65 |

*Dow-Ethocel Plastic Granules:*

| | | |
|---|---|---|
| Formulations REH, R1, R2, LT5, and LT6, 20,000 lb and over, works, Midland, Mich., freight prepaid on 200 lb or more | | 0.72 |

*Du Pont Acrylics:*

| | | |
|---|---|---|
| Lucite 140, natural injection molding and extrusion, maximum heat resistance, moderate flow, 250-lb drums, works, freight allowed and prepaid, truckload and more | | 0.55 |
|     less than truckload | 0.57 | - 0.80 |
| Lucite 129, general-purpose moldings, medium flow, truckload and over, same basic | | 0.55 |
|     less than truckload | 0.57 | - 0.80 |
| Lucite 130, injection, general-purpose molding, drums, same basis, truckload and over | | 0.55 |
|     less than truckload | 0.57 | - 0.80 |
| Lucite 29, 30, compression molding and specialty applications, granules, drums, truckload, same basis | | 0.51 |
|     less than truckload | 0.53 | - 0.75 |

*Du Pont Nylon Resin Molding Powders:*

| | |
|---|---|
| Zytel 101, natural heat-resistant; general-purpose molding, 25-lb sealed cans, works, freight allowed and prepaid, minimum truckload and more | 1.33 |
| Zytel 103, heat stabilized, electrical parts, 25-lb cans, same basis | 1.43 |
| Zytel 105, black, weathering properties, auto, electrical parts, weather-resistant moldings, 20-lb cans, same basis | 1.43 |
| Zytel 211, impact devices, parts requiring exceptional toughness, 22½-lb cans, same basis | 1.33 |
| Zytel 3606, extrusion; heat and light-stabilized, wire jacketing (field wire), 25-lb cans, same basis | 1.95 |

*Du Pont Polyethylenes:*

| | |
|---|---|
| Alathon 3, natural, extrusion, molding; base resin for wire and cable, 50-lb bags, minimum truckload or more, delivered | 0.45 |
| Alathon 4, black, extrusion; cable jackets, 50-lb bags, same basis | 0.53 |
| Alathon 5 and 5B, natural, extrusion; high frequency, high voltage insulation, bags, same basis | 0.43 |

TABLE 4.7 (*Continued*)

*Du Pont Tetrafluoroethylene Resin:*

| | |
|---|---|
| Teflon 1, general-purpose powder for molding and extrusion; chemical, electrical, mechanical, non-adhesive uses, 220-lb drums, freight allowed | 4.90 |
| 25-lb drums | 5.05 |
| 5-lb drums | 5.55 |
| Teflon 5, special granulation for molding cylinder to produce shaved tape; electrical, chemical, mechanical, non-adhesive uses, 220-lb drums, same basis | 5.51 |
| 25-lb drums | 5.30 |
| 5-lb drums | 5.80 |
| Teflon 6, special granulation for extrusion; thin-walled tubular goods, tape and wire coating, 50-lb drums, same basis | 7.85 |
| 4-lb drums | 8.00 |

*Durez Phenolic Molding Materials:*

| | |
|---|---|
| Phenolic, standard general-purpose compounds, truckload, carload or more | 0.20½ - 0.24½ |
| less than truckload, bags | 0.21 - 0.25 |
| (Drums ½¢ more than above) | |
| Impact-resistant compounds, truckload, carload, or more, drums | 0.26 - 0.59 |
| less than truckload, drums | 0.26½ - 0.59½ |
| Electrical insulation compounds, natural, black and brown, truckload, carload or more, drums | 0.22 - 0.31 |
| less than truckload, drums | 0.22½ - 0.31½ |
| Heat-resistant compounds, truckload, carload or more, bags | 0.20½ - 0.26 |
| less than truckload, bags | 0.21 - 0.26½ |

*Durez Phenolic Resins:*

| | |
|---|---|
| Water soluble phenolics, 500-lb drums, truckload | 0.18½ - 0.19½ |
| Liquid phenolics, 500-lb drums, truckload | 0.26½ - 0.38 |

*Firestone Vinyl Resins:*

| | |
|---|---|
| Exon 402A, 500, 905, 915, 925, truckload and over, Pottstown, Pa., minimum transportation prepaid, single shipment | 0.27 |
| Exon 654, plastisol, truckload and over | 0.30 |
| Exon 450, 468, 480, truckload and over | 0.32 |
| Exon 470, copolymer soluble, truckload and over | 0.48 |

*General Electric Phenolic Molding Powders:*

| | |
|---|---|
| General-purpose, black, brown, drums, 23,000 lb and over, works, Pittsfield, Mass., freight allowed | 0.21 - 0.25 |
| Mottles, walnut, same basis | 0.22 |
| High heat resistance, brown, same basis | 0.25½ |
| Medium heat resistance, black | 0.21 |
| High impact, black, brown, same basis | 0.41½ |
| Medium, impact, black, brown, same basis | 0.40½ - 0.56½ |
| Rubber-phenolics, wood flour, asbestos, black, and fabric-filled, black, brown, same basis | 0.36½ - 0.66 |

TABLE 4.7 (*Continued*)

*Goodrich Polyvinyl Resins:*

Geon 101, 101EP, 103EP, 202, general-purpose resins, 50-lb
bags, truckload and over ... 0.27
Geon 121, plastisol applications, 40-lb bags, truckload and over ... 0.30
Geon 126, for organosols, 40-lb bags, truckload and over ... 0.28
Geon 404 HI, rigid applications, 50-lb bags, truckload and over ... 0.37
Geon 428, phonograph records, 50-lb bags, truckload and over ... 0.32

*Goodyear Coating Resins:*

Pliovac AO, vinyl copolymer, dispersion resin, 50-lb bags,
Niagara Falls, minimum freight prepaid, 20,000 lb ... 0.30
   2000 to 19,999 lb ... 0.31
Pliovac DB80V, dry blending polyvinyl chloride, calendering,
50-lb bags, Niagara Falls, freight prepaid, 20,000 lb ... 0.27
   2000 to 19,999 lb ... 0.28
Pliovac DB90V, dry blending polyvinyl chloride, extrusion,
50-lb bags, Niagara Falls, minimum freight prepaid, 20,000 lb ... 0.27
   2000 to 19,999 lb ... 0.28
Pliovac EDB90V, dry blending polyvinyl chloride, electrical
grade, 50-lb bags, Niagara Falls, minimum freight prepaid,
20,000 lb ... 0.27
   2000 to 19,999 lb ... 0.28

*Hercules Hercocel Molding Powders:*

Hercocel A, cellulose acetate, transparents for injection, molding,
extrusion, self-extinguishing formulas, 270-lb containers,
20,000 lb or over, Parlin, N. J., freight prepaid ... 0.38 - 0.50
Hercocel A, for injection molding, special opaque colors,
270-lb container, 20,000 lb and over, same basis ... 0.36
Hercocel E, ethyl cellulose molding powder, 235-lb container,
20,000 lb and over, same basis ... 0.72

*Durez Hetron Polyester Resins:*

Fire-resistant, rigid and semi-rigid, tanks works, delivered ... 0.41½- 0.46½
   truckload delivered ... 0.43  - 0.48
Fire-resistant, light-stabilized, rigid, tanks works, delivered ... 0.47
   truckload delivered ... 0.48½

*Jones-Dabney Alkyds:*

Syntex H-3, rosin maleic ester; for hard, fast drying lacquers
and pale varnishes; 100% solids, drums, carload, works,
minimum freight prepaid East ... 0.26¼
*Jones-Dabney Epoxy Resins, Solutions:*
Epi-Rez 510, liquid epoxy resin; clear, light colored; for adhesive, laminating, casting, potting applications; drums, carload ... 0.80
Epi-Rez 515, adhesives and laminates; for blending with higher
and lower melting resins to vary viscosity; drums, carload ... 0.85½

TABLE 4.7 (*Continued*)

*Koppers Dylene Polystyrene Molding Materials:*

| | | |
|---|---|---|
| Crystal pellets or granular Nos. 2, 3, 4, 7, 8, regular, 50-lb bags, 20,000 lb, works, freight allowed | | 0.27½ |
| less than 20,000 lb | 0.28 | - 0.29 |
| Standard colors, regular types, 20,000 lb and over, works, freight allowed | | 0.31½ |
| less than 20,000 lb | 0.32 | - 0.33 |

*Koppers Polyethylene:*

| | |
|---|---|
| Dylan 3500, natural, injection molding; film and bottles; 50-lb bags, works, freight allowed; 20,000 lb and over | 0.41 |
| Dylan 3016, 3028, black, with anti-oxidant; pipe; 50-lb bags, 20,000 lb and over, works, freight allowed | 0.37½ |
| Dylan, colors, all types, 50-lb bags, 20,000 lb and over, works, freight allowed | 0.46 |

*Loven Molding Compounds:*

| | |
|---|---|
| Airco Vinyl Acetate D, contains diphenyl amine inhibitor, tanks, Calvert City, Ky., or tank trucks, Paulsboro, N. J., East, minimum freight allowed | 0.16½ |
| drums, carload | 0.19 |
| drums, less than carload | 0.20 |
| Airco Vinyl Acetate H, contains hydroquinone as temporary inhibitor, tanks, Calvert City, Ky., or tank trucks, Paulsboro, N. J., East, minimum freight allowed | 0.16½ |
| drums, carload | 0.19 |
| drums, less than carload | 0.20 |
| Phenolic, standard black or brown, general-purpose molding compound (LM-100), 50-lb bags, truckload and over, freight prepaid | 0.20 |
| Phenolic high-impact, natural, black or brown molding compound (LI-201), truckload and over, freight prepaid | 0.39 |
| Phenolic medium impact molding compound (LMI-301), 50-lb bags, truckload and over, freight prepaid | 0.25 |
| Phenolic molding compound, pulverized (LS-710), 50-lb bags, truckload and over, freight prepaid | 0.36 |
| Phenolic resins, pulverized (LWR), truckload and over, freight prepaid | 0.30 |

*Marblette Resins:*

| | | |
|---|---|---|
| Phenolic, casting, Nos. 71, 76, 500 lb or more, Long Island City | | 0.50 |
| Nos. 400, V65-122, same basis | | 0.46 |
| Bonding, same basis | 0.36 | - 0.46 |
| Epoxy laminating, 500 lb or more, Long Island City | | 1.07 |
| Casting, same basis | | 1.25 |

TABLE 4.7 (*Continued*)

---

*Monsanto Polyethylene:*

| | |
|---|---|
| Molding resins 705, 805, 935, 575, 50-lb bags, truckload and over | 0.41 |
| Bottle blowing and extrusion, 254, 50-lb bags, truckload and over | 0.41 |
| Film and profile extrusion, 306, 13306, 13406, 50-lb bags, truckload and over | 0.41 |
| Black compounds, 10308, 11302, 50-lb bags, truckload and over | 0.375 |

*Neville Resins, Resin Solutions:*

| | |
|---|---|
| Nevindene, coumarone-indene, high-melting extreme hardness (R-1, R-3, R-5, R-6), flake, 300-lb drums or six 50-lb bags, works, Pittsburgh, freight allowed | 0.16½ - 0.20 |
| Medium hard (R-7), same basis | 0.19  - 0.19½ |
| Hard (R-9, R-10, R-11, R-12, R-12-A), flake, drums or bags | 0.15  - 0.19½ |

*Plaskon Coating Resins:*

| | |
|---|---|
| Alkyds, tanks, works | 0.12  - 0.27 |
| Urea tanks, works | 0.19½ |
| Melamine, tanks, works | 0.32¼ - 0.34¼ |
| Modified phenolics, drums, carload | 0.21½ - 0.23¾ |

*Plaskon Molding Compounds:*

| | |
|---|---|
| Alkyd, putty type, 411, natural colors, 20,000 lb or more | 0.43 |
| less than 20,000 lb | 0.43½ - 0.50 |
| Standard colors, 20,000 lb or more | 0.43½ |
| less than 20,000 lb | 0.44  - 0.60 |
| Alkyd, granular type, 420 (one color) less than 10,000 lb | 0.39½ - 0.50 |
| more than 10,000 lb | 0.39 |
| Type 422 (natural color), less than 10,000 lb | 0.49½ - 0.60 |
| more than 10,000 lb | 0.49 |
| Alkyd, reinforced type, 440 (natural color only) | |
| less than 10,000 lb | 0.91  - 1.05 |
| more than 10,000 lb | 0.90 |
| Phenolic, lump and chipped, truckload, carload, bags | 0.26½ |
| less than truckload, bags | 0.27½ |
| Phenolic, powder, fiber drums, truckload, carload | 0.27  - 0.29½ |
| less than carload, drums | 0.27½ - 0.32 |
| Urea formaldehyde, standard colors, less than 200 lb | 0.52 |
| 200 to   4,999 lb | 0.33 |
| 5,000 to 29,999 lb | 0.33 |
| 30,000 lb or more | 0.33 |
| Fine powder of a single, standard color is .03 less per pound than above. | |
| Urea black 1596 and brown 1597, more than 20,000 lb | 0.17½ |
| less than 20,000 lb | 0.18 |
| Melamine formaldehyde (single color), more than 20,000 lb | 0.45 |
| less than 20,000 lb | 0.47  - 0.73 |

TABLE 4.7 (*Continued*)

---

*Plaskon Polyester Resins:*

Rigid types 911 and 920, tanks or tank trucks, Toledo, freight
prepaid                                                              0.53

*Rohm & Haas Acrylics:*

Plexiglas V, VM, VS, injection molding and extrusion, colorless,
clear, pellets, 200-lb drums, truckload and over, East               0.55
Plexiglas VE, colorless, transparent, general-purpose extrusion
resin, heat resistant, granules, 200-lb drums, truckload and
over, East                                                           0.51
Plexiglas Y, colorless, compression molding and general-purpose,
heat resistant, beads, 200-lb drums, truckload and over, East        0.51
Plexiglas A, colorless, for laminating resins, cements, beads,
200-lb drums, truckload and over, East                               0.51
Plexiglas, colors, V, VM, VS, VE, Y, and A, truckload or more        0.59

*Rohm & Haas Polyesters:*

Paraplex P-13, light amber, 50% polyester concentrate for
potting coils, electronic components, drums, truckload, works,
minimum transportation allowed                                       0.47
Paraplex P-43, 70% polyester concentrate, laminating, molding,
casting, drums, truckload, same basis                                0.34
Paraplex P-43HV, 80% polyester concentrate, similar to P-43 in
properties and use except for higher viscosity, drums, truckload, same basis                                                     0.36

*Shell Epoxy Resins:*

Epon 815, 820, 828, adhesives, laminates, castings, potting,
   drums, carload                                      0.80
     drums, less than carload                0.83½
Epon 834, also as vinyl stabilizer, drums, carload                   0.85½
     drums, less than carload                0.86½
Epon 864, also as vinyl stabilizer, drums, carload                   0.88½
     drums, less than carload                0.89½

*Tenite Acetate, Cellulose Acetate Plastic:*

Transparents and self-extinguishing materials for extrusion and
molding; f.o.b. Kingsport, Tenn., freight allowed U.S. and
Canada; 20,000 lb or more                                            0.50
     less than 20,000 lb              0.52 - 0.59
Translucents, metallic pearls, special grade blacks, for molding,
same basis, 20,000 lb or more                                        0.38
     less than 20,000 lb              0.48 - 0.55
Group III, dense colors and blacks for molding, 20,000 lb or more
     less than 20,000 lb              0.39 - 0.48

TABLE 4.7 (*Continued*)

---

*Tenite Acetate, Cellulose Acetate Plastic: (Continued)*

| | | |
|---|---|---|
| "A" pearls, same basis, 20,000 lb or more | | 0.65 |
| less than 20,000 lb | 0.67 | - 0.74 |
| Reprocessed black (as available), same basis, 20,000 lb or more | | 0.36 |
| less than 20,000 lb | 0.38 | - 0.47 |

(Above prices, when applicable to single items on accepted orders totaling 20,000 lb or more for shipment to one destination at one time, are reduced by one cent for quantities up to 5000 lb, and by two cents for 5000 to 19,999 lb)

*Tenite Butyrate, Cellulose Acetate Butyrate Plastic:*

| | | |
|---|---|---|
| Transparents; translucents; metallic pearls; special grade blacks; for molding and extrusion; f.o.b. Kingsport, Tenn.; freight allowed U.S. and Canada: 20,000 lb or more | | 0.62 |
| less than 20,000 lb | 0.64 | - 0.71 |
| "A" pearls, same basis: 20,000 lb or more | | 0.72 |
| less than 20,000 lb | 0.74 | - 0.81 |
| Reprocessed blacks (as available), for molding, same basis: 20,000 lb or more | | 0.50 |
| Reprocessed blacks, less than 20,000 lb | 0.52 | - 0.58 |

(Above prices when applicable to single items on accepted orders totaling 20,000 lb or more for shipment to one destination at one time, reduced by one cent for quantities up to 19,999 lb)

*Tenite Polyethylene:*

| | | |
|---|---|---|
| Group I, general-purpose molding, extrusion, blowing and film extrusion-pellets, natural, 50-lb bags, 20,000 lb or more | | 0.41 |
| less than 20,000 lb | 0.42 | - 0.45 |
| Group II, electrical materials, molding, extrusion, blowing, and wire covering-pellets, natural, 50-lb bags, 20,000 lb or more | | 0.43 |
| less than 20,000 lb | 0.44 | - 0.47 |
| Group III, wire covering-pellets, brown or black, 50-lb bags, 20,000 lb or more | | 0.46 |
| less than 20,000 lb | 0.47 | - 0.50 |
| Group IV, pipe extrusion-pellets, black, 50-lb bags, 20,000 lb or more | | 0.37½ |
| less than 20,000 lb | 0.38½ | - 0.59½ |
| Group V, general-purpose and wire covering-pellets, standard colors, 50-lb bags, 20,000 lb or more | | 0.46 |
| less than 20,000 lb | 0.47 | - 0.68 |

(Above prices f.o.b. shipping point, freight allowed to destinations in U.S. and Canada.)

TABLE 4.7 (*Continued*)

---

*U.S.I. Polyethylene:*

| | |
|---|---|
| Petrothene 100, tubular film extrusion; medium flow; blow molding; 50-lb bags, delivered, truckload | 0.41 |
| Petrothene 110, tubular and sheet film extrusion; good transparency and slip properties; 50-lb bags, delivered, truckload | 0.41 |
| Petrothene 200, all purpose resin for general molding and extrusion, film or small parts, 50-lb bags, delivered, truckload | 0.41 |
| Petrothene 201, medium to high flow resin for molding, extrusion, paper coating, blow molding, 50-lb bags, delivered, truckload | 0.41 |
| Petrothene 202, high flow resin for injection molding large parts; coating applications, 50-lb bags, delivered, truckload | 0.41 |
| Petrothene 203, medium to high flow resin for injection molding, paper coating; 50-lb bags, delivered, truckload | 0.41 |
| Petrothene 210, sheet film extrusion (Type 200), 50-lb bags, delivered, truckload | 0.41 |

(Less than carlot quantities of above are 1 to 4¢ per lb higher than truckloads.)

*Vibrin Resins for Reinforced Plastics:*

| | |
|---|---|
| Rigid, general-purpose (114, 117), drums, truckload or carload, Naugatuck, Los Angeles, minimum transportation allowed | 0.34 |
| Resilient (151), truckload or carload | 0.35 |
| Light stabilized (152-LS-4), truckload or carload | 0.35½ |
| Flexible (121), truckload or carload | 0.46 |
| Heat resistant (115A), truckload or carload | 0.38 |
| Shellcoats (X-1633A and X-1636W), truckload or carload | 0.49 - 0.70 |
| Hand layup (154), truckload or carload | |

# 5. APPLICATIONS

Of the thousands of applications for plastics, an attempt will be made in this chapter to list the more important and more typical ones. Two types of classification are used—materials and industries. The first classification includes typical applications for most of the commercial plastics. This is intended to give the reader some idea of the various materials, then he can turn to the industry which he is interested in to obtain information about its typical applications.

Many applications suggested by material manufacturers will be found in other chapters. For instance, under Films and Sheets (Chapter 3) will be found the outstanding applications of the products as listed by one company. Also, in order to present a more concrete idea of the properties, many applications are included in Chapter 2, together with the properties of the various types of plastics. With this arrangement some duplication necessarily follows, but it is thought that this is offset by the greater ease in locating desired data. To locate specific applications use of the index is suggested.

## Materials

The following list gives the most important groups of plastics in the classification of materials. Applications for each group follow.

acetates
acrylics
butyrates
casein
cellulose nitrate
coumarone-indene
ethyl cellulose
epoxy

fluorocarbons (including a separate list for Teflon)
melamine
nylon
phenolics (including a separate list for cast phenolics)
polyester

polyethylene
polystyrene
silicones
urea

urethanes
vinyls (including additional
lists under vinyl film and
vinyl sheet)

For materials not listed here see Chapter 2.

### Acetates (cellulose acetate)

acetate-coated wire screen for
   greenhouses and cold frames
artificial leather
brush backs
business machine keys
combs
displays
eye glass frames
filing tabs
flashlight cases
flower pots
fountain pens

handles
lamp shades
laminated luggage
mixing bowls
packaging film
protective coatings
radio knobs
ragid containers
table mats
toys
wallet-envelopes
window material

### Acrylics

automobile tail-lights
boat windshields
boiler peep hole covers
boxes
brush backs
combs
decorative giftwares
display racks for apparel
door pulls
housings for vacuum cleaners

lamp bases
lighting fixtures
mirrors
outdoor signs
picture frames
piped light applications
protective shields for machine
   tool guards
towel rods
windows for industrial plants

### Butyrates (cellulose acetate butyrate)

automobile tail-light
   lenses
coatings
conveyor rollers
decorative extruded strips
decoys
fisherman's tackle
football helmets
furniture strips (rattan)

gun stocks
lacquers
lawn-mower rollers
radio grilles
telephone head-sets
tool handles
vacuum cleaner parts
wallboard molding
wire guards

### Casein

adhesives
buckles
buttons
fibers
finishes for leather and paper

game counters
knitting needles
novelties
paint base

## Cellulose nitrate

advertising forms and calendars
brush handles
cutlery handles
drawing instruments
fountain pens
hammer heads
hamper tops
heel covers
identification plates
index forms
inspection panels
instrument dials
labels
optical frames
piano keys
scales
shaving brushes
shoe heels
toilet seats
tool handles
towel bars

## Coumarone-indene resins

As one of the components for:

aluminum paint
concrete curing compounds
pipe oils
rubber compounding
adhesives
chewing gum
printing inks
floor tile binders
phonograph records

## Ethyl cellulose

adhesives
extruded kitchen trim
flashlight cases
lacquers
printing inks
protective coatings
proximity fuses
radio housings
refrigerator door strips
toilet seats
toughening agent for other
  plastics
toys
wire insulation

## Epoxy

boat hulls
drop hammer dies
pipe linings
table surfaces on laboratory furniture
epoxy putty is used in foundries
  to repair defective castings
extensively used in nuclear
  research

## Fluorocarbons

bakery rolls
candy molds
capacitor insulation
chemical pipe
chemical tubing
coaxial cable spacers
collapsible bags for storage of
  liquid fuel
condenser foil for motors as
  protection against corrosion
  at high temperature
control instruments
coverings for heat-sealing plates
drum liners
gaskets
insulation parts
laboratory equipment
protective coatings
pump diaphragms
pump packing
radio and radar parts
reinforced hose
signal devices
sizing of glass fibers to provide
  lubrication
tire molds
transformer parts
valve packing
valve seats
water-repellent coatings of fabrics
  and paper
wire coating

## Teflon Applications*

Typical applications include gaskets, valve packings, expansion joints, adaptors, bellows, seals, inert laboratory equipment, etc., especially for the chemical industry. Less typical but increasing uses include tube sockets, insulator bushings, spacers for coaxial cables, insulators for high-voltage wires and cables for radio, radar, and television, as well as other electrical equipment—especially in high-temperature, high-frequency service, conveyors, and heat-sealing machines—all surfaces that contact sticky materials, where anti-hesiveness is especially valuable.

## Melamines

automotive ignition blocks
buttons
circuit breakers
coating for fabrics
electrical insulators
food containers
fuse boxes
lamp pedestals
light fixtures
radio housings
refrigerator coatings
soda fountain parts
surface coatings
switches
table dishes
tableware
television-tube supports
trays
washing machine agitators

## Nylons

bearings
brush backs
brush bristles
combs
fish nets
fishing lines
food containers
gears
impact tools
insulated wire coating
leaders for fishing
machine part
paint brushes
quality tableware
raincoats
slide fasteners (zippers)
solenoid coils
sterilizable utensils
surgical sutures
tennis racket strings
textile applications
valve seats

## Phenolics

adhesives
baskets and trays in textile mills
business machine housings
camera cases
clock cases
closures
coffee makers
containers
cups for milking machines
electric wiring devices
electrical appliance plugs
enamels
flashlight cases
fuse bases
games and novelties
handles
ignition parts for automobiles
impregnating resins
ion exchange resins
knobs
lamp sockets
meter housings
pulleys
radio cabinets
switch bases
switches
surgical instruments
telephone handsets
trays for photography
tube bases
vacuum cleaner parts
washing machine agitators
wheels

* Submitted by Dixon Corp., Bristol, R. I.

**Cast phenolics**

| | |
|---|---|
| ash trays | art work |
| cigarette lighters | jewelry |
| handles for kitchen utensils | |

**Polyesters**

| | |
|---|---|
| adhesives | laminates |
| antenna masts | lampshades |
| automatic pinsetting parts | mannequins |
| automobile parts | protective coatings |
| boats | radar tubing |
| clock cases | radio grilles |
| counter surfacing | radomes |
| desk sets | refrigerator parts |
| handles | tanks |
| housings | wall covering |
| humidifiers | washing machine parts |

In addition to the above, the following applications of polyesters may be of interest:

| | |
|---|---|
| advertising displays and signs | hobby horses and junior cars |
| corrugated and flat translucent panels for daylighting in factories and schools | helmets |
| | insulating board |
| | sandwich material |
| decorative building partitions | swimming pools |
| fishing rods and archery bows | truck bodies |

**Polyethylene**

| | |
|---|---|
| acid resistant linings | laundry baskets |
| antenna parts | packaging film |
| baby's bathtub | packing |
| bottle caps and pourers | paper coating |
| closures | refrigerator dishes |
| dish pans | squeezable bottles |
| electrical insulation | storage-battery separators |
| flashlight case | surgery items |
| flexible ice trays | tote boxes |
| garbage can | toys |
| garden mulching sheets | trashcan |
| gaskets | vials |
| housewares | washers |
| insulating tapes | wastebasket |

**Polystyrene**

| | |
|---|---|
| displays | radio cases |
| electrical equipment | radios |
| food containers | refrigerator parts |
| housewares | toilet articles |
| kitchen accessories | toys |
| packaging | wall tile |

also

packages

place mats and shelf lining

## Silicones

adhesives

bearing greases

generator coils (rewinding with silicone varnishes may increase rating by 50 to 100 per cent)

glass cloth laminates

lubricants (treating spinnerets with silicone resins eliminates much of the plugging. Silicone mold lubricants also are important.)

polishing compounds

protective coatings

radio applications

textile finishes

transformer spacers

## Urea

| | |
|---|---|
| brush backs | juice extractors |
| closures | kitchen accessories |
| coasters | radio housings |
| fan grille | tableware |
| flashlight case | trays |

## Urethanes

adhesives (one urethane adhesive is used successfully to glue glass to metal)

coatings (a liquid urethane coating is applied on airplane wing edges to protect against rain-caused erosion)

elastomers and rubbers (rubber companies estimate that only price is an obstacle to the development of a urethane modified automobile tire that will last 100,000 miles)

flexible and rigid foams (several airlines have replaced foam rubber seats weighing 14 pounds with urethane seats weighing 7 pounds)

paint base (the urethanes are used for paint bases for industrial surfaces for protection against chemical fumes)

reinforcement for airplane wings (urethane is poured into wing cavities in liquid form. It then foams inside the wing providing a solid reinforcement with an appreciable saving in weight)

wire coating

## Vinylidene chloride (saran)

| | |
|---|---|
| bristles | filter cloth |
| chemical piping | fittings |
| filaments used in weaving upholstery fabrics, rugs, carpets, awnings | latex coatings |
| film for home packaging (for this application it compares favorably with polyethylene) | window screens |

TABLE 5.1. FILM, SHEETING MATERIALS, AND APPLICATIONS
SUGGESTED BY BAKELITE

*Materials:*

Vinyl chloride and copolymers:
    Calendered rigid sheeting
    Cast film
    Planished elastomeric sheets
    Planished rigid sheets
    Plasticized calendered film and sheeting

*Applications:*

Bookbinders and covers
Drafting and calculating instruments
Household products
    Draperies
    Mats
    Shower curtains
    Tablecloths
    Upholstery
Inflatables
    Beach accessories
    Mattresses
    Swimming and wading pools
    Toys
Lamp shades and light fixtures
Nursery items
Rear windows for convertibles
Recording disks
Signs and tags
Sporting equipment
Tapes
Templates
Three-dimensional products
    Advertising displays
    Doll faces
    Novelties
    Plaques
    Relief maps
Wearing apparel and accessories
    Handbags
    Luggage
    Protective clothing
    Rainwear
    Sportswear

**Vinyls (see also vinyl film and vinyl sheet)**

bill folds
belts
clothesline
coated paper
fabric backing for automobiles
   (especially interior side walls)
floor tiles
handles
leather substitutes
luggage
note book covers

paint brush bristles
purses
shoe soles
table covers
table mats
toys
upholstery
wall tile
welting
wire insulation

**Vinyl film**

aprons
draperies
electric tapes
inflatable items
rain wear

shower curtains
table cloths
wall covering
baby pants

**Vinyl sheet**

displays
lamp shades
light-diffused panels

printing stock
umbrellas

## Industries

The industrial applications have been described under the following headings:

architecture
automotive and aircraft
electrical
home and home appliances
packaging and containers
printing and coatings
textiles
toys and sports

In most uses cited, one of several different materials may be used. Usually the most appropriate plastics are given but if there is doubt as to which is the best for a given application reference to Chapter 2 on properties of the different plastics might supply the answer.

There are, of course, applications in many categories not listed here, such as ion exchange resins, oil wells, and medical, but these are special cases and it is difficult to specify a typical application. It is best to secure information for such specialized cases direct from the manufacturer or by referring to some of the earlier lists in this chapter.

**Architectural Uses.** Plywood and laminates are rapidly becoming the chief materials of the general builder. Plywood, although related to veneered wood and inlaid wood, is actually a specific type of material. When bonded with resins it has proved more serviceable than conventional lumber for many applications. Many designs are available including a metal-plywood panel. Another panel is surfaced with phenolic resin impregnated paper. A popular type has a low-density core, sometimes in the form of a honeycomb of resin impregnated paper. Most of the adhesive-type resins are used in one design or another but the newer resins are encroaching on the more familiar phenolics. (See Plywood, Chapter 3)

The shortage of heavy timbers has led to the use of thick laminated structural members. Barns and other buildings have been built with roof supporting trusses consisting of laminates of relatively small pieces of wood bonded with phenolic glues.

Prefabricated houses have turned to laminates in order to reduce costs. Some of the laminates used have included an aluminum reflecting sheet for insulating purposes; others have embodied plastic foam for the same purpose.

The leading adhesives used in architecture, not only for laminates but for cabinets, school seats, kitchen counters, and similar items are ureas, phenolics, acrylics, epoxies, and vinyls.

Molded plastics are used for door knobs, desk drawers, furniture casters, lamp bases, and a variety of other products in the building industry. Extruded plastics are used for baseboards, curtain rods, trim for elevators, stair rails, panel moldings, and floor tile. Coating materials such as alkyds and vinyl resins are used for decorative fabrics, wall covering, and combined with many other types of resins for paints, enamels, and lacquers.

Window screens are made of vinylidene chloride and polyethylene. Roofing tile is made of polystyrene and acrylics and floor tile of vinyls and polyethylene. Venetian blinds are made of vinyls and polystyrene.

The largest volume application of reinforced polyesters today is in the building industry where a high strength-to-weight ratio, translucency, low heat transmission, and weather resistance are important advantages.

Plastics in quantity have been added to the large amounts of traditional materials used for house construction. One authority estimates that more than 400,000,000 pounds of plastics are now consumed annually in building construction.

Durability, ease of maintenance, and beauty have encouraged widespread use of plastics in flooring, counter and wall surfacing, lighting fixtures, glazing, and roofing. Some uses of plastics in a typical home of today, as given by The Manufacturing Chemists' Association, are:

architectural trim
door handles
draperies
drawer pulls
light diffusing ceilings
outdoor furniture
shower stalls and curtains
table tops
translucent panels
underground piping and wiring
venetian blind tapes
window seals and screens

A new wall covering consisting of a vinyl plastic backed with resin-treated cotton fibers which are laminated under heat and pressure to prevent shrinkage has been announced by Monsanto Chemical Company.

By pouring or spraying polyurethane liquids into the wall cavities of houses and letting the liquids foam and harden, a construction is provided which gives added insulation as well as soundproofing and mold, mildew, and fire resistance. The urethanes have been a great boon to home builders. In addition to their many other uses, they can be easily colored to any shade and made into decorative panels by producing a sandwich of foam between two pieces of clear plastic.

**Transportation Industry.** The use of plastics in the average automobile is increasing each year. Nearly all the different types find some application. The ureas probably were the first light-colored plastics to be used but many applications in which these were used have given way to thermoplastics which can be injection molded. Phenolics are used for many electrical parts, including distributor heads, switches, coil parts, magnetos, ignition parts, and even instrument housings. Butyrates have replaced acetates to some extent because they have better resistance to weather and shrinkage. They are used for instrument panels, steering wheels and, in some instances, for tail lights although the acrylics are gradually usurping the latter field. Polyethylene also is used for steering wheels and, in molded or extruded form, it is applied over metal for automobile hardware. Polystyrene is used for instrument dials and in other places where it will not come in contact with gasoline. The vinyl family, formerly represented in the automotive field primarily for the production of safety glass, is rapidly replacing most fabrics either as a coating for textile liners or as self-supported side walls.

Vinyls are used for fender anti-squeak parts. Arm rests often are post-formed melamine laminates, although molded phenolics, as well as butyrates and ethyl cellulose are used. In addition to the butyrates which are used for steering wheels, ethyl cellulose and the vinyls should be noted, as they appear to be coming into greater demand for this application.

*(Courtesy Celanese Corp. of America)*

Figure 5.1. This Texas monorail coach is constructed of a steel-ribbed frame covered with a reinforced polyester shell. This shell is composed of two layers of 3 oz. fibrous glass mat, sandwiched between single layers of glass cloth, each layer being impregnated with polyester resin. Blue pigment was added to the resin before application thus providing permanent color. About 2000 lb of resin are used for each coach.

Nylon finds a market in leaf spring pads and for many of the gears used in automobile construction; in the form of nylon fabric, it is used for head linings and other interior textiles.

For production figures covering plastics used in automobiles see Table 4.3.

Cabins for small private airplanes often are made of polyester fibrous glass laminates. Fuel tanks are also made of the same materials.

Typical applications of plastics in aircraft include canopies, radomes, wing tanks, windows, structural parts, and insulators.

Molded nylon is used in the speedometer, dome-lights, door locks, and in gears and bushings in both automobiles and aircraft.

An estimate in the Manufacturing Chemists' Association Book of Facts gives the following figures for some of the plastics used in American automobiles based on 5,700,000 passenger automobiles in 1955: acrylics, 7,400,000 pounds; butyral sheeting, 17,000,000 pounds; butyrates, 5,200,000 pounds; phenolic molding materials, 5,200,000 pounds; vinyls, 21,000,000 pounds and nylons, 3,800,000 pounds.

The above figures are given here for convenience even though they are included in a table in Chapter 4.

Aircraft windshields have been treated with a modified silicone vapor to render them water repellent. High-speed air contact then removes rain and promotes good vision.

**The Electrical Industry.** Some of the new plastics have such excellent electrical properties that they are almost indispensable in the construction of electrical equipment, but the older materials still hold the market in the "run-of-the-mine" applications. Phenolics are used for switches, switch plates, plugs, magneto parts, phone parts, and similar items. Ureas can be used in most of the same applications to add a lighter touch but they do not have quite as good heat resistance. Phenolics are satisfactory up to 300°F but ureas should not be used where the temperature is apt to rise above 220°F. The polystyrenes with their low loss factors are used in much of the high-frequency radio production.

The polyethylenes are superior for many applications in the electrical industry. They have almost completely replaced gutta percha for submarine cables. They are considered the best material for many types of communication and power cables. They are used for radio spaghetti tubing, for antenna wiring, and in the construction of television sets. The silicones are introducing new design possibilities to motor and generator construction through their high heat resistant insulating properties. Motor commutator designers often find a combination of fiber glass and a thermosetting resin to be their best material. Fabric base laminates bonded with ureas or phenolics are used for telephone switchboards and panels. Lighting fixtures make extensive use of ureas where modified light distribution is desired. Acrylics also are used for electrical dials and knobs. The vinyls find application in wall plates, terminal blocks and, in considerable volume, in wire insulation. Antenna masts often are made of a glass fiber polyester combination. The polyesters also are used for radar tubing and for radomes.

Although the acetates have rather mediocre electrical and heat resistant properties, they have, nevertheless, been used for telephone receiver bases and housings because of their toughness.

A fan blade for an electric fan, made of polystyrene, weighs 10 oz. compared to 13 oz. for the cast magnesium part it replaces. In addition it costs less and operates more quietly.

*(Courtesy Barrett Div.)*

Figure 5.2.  An assembled automobile ignition coil and two spark plug lead insulators. The top of the coil and both insulators are molded of mineral-filled alkyd which gives good arc resistance and high dielectric strength, as well as heat resistance which is important in modern, high-compression engines. Dimensional stability also is important in both applications.

Nuclear research requires all types of specialized materials and an indispensable role is performed in this field by plastics. Unusual conditions such as high radiation fluxes, vacua and great magnetic forces are overcome with the equally unusual properties of some of the plastics. An important piece of equipment consisting of two 6-in. cast epoxy insulating rings and a center metallic electrode, cemented together with epoxy cement, is known as an electrostatic focusing lens. The rings must withstand 30,000 volts across their 1 in. width. An epoxy casting whose dielectric constant had been adjusted by the addition of a glass bead filler was successfully used for a cable terminal operating under extremely high voltage. James O. Turner of the Radiation Laboratory, University of California, states: "We are repeatedly faced with the problem of carrying electrical circuits through the walls of vacuum vessels operating under high vacuum. This requires bushings that are vacuum tight, do not outgas and will withstand high voltage." Here, again, designers have turned to epoxies. Successful bushings are constructed of epoxy resins filled with tiny glass beads. Coils for the Bevatron are constructed on forms machined from acrylics. Later the coils are saturated with epoxy resin and cured. Radiation shields use sandbags made of heavy gage polyethylene film, filled with wet sand. Containers for liquid hydrogen are made of expanded polystyrene but foam-in-place polyurethanes are being studied for this application. Cloud chamber windows are made of cast polyester. Many other applications of plastics are vital in this new and interesting research work. These include silicones, fluorocarbons, nylons, and vinyls.

Transformers with molded plastics covers and bushings are being made by General Electric Co. The covers are polyester reinforced with fiber glass. The resin is made non-tracking by a special process. The bushings are epoxy resin modified to increase their impact strength and to make them non-tracking.

**Homes and Home Appliances.** An appreciable part of the tremendous increase in the sales of plastics during recent years has been due to the improved acceptance of plastics by the average housewife. This is due not only to better labeling on the part of manufacturers but also to a better selection of materials and to an actual improvement in the materials themselves. Most of the various types of plastics find some application in the home or in home appliances.

The acetates are low priced, easily molded, and tough and so are used extensively for such items as vacuum cleaner housings, shelf brackets, clothes hamper covers and even, in some cases, for toilet seats. The latter, however, are in a most competitive field and many plastic types have been tried. The phenolics probably lead but the butyrates, ethyl cellulose, and polystyrene have all had some success in this field. Urea and melamine also have been used to some extent for toilet seats of the flat bottom type when color has been desired.

The butyrates have greater dimensional stability than the acetates and therefore have been used for trim for refrigerator interiors and for molding around metal inserts such as required for some egg beaters and other kitchen utensils. The butyrates also have been used for picture frames, furniture strips, lawn-mower rollers, and tool handles.

The acrylics find use in the home for decorative articles such as candle holders, handkerchief boxes, salad bowls, and serving trays. They are also used in modern lighting arrangements where their peculiar power of piping light is effective. Towel bars and door knobs frequently are made of acrylics.

Figure 5.3. A dresser made with phenolic one-piece molded drawers.

Caseins are the most widely used material for buttons. In addition, they are used in the home for game counters, knitting needles, and novelties. The nitrates, because of their inflammability, are discouraged for most home applications. Their uses however include optical frames, piano keys, and fountain pens, to mention but a few.

The melamines, of course, are used for table dishes but these have not made very deep inroads into the average home. They are being used more and more extensively in camps and summer homes, but their chief use remains in airplane service.

Nylons in the form of fibers are used for tooth brush bristles. Nylon moldings are used for brush backs and combs. Phenolics are found most everywhere in the average home. Some typical applications include clock cases, bottle closures, flashlight cases, lamp sockets, switches, washing machine agitators, and telephone handsets. A recent development is the one-piece molded dresser drawer. Plastic ash trays usually are made of phenolics.

*(Courtesy The Richardson Co.)*

Figure 5.4. Desk drawers compression molded in one piece of special phenolic material. They clean with wet or dry cloth, won't stick or warp, and stay the exact size to fit.

Polyethylene, which shows the fastest growth of any plastic, owes much to the demand from the average home. Garden hose today is either made of vinyl or polyethylene. Ice trays and refrigerator dishes and squeeze bottles are typical polyethylene applications. Other home uses include trashcans, waste baskets, toys, and kitchen packaging film. The peculiar resilience and slightly soft surface of polyethylene has led to the development of many new uses. An orange juice container with a leak-proof lid which fastens by friction could only be made of polyethylene. Corks of polyethylene are said to be tighter and yet easier to apply than the conventional cork.

Recent designs of refrigerators and washing machines make extensive use of polyesters. Large panels usually are polyester-glass laminates or else similar laminates of high impact polystyrene and glass. Other polyester applications in the home include antenna masts, lamp shades, and wall coverings. Corrugated translucent panels of polyesters and glass are becoming popular in modern home construction for terrace roofs, garage doors, wind breaks, and similar forms.

*(Courtesy American Cyanamid Co.)*

Figure 5.5. This electric hand mixer has the housing and handle both made of molded melamine. The handle is molded in a contrasting color. The mixer weighs less than 3 lb.

Polystyrene, although brittle in thin sections, is widely used in the home. Kitchen accessories, toilet articles, food containers, measuring cups, and radio cases are typical uses. The silicones as yet have not invaded the home to any extent. Some appliance coatings use silicones and some silicone glass cloth laminates are made into decorator items. Urea competes with polystyrene for juice extractors and other kitchen accessories.

Cold-molded plastics perhaps should be mentioned here. Most of these borderline plastics materials are bituminous although phenolic resin or cement binders may be used to produce a cold-molded product. They withstand high temperatures (600°F) and are used for electric stove heaters, coffee maker bases, and other electrical heating devices.

Figure 5.6. Polyethylene makes this interesting application possible. A 28 oz. laundry basket has just been molded on an 80 oz. Hydraulic Press Manufacturing Co. injection press. The design, engineering and tooling for this item took about a year and the tooling cost ran to more than $30,000. The mold alone weighs 10,000 lb. The press is a massive piece of equipment which cost about $80,000. The molder is Columbus Plastics, Inc., Columbus, Ohio. The molding rate is one basket every 40 sec.

The vinyls are the most versatile household plastic. Applications include floor and wall tiles, upholstery, table mats and covers, belts, luggage, purses and handbags, heel covers, shoe soles, raincoats, and dozens of other familiar items. Electrical wire insulation generally is a vinyl. Vinyl film is used for rain wear, shower curtains, and wall covering, to mention but a few of its many uses. Lamp shades are a natural for vinyls as are also billfolds and card cases. Urethane foam is used in upholstery. One company is said to be making a floor wax out of a styrene-based polymer.

The drainboard, counter tops, wall and floor tile in a kitchen might be plastic—perhaps polystyrene for the wall tile and a tough, resilient vinyl for the floor. Other kitchen applications might include vinyl film curtains, an acrylic panel light diffuser over the sink, vinyl coated cloth Venetian blinds, a laminated phenolic counter and back-splash, formed in one piece to eliminate dirt-catching cracks, and many electrical appliances with molded phenolic or urea handles.

As for the breakfast nook one designer says: "There is scarcely any soil you can think of—butter, catsup, coffee, lipstick or ink—that cannot be just wiped off anything in today's plastic nook."

(Courtesy Monsanto Chemical Co.)

Figure 5.7. This modern luncheon scene has vinyl mats and upholstery, melamine dishes, and a table top of melamine spillproof laminate.

Among kitchen dishes and utensils good design might indicate a polystyrene funnel and wire mesh strainer, an ice bucket of reinforced polyester, translucent colored polystyrene canisters, zippered food bags of polyvinyl chloride, and a cellulose acetate fruit juicer. Polyethylene ice cube trays are convenient when but three or four cubes are desired.

Structural uses of reinforced plastics look bright for the future. An all-plastic refrigerator, with reinforced polyester panels, foamed styrene for soldering irons are made of phenolics.

cores and epoxy adhesives was announced during a recent exhibit. Handles

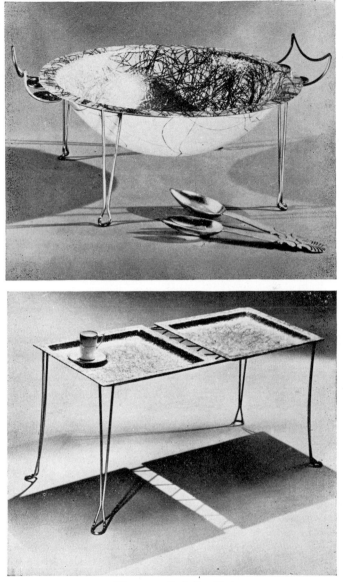

*(Courtesy Bakelite Co.)*

Figure 5.8. New designs in table servers, trays, bowls and other home giftware are made of lightweight, durable plastic laminates that incorporate decoration with protection. The art effects are fused between rigid vinyl sheets. Foods, alcohol, and water accidentally spilled do not stain or mar the colorful decoration thus fused. The salad bowl is 18 in. in diameter and weighs only 4½ oz. Each shape can be made with black, white, or clear rigid vinyl sheet as a background for the design. Removable serving trays in square shapes fit the wire frames of the cocktail table.

**Packaging and Containers.** This is a big field where plastics not only form one of the principal materials but where they have been responsible for much of the development. No other material, for instance, could serve as a package for frozen food and at the same time as a means for preparing the food without removing it from the package. Rolled film, 0.010 in. thick and thinner, forms an important package material, and elaborate automatic machinery has been developed for processing it. The leading plastics used are the vinyls, polyethylene, cellulose acetate, ethyl cellulose, and regenerated cellulose.

Figure 5.9. Meat and other products may now be frozen, and later cooked in the same container. This shows meat balls which have just been cooked in a Mylar polyester film container.

Shipping containers, generally, continue to be paperboard—but a far different paperboard from that used years ago. Rugged and weatherproof shipping materials were developed during World War II from dense, sized, water-resistant paperboard bonded with ureas and sealed with starch adhesives.

The use of transparent containers has grown by leaps and bounds during the last few years. Manufacturers have discovered that many products sell better when they can be seen. Both rigid and non-rigid sheets and films are available in transparent materials; these are fabricated by various processes into boxes of diverse shapes, and printed in black and white or in color. Moldings also are used for containers, usually to add a sense of quality to the product.

The acetates are used both for rigid containers and for non-rigid packaging film. Polyethylene is an important plastic for the non-rigid type of package which is becoming popular.

Some of the products that are being merchandised in rigid transparent packages are the following:

Bakery goods
Candy
Cigars and pipes
Drugs (not hydroscopic)
Flowers
Hardware
Jewelry and watches
Toiletries and cosmetics
Wearing apparel

Closures might be considered as part of the general container group. Here, the thermosetting materials are important. Great quantities of bottle closures are made in a threaded design. These are made on elaborate automatic machines which mold the caps over metal threads and then spin the caps off the threads after they have set. Other machines, instead of unscrewing the cap moldings, force them off the threads while they are still warm and soft enough to return to their original molded shape. The phenolics are popular for closures but ureas are used where light colors are desired. Ureas are odorless and tasteless and can be used for packaging medicines and foodstuffs. Polyethylene is used for medicine bottles as well as for closures on such bottles. It also is coming to the front in the food packaging field.

Polystyrene with its good chemical resistance is used for some acid containers and for collapsible tubes. Metal parts (tools) are being packaged by a special method of vacuum forming. The parts, mounted on cards with prepared surfaces, are placed in rows under the forming sheet. Vacuum forming of the sheet over the parts then tightly seals the sheet to the card thus producing individual packages ready for display and sale. Saran sheets are used for packaging instruments and large metal parts.

A "sandwich" of paper and foamed styrene is produced in continuous operation by the St. Regis Paper Company. This consists of a core of stiff foamed plastic with a sheet of kraft paper on either side. Good compression strength under conditions of severe humidity and good insulation qualities are claimed for this product. It will be used for making containers.

A polyethylene can, said to be on the threshold of matching the price of metal cans, has been announced by American Can Co. Originally developed by Bradley Container Corp. it came in the American Can Co. camp with that company's recent purchase of the Bradley company.

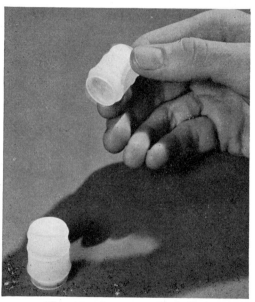

(Courtesy Armstrong Cork Co.)

Figure 5.10. This newly designed polyethylene cork gives a tighter seal than the conventional type.

The container looks much like a metal can. It is a seamless extruded cylinder of polyethylene with metal ends crimped on by a cold mechanical process. The new high-density polyethylenes are expected to make possible thinner walls while retaining the same rigidity.

Bulk containers, once exclusively made of steel or wood are now turning to plastics. Drums and carboys made of plastics are used for shipping chemicals and other liquids. However steel containers lined with resin lacquers no longer present their former corrosion problems and so are retaining much of the bulk container business.

The following have been suggested as important materials and applications in packaging:

*Materials:*
   Polyethylene resins and compounds, vinyl copolymers, cast film, coated paper

*Applications:*
   Closure liners
   Drum liners
   Hardware packaging
   Horticultural supply packaging
   Moisture and gas barrier laminates
   Produce packaging:
      Candy and nuts
      Fresh fruit
      Frozen foods
      Meat by-products
      Poultry
      Vegetables
   Rack-items packaging
   Refrigerator and food locker bags
   Soap and cosmetics packaging
   Textile packaging

**Printing and Coating.** Technical advances in printing have caused an increased switch from the natural resin binders used in printing inks to materials offered by the synthetic resin industry. The phenolics and the alkyds are perhaps the most commonly used binders. The phenolics are used in gravure and heat-set inks where high-speed press action calls for drying the solvent by evaporation. Alkyds are used in lithographic and topographic inks where their toughness and fast drying properties are advantages.

For printing on special surfaces such as glass and plastics many other resins have been pressed into service, including the acrylics, ethyl cellulose, melamine, the nitrates, ureas, and the vinyls.

In addition to the use of plastics in the formulation of inks there are many other applications of plastics in the over-all printing industry. Kraft paper impregnated with ethyl cellulose is used extensively for book covers. Such covers are relatively water proof and are not affected by alcohol and common acids. The problem of the right adhesive to bond covers to the end papers of a large book has not been fully solved. For magazines and small books, flexible adhesives such as vinyl acetate are satisfactory.

Vinyl printing plates have successfully replaced electrotypes in some cases. Vinyl rigid sheets can be used as electrotype molds. These take the impression of the type by use of heat and pressure. The impressed sheet is then copper plated and the copper, stripped from the sheet, forms the electrotype.

Printing on plastics often is accomplished by the roll leaf method. The roll may be composed of pigment colors mounted on paper tape. In operation the tape winds under the die and over the work to be printed. The stamping operation then is synchronized with the forward movement of the tape.

Synthetic resins gradually are supplanting some of the natural gums, resins, and oils in the production of modern surface coatings. Some oils are retained in most formulations, however. The use of ureas and phenolics in the general fabricating industry pioneered the way for their use in the coating industry. The phenolics were modified to give them oil solubility. The ureas were similarly modified by reacting them with butanol. High polymers have been produced in relatively low molecular weights to obtain solutions of high solids content.

The phenolic type coatings are used, among other things, for chemical-resistant paints, colored baking enamels, floor coatings, lacquer undercoaters, and traffic paints.

Alkyds, which are more largely used for coatings than any other resin, may be modified with the fatty acids of drying or semi-drying oils and the finished resins will then depend on the conversion of these oil radicals for drying. The alkyds are nearly always combined with other resins in the preparation of coatings. However, they constitute the major part of many air-drying and baking finishes. When unmodified the alkyds form the coating film by condensation, and when modified with other resins the film forming usually is by evaporation. Some typical applications of modified alkyd coatings are furniture lacquers, and refrigerator and washing machine finishes. The following properties explain the extensive use of the alkyds in coatings: retention of initial appearance after long exposure to severe weather, adhesion, flexibility, and ease of application.

An important development in coatings is the use of dispersion resins, where the resins instead of being dissolved in a solvent are held in suspension in an emulsion. The resin particles of such an emulsion are colloidally fine but still are relatively large compared with a solution. Due to their size they have little tendency to penetrate fibrous materials and therefore find use where surface irregularities are to be overcome. Typical dispersion coating applications include plywood panels, boats, structural steel, and sealers for wood furniture.

The melamine coatings have good color retention at high temperatures and are fast curing even at relatively low temperatures. Vinyl coatings are odorless, tasteless, and can be made colorless. A wide range of physical properties can be secured by varying the degree of polymerization. When pigmented the vinyl coatings form excellent swimming pool paints.

The newer polystyrene coatings are alcohol and water resistant and have been used to some extent for coating metal refrigerators.

Coatings resistant to 600°F are produced from silicones; these find use in the electrical field. They are compatible with the phenolics and some other resin coatings. However, they generally require baking at about 400°F for 1 hour for satisfactory curing.

Metalized polyester sheets with pressure sensitive backing find applications in the label, decal, sign, display, and other fields. They are offered by Coating Products, Englewood, N. J. Stock sheets of unsupported Mylar now are offered in high luster chrome finish, 1-mil gage, backed with pressure sensitive adhesion. High tensile strength of the material permits rough handling without need of lamination to supporting materials. Sheets are now 20 in. by 25 in. with other sizes on special order.

**Textile Industry.** Not only are plastics important as materials from which textile fibers can be made but they are almost indispensable in the treatment of textiles made of both natural and synthetic fibers. They also find extensive application in the design and construction of the equipment used in a textile plant.

Rayon, which is a regenerated cellulose fiber, and therefore not a true synthetic is, nevertheless, often considered in the plastics family. It has the largest production of all the man-made fibers. The first and probably the best known true synthetic fiber family is the polyamide group of which the chief fiber is nylon.

In the textile field the term nylon covers fibers, filaments, yarns, and fabrics made of a nylon-type of polyamide. Other synthetic fibers include the polyesters of which Dacron is an example.

The following are other examples:

| Type | Example |
|------|---------|
| polyacrylo-nitrile | Orlon |
| polyvinyl chloride-vinyl acetate | Vinyon |
| polyvinylidene chloride | saran |
| tetrafluoroethylene | Teflon |
| polyacrylonitrile vinyl chloride | dynel |

In addition to the above, are the polyethylene fibers which are the lightest of all textile fibers, with a specific gravity of 0.92. Woven fabrics of polyethylene are used for automobile upholstery, for curtains, and in the industrial field for filter cloths, and other applications where chemical inertness is important.

The spinnerettes used in making some fibers whirl at perhaps 10,000 rpm and the only material which would combine a highly polished surface and light weight to withstand the centrifugal force has been a steel wire-reinforced phenolic.

The coating of bobbins in the textile industry has long been a problem because of continuous wear of the thread passing over their surfaces. Some of the recent vinyl coatings have exhibited excellent wear resistance in this application.

TABLE 5.2.  SYNTHETIC LATEX APPLICATIONS, BY TYPE,
IN TEXTILE OPERATIONS

| Textile Application | Type of Latex | | | | | |
|---|---|---|---|---|---|---|
| | Butadiene-Styrene | Butadiene-Acrylonitrile | Neoprene | Polyvinyl Chloride | Polyvinyl Acetate | Acrylic |
| Non-woven fabric | X | X | | X | X | X |
| Backcoating (carpet, upholstery) | X | X | | X | | X |
| Fabric sizing-finishing | X | X | | X | X | |
| Warp sizing | | X | | | X | |
| Coating | X | X | X | X | | X |
| Textile printing | X | X | | | | X |
| Pigment dyeing | X | X | | | | X |
| Cord dip | X | X | | | | |

Courtesy Goodyear Tire & Rubber Co.

The vinyls and ethyl cellulose find extensive application in the coating of fabrics, usually by calendering, but also by doctor knife.

The caseins rely on the textile industry for much of their production because clothing requires so many buttons, buckles, and ornaments.

The melamines and ureas are used for cotton and rayon treatment to impart wrinkle resistance. The alkyds find a limited application in the finishing of hats and to give a stiff "hand" to rayon and acetate fabrics.

Within three years, according to Brand & Oppenheimer, Inc. of New York, upwards of 15 million square yards of urethane foam will be used annually for interlining clothing, making this material a dominant factor in the clothing industry. About one million square yards of this material, annually, is currently being used as an interlining in outerwear garments.

Synthetic latices are used in today's textile processing to modify the properties of the yarns or the fabrics. The improved properties of the fabrics include: better hand, abrasion resistance, crease recovery, wash fastness, appearance, and long life. In addition, latices frequently are used in textile printing to impart better pigment binding properties.

TABLE 5.3. WEIGHT AND PER CENT OF LATEX CONSUMED
IN TEXTILE APPLICATIONS

| Textile Application | Amount Used | % Latex in Compound |
|---|---|---|
| Non-woven fabric | 5-50% * | 85-100% |
| Back sizing | 0.5-10 oz/sq yd | 25-100 |
| Fabric finishing | 1-5% | 100 |
| Warp sizing | 4-8% | 15-100 |
| Coated fabric | 1-16 oz/sq yd | 50-100 |
| Textile printing | 0.5-4 oz/sq yd | 50-80 |
| Pigment dyeing | 1-4 oz/sq yd | 50-80 |
| Cord dip | 4-8% | 85-100 |

* Given as % of total weight because of wide variations in weight of material.

The present trend toward fabrics that wear well and which can be cleaned easily, has led many manufacturers to turn to resins as finishes for upholstery fabrics, as well as to synthetic fibers and plastics sheets for the upholstery material itself.

More than 41,000,000 pounds of urea and melamine resins were used for coating and treating textiles in 1955, and the 1956 total was not much less. Other resins were also used for this same type of application. The total of all resins for textile use was well over 100,000,000 pounds. The vinyls probably were most extensively used in this field.

**Toys and Sports.** Sales of plastic toys have increased rapidly in recent years as designs and materials have improved. Manufacturers have at last come to realize that sharp edges and thin sections which might break must be avoided. The soft pliable nature of polyethylene has made it possible to make many toys and sports items which formerly seemed to call for more rigid materials. Even chessmen, dice, and game chips are receiving public acceptance when made of polyethylene.

Toy furniture of polystyrene is being made on a mass production basis at low prices and seems likely to completely usurp the market. Polystyrene also is used successfully for blocks, animals, and toy trains. The acetates seem to be favored for such items as doll heads, balls, rattles, and floating toys because of their toughness in thin sections. Other thin parts are made of vinyl plastisol resins by slush casting. In this operation the plastisol is poured into a heated mold and then poured out leaving a relatively thin coating over the interior mold surface.

Their good resistance to weathering has given many plastics entry into the sports world. The butyrates, for instance, are used for gun stocks, duck decoys, artificial bait, fishing reel parts, football helmets, and boat buoys. The phenolics are used for field glass cases and shuffleboard disks to mention two of the many applications. Reinforced phenolics are preferred by many for football helmets, and phenolic bonded plywood is used for toboggans and skis.

Other typical applications of plastics for sport items include nylon for tennis racket strings and fish nets, glass-fiber reinforced polyesters for fishing rods and archery bows, nitrates for ping-pong balls, and silicone rubber for golf ball cores. Because of their heat sealability and water resistance the vinyls are preferred for many beach appurtenances such as inflated balls, mats, and sleeping bags. Glass fibers bonded with epoxies and with various other plastics binders have been used for boat hulls.

Reinforced plastics baby carriage bodies are produced by Popular Fibreglass Products Corp., Northport, N. Y.

Roller skate wheels are made of a compound of phenolic and synthetic rubber. Two types are available for the reported 23,000,000 skating enthusiasts—precision wheels for the better skater and open-bearing wheels for the average devotee.

# 6. PROCESSES

This chapter gives brief descriptions of most of the processes required in the final fashioning of plastics products for the consumer. Sometimes in describing an operation it is difficult to separate the process from the end product and therefore some duplication exists between this chapter and Chapter 3 which describes plastic forms. Both chapters should be referred to by the reader of general interest.

The following processes are included here:

| | |
|---|---|
| calendering | shell molding |
| casting | transfer molding |
| coating | blow molding |
| extrusion | plastisol molding |
| forming metal | reinforced-plastics molding |
| laminating | mold making |
| low-pressure laminating | molding details |
| machining | molding of alkyd resins |
| molding (general) | post-forming |
|    compression molding | potting and encapsulation |
|    high-frequency molding | heat sealing |
|    injection molding | vacuum forming |
|    jet molding | |

## Calendering

Probably the highest production method of forming film and sheeting is calendering. At first the calendering of plastics was merely an adaptation of the rubber technique. However, it soon became apparent that the use of two banks of rolls did a better job than one, when working with the higher temperatures called for with plastics. In one system, the plastic mass heated and worked to the proper condition on a horizontal two-roll mill is then transferred to the nip between the upper and middle rolls of a vertical three-roll mill where it forms a bank. These heated rolls have a speed differential which applies a smearing action to form a film which is carried around to the lower roll. This film may then be taken off and stored on a wind-up roll with a liner introduced to prevent adhesion. As a modification a sheet of fabric may be introduced and various coating and impregnating effects may be produced in the fabric by varying the speed differential of the lower two rolls. The temperature of the rolls, which may vary from 300 to 350°F or higher with different resin formulations, is an important part of the process.

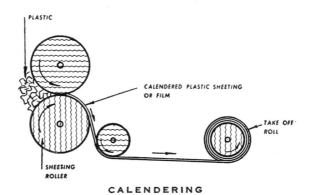

CALENDERING

Figure 6.1. One arrangement of rolls in a simplified calendering operation. Many other arrangements are possible, each with some special purpose. The rolls are hollow and heated. (*Courtesy The Society of the Plastics Industry*)

The vinyls are the materials most frequently processed by calendering. The complete equipment for the production of vinyl sheeting by this method is expensive—in the neighborhood of $100,000—but when once set up and operated at high production the unit cost of vinyl sheeting is lower than that produced by any other process. For polyethylene, extrusion is a competitive operation.

Equipment for vinyl calendering usually consists of a Banbury mixer, a conveyor to a two-roll plastics mill, a three- or four-roll calender, and a suitable "wind-up." The wind-up is an important part of a well functioning system. It must apply a steady moderate tension, adjusted so that the increase in diameter doesn't increase the tension. Roll edges must be kept uniform and some provision must be made for transferring from a full roll to an empty roll without interfering with the continuing operation of the calender.

## Casting

The pouring of liquid plastics into molds where they solidify by heat or catalyst, without pressure, is one form of casting. Because of the simple equipment required and the absence of pressure this method finds many uses. In another form of casting a film is produced on large moving drums or on moving metal belts. The base material for the film is usually dissolved or dispersed in a solvent in which case the wet film passes onto the belt and through an oven (or heated zone of the drum) where the solvent is evaporated leaving the solidified film, which is later stripped from the belt (or drum). A modified type of film casting deposits the film on a paper carrier. This method will be described in a little greater detail later (see Chapter 9).

To return to the process ordinarily referred to as casting, this seemingly simple fabricating method nevertheless involves some problems. When a large bulk of material is involved precautions must be taken to avoid shrinkage difficulties. The usual answer is special formulation and slow curing. Special fillers also may be introduced. The more common liquid casting resins are the phenolics, the polystyrenes, the acrylics, and the polyesters. Phenolic casting resins are cured over long periods at temperatures between 140 and 160°F. Shorter periods are obtained with catalysts. The ureas and melamines are sometimes cast, using a finely divided composition with fillers, the batch being made liquid by addition of liquid activators.

The design of molds for casting is an important detail in the process. Straight-draw lead molds are generally used. In making such a mold a dipping arbor is prepared. This commonly is a highly polished steel master or arbor. The mold is made by dipping this steel arbor into molten lead, then removing it with a continuing steady motion and promptly cooling it in water. One dip usually provides a lead form sufficiently thick for a casting mold. The lead is stripped from the steel with a knockout rack, providing a female open-ended mold with a smooth interior. Various fluted designs or other variations are permissible but all must have taper and must run toward the open end to permit removal of the casting. The form is used once and then remelted.

The simplest way to cast a piece with an undercut is with a rubber or elastomeric mold. For such a mold a model of wood or plaster of Paris is dipped successively in a bath of rubber latex until the desired thickness has been built up—usually about ⅛ in. It is then split and removed, encased in a plaster of Paris mold, and filled with the casting resin. After curing the plaster of Paris and the rubber mold are removed, leaving the undercut cast piece intact.

## Coating

Plastics are used as coating materials on many different products. The nature of such coatings is described in Chapter 3 and the common methods of coating by brushing, spraying, and dipping are mentioned briefly elsewhere. Here, coating by a so-called "doctor blade" is briefly described. This method is sometimes called "spread coating." The material to be coated—paper, leather, even wood—passes first over a table or counter where it can be examined and smoothed if necessary and then over a supporting roll. Close to this roll, but between it and a following support-

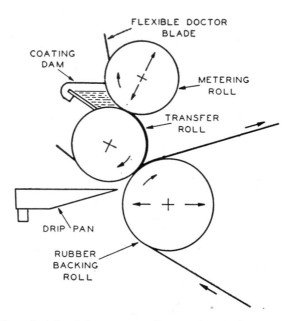

Figure 6.2. The principle of the reverse roll coater is metering an accurate thickness of coating with two precision ground chilled iron rolls, and applying the premetered coating to the web, supported by a rubber backing roll. The amount of coating applied is controlled by the opening between the metering roll and transfer roll as shown, and is independent of variations in web caliper. The metering roll surface is continuously cleaned by a flexible steel doctor blade. The coating width is controlled by variable positioned edge dams. (*Courtesy John Waldron Corp.*)

ing roll, is located an adjustable coating knife or doctor blade. The coating compound (in a soft state) is introduced on the material to be coated just behind the blade in its forward movement. Thus as the material travels it is spread with a film of the coating plastic. The thickness of this film is determined by the adjustment of the blade or doctor knife and the speed of the travel.

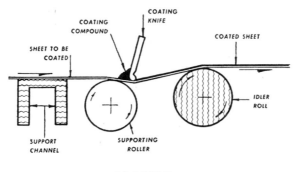

COATING

Figure 6.3. A simple method of coating sheet material. Both the coating knife and the supporting roll are adjustable. After being coated the material passes through an oven for curing.

There are many variations from the simple method shown in Figure 6.2. One such variation is to have the plastic picked up by a second or third roll and then deposited on the traveling material. Coating on a paper carrier is described in Chapter 9. This is similar to casting of film.

## Extrusion

Extrusion is a continuous operation. As all industry favors the development of such an operation this method of processing plastics is gaining considerable importance. The usual method of extrusion is called "dry extrusion" and may be divided into three types: (1) direct extrusion in which the design of the extruder die and of the take-off device determine the shape of the extruded article; (2) semipositive extrusion in which the most important surfaces are controlled by a forming die or mold after the material leaves the extruder; and (3) positive extrusion in which all surfaces are controlled by a mold after the material has left the extruder. This latter is called "extrusion molding" but it is not a continuous process.

The normal process of extrusion of plastics consists essentially of conveying, heating, and then forcing a thermoplastic resin under controlled conditions through an orifice (die) of specific dimensions. While there has been marked improvement in know-how and equipment design for this operation during recent years the basic principle of a rotating screw in a heated cylinder remains standard. Some manufacturers use two parallel screws either meshed or non-meshed but the arrangement shown in Figure 6.4 represents the general practice today. This machine consists essentially of four parts: a feed hopper, a heated cylinder, a revolving screw, and a die. Especially prepared and conditioned extrusion material is introduced into the feed hopper from which it is forced by gravity onto the feed end of the revolving screw. It is then mixed, heated, and forced forward through the die by the action of the revolving screw in the heated cylinder.

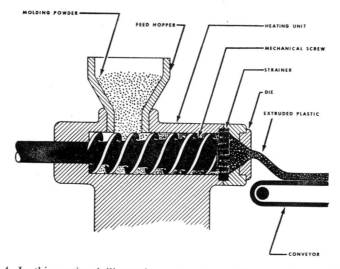

Figure 6.4. In this sectional illustration, extrusion molding powder, carefully conditioned as to moisture content and particle size is introduced into a suitable hopper from which it is gravity fed to the rear end of a screw. The screw, which revolves in a heated cylinder, is an important part of the extruder. It may have many different forms. It may be cored so that it may be heated or cooled as desired. The flights may be uniform or tapered toward the front end so that pressure builds up as the melting material approaches the die. It may have a torpedo, or enlarged smooth section at the die end, or the flights may extend throughout its length. Usually the design of the screw is determined in relation to the material to be extruded.

The cylinder, which is indicated here as the heating unit, is not as simple as shown, but is divided into heating zones—usually four for a standard extruder. These are within the cylinder walls as a rule (usually electric but sometimes oil heated) and are separately regulated so that the temperature of the plastic may be controlled clear to the die.

Extrusion as a means of either fabricating or compounding plastics is always one of the first methods to be investigated. Molding powders in dry blends may include materials with differing properties as well as colorants. Temperature control is important. First the temperature and moisture content of the powder should be carefully regulated and then the temperatures of the zones of the extruder barrel or cylinder. In many of the newer machines electric heating is used for the cylinder zones. The control instruments should regulate with a minimum of cycling. On and off control is not recommended but rather a proportioning type to give smoother temperature regulation.

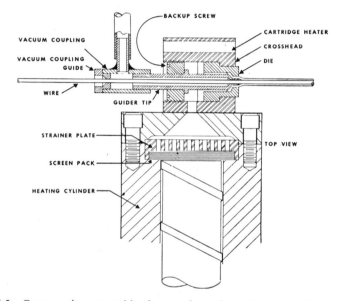

Figure 6.5. Cross-section assembly for coating wire with nylon. The wire is fed through the center of the extruder die and the hot molten material from the extruder flows around the wire to which it adheres in a coating of regulated thickness.

Sometimes it is desirable to cool part of the cylinder or barrel. This has been one of the problems in electrical heating. However, several successful methods of cooling are now available. Small blowers below the zones to be cooled probably are the cheapest. Cooling coils for water may be cast as an integral part of the cylinder, or copper tubing for water may be wrapped around the extruder barrel.

Several stages may be used in the operation of an extruder. However, single-stage operation is by far the most common. The barrel may run to a length of about 16 times the diameter for single-stage and about

20 times the diameter for multi-stage extruders. This proportion is based on the diameter within the barrel. Screws vary in design. Differences include such factors as pitch, flight depth, and screw clearance. As the material moves along the screw both temperature and pressure increase and its volume per unit weight decreases. Thus long screws usually discharge at greater pressure than short ones. To compensate for the decrease in volume of the material it is usual to gradually decrease the depth of thread or the pitch of the screw as the die end is approached.

Figure 6.6 A schematic diagram of a single-stage screw of a widely used type. Note the decreasing depth of thread. The compression ratio of such a screw is ascertained by comparing the volume of the first flight with that of the last flight.

The over-all design of an extruder may vary with different materials in order to give maximum efficiency. Multi-screw extruders often are recommended, for instance, for extruding rigid vinyl compounds.

While most thermoplastics may be extruded, the nine most common commercial materials used in extruders are as follows:

acetates
butyrates
ethyl cellulose
acrylics
polyamides (nylons)
polyethylene
vinyls
polystyrene
polyvinylidene chloride (saran)

Because the thermal life of saran is short, special precautions must be taken in the design of extruding equipment. A speedy unrestricted passage through the cylinder and screw should be assured.

Some materials such as nylon need a screen-pack ahead of the die in an extrusion machine to build up back pressure so that an even flow of material can be secured through the die.

The number of extrusion machines in operation in the United States during 1956 increased by more than 20 per cent; during this same period the number of injection molding machines in operation increased only 12 per cent.

Recent developments in extrusion include several methods for interrupted flow, making it possible to use an extruder for the molding of small, simple shapes such as closures. Greater progress in this general field is predicted for the future.

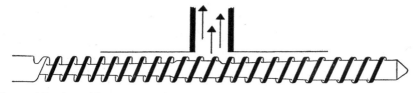

Figure 6.7. A multi-stage extrusion screw. Extruders of this type are equipped with provision for devolatilizing gaseous vapors. Somewhere along the screw a place is open to the atmosphere as shown by the arrows at the center. Leakage of material is prevented by placing a restriction in the screw before the vent which causes a pressure drop across this restriction; this is indicated by the sharp decrease in thread depth shown.

### Forming Metal

Plastics, especially epoxies, often are used for tooling, that is, for making molds or die pieces with which metal is formed.

A typical operation starts with a wooden pattern furnished by the customer. It is suitably placed and the entire exposed surface is coated with a release agent. Several layers of glass fabric bonded with a laminating resin are placed over the wooden model. Epoxy resins are used in the compounds because of their excellent bonding characteristics and the fact that they cure without heat or pressure. After the build-up of glass fabric and resin this part of the forming die is backed with a mixture of the laminating resin and buckshot. The finished die is a very strong, dimensionally stable reproduction of the pattern. After the die is made, another compound, a flexible epoxy, is cast in a plaster mold taken from the original wooden pattern. After removal from the mold this casting becomes a resilient punch for use with the die previously made. This punch is strong enough to form most metal sheets without fracturing. The punch used may also be cast directly against the finished plastic female die after waxing the surface to prevent adherence.

### Laminating

The term "laminating" usually refers to high-pressure laminating as distinct from low-pressure laminating and reinforced plastics. The phenolics were the first binders for laminates. With the newer types of paper these made it possible to produce strong, rigid, and durable sheets, but they were limited to dark colors. With the advent of the ureas light colors and decorative patterns became possible. Fabrics were used as the reinforcing material to add new properties. The laminates, as forms of plastics, and a brief description of the laminating process are described in Chapter 3. Several processes are used for making laminates. The simplest method is to cut resin treated material (paper or fabric) to size and then pile up the cut sheets to secure the desired thickness and place the stacks between polished steel plates in a hydraulic press, provided with heated platens. The heat and pressure cause the resin to flow and then harden, thus forming the stacks of sheets into solid structures. For making laminates with phenolic or urea binders, pressures of about 1500 psi and temperatures of about 350°F are used. An outer face sheet of higher resin content may be used to give better appearance.

*(Courtesy R. D. Wood Co.)*

Figure 6.8. A 2,000-ton multiple-opening hydraulic platen press, designed specifically for precision lamination of plastic industrial and decorative panels from impregnated paper or cloth. It will produce laminated panels up to 40 in. by 80 in. in size.

A modified process, sometimes called "molding of laminates," uses the buildup of sheets described in the above method. However, instead of the flat press application various curved forms with their press modifications are used in a type of compression molding technique. By using coils of impregnated sheets such items as gear blanks and castors are made.

**Low-Pressure Laminating.** The usual pressures employed for low-pressure laminates range from 50 to 350 psi. Dies or forms thus can be of inexpensive materials such as wood, cement, or even plaster of Paris. One method is to use half the usual die, and to place the impregnated stack of sheet material over it. The rubber or other flexible blanket used to cover the assembly is then drawn down, by air pressure or by vacuum, thus forcing the sheet material against the die half. A variant of this method, known as "bag molding," places the entire assembly in a flexible bag, applies vacuum to the bag to bring the mold and sheet material into close contact, and then places the assembly in an autoclave for curing at the desired temperature, and pressure.

In one alternate method, for instance, in making a boat, fibrous matter in relatively small sheet form is laid, or built up over a shaped surface. The various pieces of material are arranged in the desired thickness over the form or mold, and smoothed down to give a fairly even layer. Then the liquid resin binder is applied. A male mold should be used and if volatiles are present they should be allowed to evaporate before successive layers are put in place.

The fibrous material is sometimes impregnated with a binder before being placed over the mold. The binder is either cured with heat or by adding a catalyst.

Both thermosetting and thermoplastic resins are available for low-pressure laminating. Some contact pressure materials can use pressures of less than 1 psi which means that the weight of a die or mold would be sufficient. The polyester resins frequently are used in low-pressure laminating to produce flexible sheet products. Continuous lengths of low-pressure laminates are possible and find application as table top covering, wall covering, and similar products. The terms "low-pressure laminates" and "reinforced plastics" sometimes are used synonymously. See Chapter 3.

## Machining of Plastics

Most of the machining operations performed on wood or metal may be used on plastics with some modification in the technique. As with metal cutting, speeds may be set at the highest speed at which overheating of

*(Courtesy Resistoflex Corp.)*

Figure 6.9. A vinyl conveyor belt used to facilitate handling of small machined parts.

the tool or material can be avoided. Also, as with metal, coolants or cutting fluids generally are used. In the case of plastics plain or soapy water or, less frequently, oil may be used. The teeth on band saws should have a good set to clear away chips. Guides should be set close to the work. Twist drills are made especially for use on plastics. They should have two flutes and a point with a 60 degree angle (30 degrees from the axis). All tools should be kept sharp and well polished. Sharp edged tools should be used for punching and shearing. Sanding and centerless grinding follow along conventional lines. One use for centerless grinding is in the preparation of Teflon rod for automatic screw machines; it is difficult to keep to accurate dimensions in extruding this material.

The welding technique for plastics closely follows that for metal when they do not have a sharp melting point. Polyethylene and the vinyls are especially good materials for welding. The normal process consists of feeding gas through a pressure regulator, then through a heater, and finally directing the hot gas to the point of welding. The plastic used for most welding is in the form of a rod which is held close to the prepared surfaces of the two pieces which are to be joined, and at the center of the directed stream of hot gas.

## Molding

This is a general term often used to include most of the operations, except calendering, which transform materials into finished plastics items. It is used here to describe the following:

> compression molding
> high-frequency molding
> injection molding
> jet molding
> shell or slush molding
> transfer molding
> blow molding
> mold making
> plastisol molding

**Compression Molding.** Thermosetting plastics usually are molded on compression molding presses. This is one of the oldest and one of the simplest means of converting plastics raw materials into finished products. Parts varying from a few ounces to 40 pounds or more are molded in this manner. The process also is used occasionally for producing both thermoplastic and cold-molded products, but generally it is a thermoset process and is used for a great variety of items from buttons, electrical devices, radio tube bases, and bottle caps to washing machine agitators and television receiver housings.

It consists essentially of a press and a mold. The mold, in simplest form, consists of two parts, an upper part known as a mold plunger or force and a lower part called a mold cavity. The molding compound is introduced into the heated cavity which is held in the lower part of the open press, and the press, with the plunger in the upper part, is then closed. At the closed position the space left between the two parts of the mold represents the form of the finished item. This description is almost an over-simplification and of course is a far cry from the operation of a modern high-speed automatic compression press producing complicated parts. In such a case the molding material may be introduced as preheated preforms or tablets. The preforms are produced and heated on a separate machine adjusted to feed them to the press, at just the right time cycle.

In this case the preforms are of the proper shape, size, and temperature for optimum operation.

Normally hardened steel molds are used and the molding compound is added in powder form or a preform is introduced into the mold cavity by an operator, where it is subjected to a pressure of from 2000 to 4000 psi and a temperature of 300 to 350°F. The combination of pressure and heat softens the compound and causes it to flow filling the mold. A small clearance—perhaps 0.003 in.—is allowed between the mold cavity and the plunger to permit escape of gases and any excess material. The mold is kept closed while the thermosetting plastic hardens—an interval of from seconds to minutes, depending on the size and thickness of the part. Then the mold is opened and the molded piece is discharged by means of ejector pins.

*The General Electric Co. Ltd, Brown's Lane, Allesley, Coventry.*

(*Courtesy G. B. Lewis Co.*)

Figure 6.10. Industrial tote pans are molded from fiber glass reinforced polyester, with a minimum glass content of 33 per cent of the total plastic weight. The nesting design pan will both stack and nest within its own dimensions. It is molded in a variety of sizes, in hydraulic presses ranging from 75 to 250 ton, depending upon the size being molded. An independent testing laboratory, on the basis of compressive tests, indicates a *safe* load of 3000 lb for the pan when stacked, and 2500 lb nested.

Undercuts in the design of moldings are taken care of by means of retractable cores or by split mold design where the mold parts are separated sideways as well as vertically. When the design gets too complicated it may be best to resort to transfer molding.

**High-Frequency Molding.** Although this is a method of heating rather than of molding it is important and some comment about it should be made. It involves heating the molding material, usually a thermosetting plastic, in a high-frequency electrostatic field. This heats the whole mass uniformly from the inside. Accordingly the molding material can safely be brought up close to the correct molding temperature. It is then transferred as a soft, hot preform to a hot die whereupon molding is performed in the conventional manner. In this way the time in the press, usually a compression molding press, is greatly shortened. In fact, a well organized high-frequency thermosetting compression molding sequence will approach the speed of injection molding of thermoplastic materials.

**Injection Molding.** A large portion of all plastics materials reach their final form through the process of injection molding. Briefly, this consists of injecting a heat-softened and flowable material from a heating cylinder into a cold closed die. Conditions of temperature and pressure are such that the molded article solidifies quickly and thus can be quickly ejected. Thermoplastic materials are used, generally in the form of molding granules, which are placed into a hopper integral with the press and from which they are fed into a heating cylinder. The cylinder is equipped with a piston which forces the material into the mold and with a discharge

TABLE 6.1. SOME TYPICAL MOLDING MATERIALS AND APPLICATIONS

*Materials:*

    Fluorocarbon resins and compounds
    Phenolic resins and compounds
    Polyethylene
    Polystyrene
    Polystyrene rubber compounds
    Rigid and plasticized vinyl chloride and
       copolymer resins and compounds
    Silicone compounds
    Styrene-acrylonitrile resins and compounds

*Applications:*

    Appliance components
    Automotive ignition parts
    Bottles and closures
    Buttons
    Communications equipment
    Electrical insulating parts
    Electrotype molds
    Housewares
    Phonograph records
    Printing plates
    Television and radio cabinets
    Textile, photographic, and chemical equipment
    Toys and dolls
    Wall tile
    Wiring devices

nozzle through which the hot material passes. Accurate temperature control is maintained in a prescribed manner throughout the cylinder. This is usually done by wrap-around electric heating units but may be accomplished by any of several other methods.

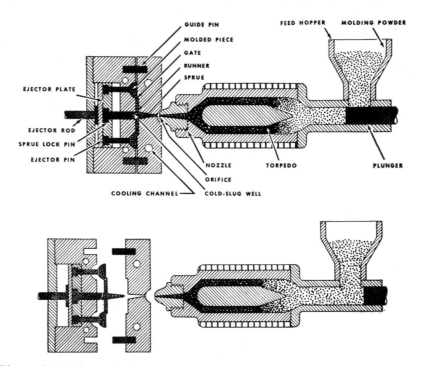

Figure 6.11. Schematic diagram of an injection molding operation with the mold closed (above) and with the mold open (below).

The temperature of the mold is lower than the softening point of the material and thus the mold rapidly absorbs heat from the soft plastic, causing the material to harden. Usually the molded articles are removed from the mold in a space of seconds either automatically or by an operator. In fact, the molding cycle for most thermoplastic materials averages from 10 to 30 seconds. By the time an article is ready to be removed from the mold a fresh charge of material has been softened in the heating cylinder and the cycle is ready to be repeated. The rapid succession of injection of the soft plastic and ejection of the molded article is perhaps the most important factor in processing plastics, as it has made possible production of a great variety of molded articles at a relatively low price. While the material used in this process is thermoplastic, thermosetting materials may be molded by modifications of the process, one of which is called "jet" or "transfer molding," as explained elsewhere. Most thermo-plastic materials can be injection molded; the most common of these, however, are the acetates, the butyrates, polystyrene, the vinyls, and the acrylics.

A schematic diagram of an injection molding assembly is shown in Figure 6.11. A measured quantity of molding powder (granulated solid) is fed into the hopper at the right. The plunger then forces it into the heating zone which has the type of cross section indicated in order to present a large hot surface area in contact with the material. Subsequent strokes of the plunger bring in more molding powder which forces forward the material already in the heating zone. At the nozzle end of the heating zone the material will have reached a fluid state, ready to pass through the orifice into the mold cavity.

The two parts of the mold are held in tight contact by a locking device which prevents them from being forced apart by the pressure of the fluid material. However, as soon as the molding has solidified, the locking device is released, permitting the mold to open as shown in the lower section of Figure 6.11.

The amount of material fed into the heated cylinder at each stroke of the plunger is regulated so that it is equal to the amount required by the mold. Thus there is a continuing but intermittent flow of material through the machine with a reservoir of heat-softened plastic available at all times during the operation.

The ejection of the molding is timed to take place as soon as the molded piece is sufficiently rigid to hold its shape.

**Jet Molding.** Although sometimes identified with transfer molding, jet molding actually is more closely associated with injection molding. It is an adaptation of the injection process to accommodate thermosetting materials. This is done by means of a special nozzle having very high heat—up to 1000°F in some cases—and a small aperture. Provision is made for quickly cooling the nozzle. This is insulated so that its high heat does not flow back to overheat the material in the cylinder behind it. The cylinder is similar to that of an injection press. In fact, it usually is the cylinder of such a press. The difference is that with thermosetting materials the temperature in the cylinder is kept low—just high enough to make it possible for the ram to push some of the material forward into the hot nozzle. The mold is heated and the final cure takes place under the heat and the pressure in the mold.

**Reinforced Plastics Molding.** A slight confusion of terms exists here, as low-pressure molding, bag molding, contact molding and reinforced plastics molding sometimes refer to the same processes. Low-pressure molding has already been described. When a flexible membrane is used to apply pressure the process usually is called "bag molding." For many relatively small products a male form (often wood) with its lay-up, is placed in a rubber (or similar) bag with pressure applied by vacuum, and the whole is then cured in an autoclave. With this method only one smooth surface (that against the mold) results. A female mold can be used with this process when a smooth convex surface is desired. The foregoing processes have the advantage of low cost for prototype or other small volume production, but are not adaptable for high production. For such items as bread trays, tote boxes and luggage, matched metal molds are used.

A modified method consists of winding the impregnated sheet material around a mandrel to produce cylindrical or similar shapes.

**Shell Molding.** This term should not be confused with metal foundry shell molding. Shell molding of plastics—sometimes called solvent molding—is based on the adherence of a resin solution to a dipped mold. If the mold is hollow it is filled with the solution and then emptied, leaving a layer of plastic film adhering to the surfaces of the mold. This process is repeated until the desired thickness of the film is secured. When the completed film has hardened it is removed, facilitated either by its own resiliency as with a bathing cap, or else by use of a two-piece mold. Often the mold itself becomes part of the end product, as for instance, the coating on a metal tube.

In foundry shell molding a resin—usually phenolic—is mixed with the foundry sand to produce castings with more accurate and smoother surfaces.

Shell molding of plastics also is called "slush molding."

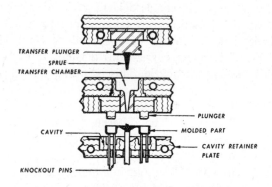

**TRANSFER MOLDING**

Figure 6.12. A transfer three-part mold in the open position. The thermosetting material is introduced into the transfer chamber where it is heated and then forced, or transferred, into the mold cavity by the transfer plunger. Timing is important in the sequence of operations.

**Transfer Molding.** An important molding process developed for handling thermosetting materials is known as "transfer molding." It also is called "step molding" and a modification is called "jet molding."

(*Courtesy Shaw Insulator Co.*)

Figure 6.13. A self-contained transfer molding press.

Transfer molding differs from compression molding in that the material to be molded is heated in a chamber which is separate from the mold which shapes the product. It often is carried out on a conventional compression press with the modifying features incorporated in the mold. The essential difference between transfer molding and injection molding is the fact that for transfer, only enough material is heated at each cycle to fill the cavities, whereas for the injection operation a reservoir of heated material is maintained with only a part of it used at each plunger stroke. With transfer molding the molding powder is placed in a heating or transfer chamber and then rapidly brought to a plastic state by a combination of heat and pressure. At the proper temperature a ram forces all the material into the mold. The amount of the material is just enough to fill the entire cavity. It is then held under pressure until curing is completed. The process is successfully used for filled phenolics and even fabric-filled melamines.

**Blow Molding.** Blow molding is a method of forming a thin shell of thermoplastic material against a female mold. A lump of semi-molten materials is roughly shaped into a hollow form similar to that of the finished product. This is then inserted into the female mold and air is introduced inside of the shaped material much as one would inflate a balloon. In this way the material is flattened out against the walls of the mold where it hardens and takes the shape desired. Then the mold is opened and the molding is removed. An alternate method is to use a thermoplastic sheet which is clamped between a mold and its cover, and to introduce air pressure between the sheet and the cover thus forcing the sheet into the mold and in close contact with the mold surfaces. The sheet usually is heated for this operation and is cooled and solidified after taking the form of the mold or die. See vacuum forming.

**Plastisol Molding.** Pourable plastisols are used for this process. Molds are coated, usually by dipping or pouring, and then are heated. If vinyl plastisols are used the temperature is about 350°F. Curing or conversion is almost instantaneous once this temperature is reached. A vinyl sponge type of plastisol is now available. An external mold may be dipped into a plastisol bath and the material which adheres may then be cured with heat and stripped from the mold. Molds often are preheated before dipping. For making spark plug covers this simple operation has been highly mechanized.

## Mold Making

An important part of any plastics molding job is the mold itself. It is the heart of the operation. If the product is not right the first place to look for the cause of the trouble is the mold. Molds usually are made of steel, although other metals are used and for some short runs plastics themselves may be used.

It almost always pays in the end to have a good mold. Economy in mold making may become extravagance in production of moldings. The length of run, rate of production, and accuracy of detail required are paramount factors in mold design and production. Because of the specialized nature of mold making a large number of mold and die makers have been established to produce molds for the plastics molder; however, mold making often forms an important department in a well established plastics molding company.

This requires specialized machines and trained toolmakers. Care must be taken in selecting the steels for molds. The steel companies are ready to help with such selection. A general-purpose hot-rolled machine steel is a common material. It is easy to machine and may be surface hardened by carburizing. Softer steels are available for "hobbing," which is a method of making a mold by pressing a very hard steel form or pattern into a softer metal. Hobbing is a convenient way of duplicating mold cavities to speed up production of moldings. Steel molds often are chromium plated to prevent deterioration of the mold surfaces on long runs. Hard chromium plating may be electrolytically deposited directly onto the steel surface of the mold. The general practice is to deposit an average of from 0.0003 to 0.0005 in. of chromium on steel.

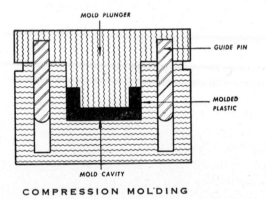

COMPRESSION MOLDING

Figure 6.14.  A cross-section of a simple compression mold, in the closed position with the mold cavity filled. As soon as the molded piece solidifies the mold plunger will be raised and the piece removed, freeing the cavity for the next molding operation. If necessary, ejector pins may be used (not shown) to help in removal of the piece. A jet of air helps clean the cavity of any loose material. *(Courtesy The Society of the Plastics Industry, Inc.)*

In a large plastics molding plant duplicating machines are standard tools in the mold making department. With these, patterns or models are clamped to one side of the machine and then a tracer is moved over the surface of the pattern. This movement actuates a cutter spindle which cuts a duplicate form in a steel block. Some hand finishing is then needed but for routine work this operation saves a great deal of the toolmaker's time.

Where materials being molded have a tendency to corrode steel mold surfaces, one way to solve the problem is to make the molds of stainless steel. In typical cases steel molds have had to be repolished every three or four months but when replaced with stainless steel molds they can be used continuously for eighteen months or more.

Three types of molds are used for compression molding: the positive, the semipositive, and the flash mold. In the positive mold the charge of molding powder is carefully measured so that when compressed it just fills the cavity. The plunger fits closely to the side of the mold and the full pressure is exerted on the molded piece. There is no escape for any excess material. With the semipositive mold there is perhaps an 0.003 in. escape opening when the plunger is fully seated. The flash mold frequently is used to avoid excessive wear on a close fitting plunger. With the flash mold the excess material is pushed out as the mold closes. This excess, known as "flash," appears as a fin on the edge of the molded piece. The fin or sprue often can be reused.

## Molding Details

Emphasis on the newer materials has been part of the plan of this book, and while the alkyd resins have been well established as coating materials for many years the development of granular, free-flowing alkyd molding powder is a fairly recent accomplishment. The following article by Mr. Moylan which describes in some detail the molding of alkyd resins is included here partly because of the recent character of some of the processes and partly because it will help the reader to understand the molding of other materials for use in cases where the molding process has not been particularized to such an extent.

## Molding of Alkyd Resins*

The diversity of applications for which alkyd molding compounds have gained acceptance has resulted in the development of many types. While the general characteristics of fast-cure and low-pressure requirements are common to all of these compounds, they may be divided into three different groups corresponding to physical form before molding.

*Granular Materials:* The physical form of materials in this group is that of a free-flowing powder. Thus, these materials readily lend themselves to conventional molding practices such as volumetric loading, preforming,

---

* This section by J. J. Moylan of the Glendale-Plaskon Laboratory, Barrett Division, Allied Chemical & Dye Corp. is included here by courtesy of Modern Plastics Encyclopedia Issue, 1956.

and high-speed automatic operations. They have found extensive use as high-grade electrical insulation, especially in the electronics field. Typical applications are television tuner segments, electronic tube bases, sockets, and resistor housings.

*Putty Materials:* This group contains materials which are furnished in soft, putty-like sheets. They are characterized by very low-pressure requirements (less than 800 psi) and find use in molding around delicate inserts and in special loading problems. The molder customarily extrudes the material into a ribbon of a specific size which is then cut into preforms before molding. Putty materials have found widespread use in encasing electronic components such as capacitors, resistors, small coils, etc.

*Glass-reinforced Materials:* Among the most recent additions to the alkyd family are materials which combine the molding characteristics of polyester resins with the reinforcing action of fibrous glass fillers to attain very high strength. These materials have already found widespread use in such applications as insulating brackets and bases, rocker rings, circuit breakers, heavy-duty coil forms, and similar applications where high strength and good electrical characteristics are important. In many cases they have replaced metal assemblies and insulating materials. Recent developments in materials of this type include a compound having markedly superior handling characteristics.

Within each of the three groups of alkyd materials described above, several distinct types are available. For example, some types are self-extinguishing, some have approval under military specifications, some have improved high-humidity performance. The manufacturers' literature on these materials should be consulted before selecting a material for a specific application.

**Presses and Equipment for Alkyd Molding.** Although full realization of the advantages of molding alkyds is best attained through the use of high-speed, lightweight equipment, most modern compression presses are suitable for use with these materials. Some presses may be encountered, however, which are so slow that it is necessary to speed the ram travel by using a high-volume pump or to decrease the amount of travel by mounting the mold on blocks to reduce daylight. Because of the low-pressure molding characteristics of alkyds, the high-pressure line may sometimes be cut out completely and only the low-pressure side of the system used. In general, not more than 4 seconds should elapse before charging the mold and applying full pressure in the case of granular and putty types, or 8 seconds in the case of fibrous glass-reinforced material.

In selecting a press to operate a specific mold for alkyds, the following rule should prove useful: for average draws, the press should furnish about 1500 psi over the projected area of the cavity and lands for molding granular alkyds; about 800 psi for alkyd putty; and about 2000 psi for glass-reinforced alkyd.

Marked savings in labor, maintenance, floor space, power costs, and depreciation are possible through the use of presses specifically designed for alkyd materials. Detailed information and specifications are available directly from the manufacturers.

**Design and Construction.** Alkyd parts are in successful production in positive, semipositive, and flash molds. In general, the semipositive and positive types are recommended to obtain uniformly dense parts with lowest shrinkage. Since the flash types rely on the back pressure of the material for density, they do not usually produce parts of maximum density due to the soft flow characteristics of alkyd materials. However, flash molds are frequently used with alkyd putty because of its low bulk factor. In any case, the use of polished, hardened, chrome-plated steel molds is recommended.

Positive and semipositive molds should be designed with enough freedom to allow escape of material and thus prevent over-pressuring. Punch clearances on positive molds of the order 0.004 to 0.005 in. are generally recommended for the granular and putty types. Slightly greater clearances are customarily used for glass-reinforced materials. Excessive clearances should be avoided since they decrease the effective molding pressure on the material, reducing the strength.

An allowance of 0.004 to 0.007 in./in. should be made for shrinkage from a cold mold. This shrinkage is dependent upon mold design, shape of the piece, and in some cases on the pressure and temperature of the operation. It is usually reproducible on a given part. There is no measurable after-shrinkage on alkyd parts over an extended period since there are no residual volatiles or continuing chemical reactions involved after molding.

The use of transfer or plunger type molds is not generally recommended for putty or granular alkyd. In many such molds the plastic phase is too "short" to permit the material to complete its cycle through the gates and runners before cure sets in. Precuring, even when it does not preclude complete filling of a mold cavity, can result in porosity, uneven density, and incomplete fusion. Such conditions obviously lead to loss of mechanical and electrical properties and to sharp deterioration in water resistance. In some cases, defects occurring in a transfer-molded piece may be invisible but will cause trouble in testing or in service.

On the other hand, in many cases transfer molds can be successfully used with granular material. Transfer molds must meet the following design requirements: (1) cavities must be small; (2) they must be grouped close to the transfer pot; and (3) wide open runners and liberal gating should be used.

It has also been noted that parts molded in transfer cavities gated at two locations show poor mechanical strength, especially at the weld line. In general, parts molded by either straight transfer or plunger methods are lower in mechanical strength and lower in electrical insulating properties than similar parts which are compression molded.

Reinforced alkyd may be transfer molded but the strength of such pieces is somewhat lower than that of compression molded pieces, the magnitude being almost entirely dependent on the size of the gates and the number of times the material changes direction before entering the cavity. Since these changes are dependent upon design, pieces will have to be tested individually in order to determine the suitability of the material for specific applications.

Multiple gates should normally be avoided because of the knitting effects between gates. An exception to this is the transfer molding of circular pieces where knitting must occur to fill the cavity. In such cases, continuous circular gating is recommended. Better strengths are usually achieved by gating at the end of the piece rather than in the middle. When shrinkage tolerances are critical, it is recommended that both transfer ram and clamping pressures be sufficient to insure dense pieces.

**Molds for Alkyd Molding.** To date, most alkyd molding has been done in molds utilizing conventional mold steels hardened by standard heat-treating methods. Other metals have been used for experimental and short-run molds. Some production molds have been chrome-plated while others are only highly polished, depending upon the preferences of the designer. The fact that the alkyds can be molded at low pressures has presented the possibility of using molds other than steel.

Alkyds, being mineral-filled materials, are somewhat more abrasive than general-purpose ureas or phenolics, and somewhat greater mold wear may be anticipated. However, because of their lower molding pressure and greater plasticity, mold wear is not as great as it is with mineral-filled phenolics. The use of minimum pressures that permit satisfactory molding tends to reduce the effects of mold wear.

The usual precautions should be taken in designing pieces for thermoset molding. Particular attention should be paid to the use of flowing curves and generous radii rather than sharp knife edges. Sections should not be designed in any case for less than 1/16 in. thickness, and projections and ridges should be designed with generous allowances for material.

The fast-curing characteristics of alkyd molding compounds should, of course, be taken into consideration when designing the number of cavities for a given production mold. The high production rate per cavity of these materials represents a definite savings in tooling cost.

## Post Forming

Although cured thermosetting sheets and laminates by definition cannot be remelted, as thermoplastic sheets can, they can be reformed to some extent; the process by which this is done is called "post forming." Thermoplastic sheets of course have much greater reforming possibilities, but the process used is seldom designated as post forming. Also the reforming of thermoplastic sheets sometimes runs into some difficulty because of their cold brittleness and (often) lower heat resistance.* Post forming of thermosetting sheets is possible because an appreciable amount of uncured resin is usually present even in cured high-pressure laminates. However, the process is limited to simple bends and moderate contours, and in practice, to but a few types of laminates. Most adaptable for post forming are cloth-based phenolic laminates and, for simple bends, paper-based phenolic laminates. Resins which soften at near 300°F produce laminates which are most readily postformed. Loosely woven glass-filled laminates are postformed to produce aircraft ducts, fairings, ammunition chutes, and cable guards, as well as many automobile parts.

Figure 6.15. Simple forming dies of metal are used for most postforming production.

Quick heating is desirable in post forming because prolonged heating tends to give less flexible stock. High-frequency heating is popular whenever the quantity to be formed warrants. Otherwise radiant heat, hot air, steam, and even liquids may be used.

In general, the dies used for post forming are simple metal forming dies such as shown in Figure 6.15.

## Potting and Encapsulating

The development of some of the new foaming materials, such as the polyurethanes, has brought into prominence the encapsulation of electrical assemblies for better protection of insulation and for more rugged total

---

* See vacuum forming.

construction of housed units. Encapsulation is the embedment of units such as resistors or capacitors, or of entire wiring assemblies, in a plastic foam-like material which completely fills the space between the assembly and its housing. A case in point may make this clearer. The wiring assembly—transistors, condensers, etc.—for a loud speaker attachment for a telephone, may be placed in, say, a phenolic housing. It must then be fastened in some way to the housing which ordinarily would leave considerable air space between the assembly and the housing. This encourages vibration and resonance. However, if encapsulation is to be used, the assembly is merely placed in the housing and a mixture of foamable resin is introduced. Under proper conditions of vacuum and temperature the resin will expand to fill the total space between the assembly and the housing making it one solid unit. Not only is such a unit resistant to rough handling but insulation is protected and acoustical properties are improved. In distinction from encapsulation, potting is the deep impregnation of units such as resistors and solenoids, to improve insulation as well as to solidify and protect against handling.

## Heat Sealing

Films and sheets may be joined by overlapping and cementing. This usually is a hand operation, the operator spreading the cement with a camel's hair brush and then subjecting the joined pieces to moderate pressure. Or it may be a semiautomatic operation with the cement applied by a roller. A similar method uses solvents in place of cement.

A more common way of joining films and sheets is by heat sealing. This takes several forms and makes use of elaborate equipment. The simplest form makes use of metal bars containing electric heating elements. These are used for bonding cellophane, vinyls, and some rubbers but the method is giving way to high-frequency or electronics heat sealing where the heat is generated within the film or sheet being bonded. Heating with pressure creates a good bond and may be applied with bars or on a continuous basis using an electronic sewing machine, which is much like the conventional sewing machine. Instead of using thread, however, the work passes under a sealing head and intermittent electronic seals are made at close intervals. A modification of this method uses two rotating discs between which the material passes, with the electronic impulse generated between the discs. This may develop an almost continuous seal.

The electronic bar sealer is commonly used for vinyls for such items as billfolds and purses. It has a capacity for handling thicknesses from 0.002 to 0.04 in. and may be used to seal vinyl film to fabric. The time required for bar contact with the material varies from a quarter of a second or less to several seconds. Pressure of the bar against the work usually is applied by air from an air compressor.

For complex products to be sealed (e.g., a raincoat) both types of sealer may be used—the bar sealer for simple joining and the electronic sewing machine for hems and curves. A recent high-speed sealer is known as an impulse sealer and is used on automatic package sealing.

### Vacuum Forming

This process consists of drawing a heat-softened thermoplastic sheet into a mold by means of a vacuum developed through holes or openings in the mold. Automatic and semiautomatic machines have been developed for this operation. A sheet from a roll is drawn across the mold, and its edges are securely clamped; it is then heated from above and when the desired temperature of the sheet is reached the vacuum is turned on thus drawing the softened sheet down tightly into the mold. The sheet in its new form cools and sets rapidly and is released ready for the next forming.

# 7. SELECTING THE PLASTIC

The manufacturer who plans to bring out a new plastic product has before him the problem of selecting the best material for his particular application. This chapter is intended to help him with that problem. It is only a guide, however, and many other factors should be explored before the final decision is made. One of the most puzzling problems concerns how the product in question is to be made and the answer has a lot to do with determining the material to be used. The following tables have been prepared in cooperation with George K. Scribner, President of Boonton Molding Co. and many of them appeared in that company's booklet published in 1956. Used in connection with Chapter 5 on applications, it is hoped that these tables will not only help the manufacturer to design new products but also to check on the established practice.

Chapter 6 should help in determining the method of making the desired item. If it is to be a film or sheet, several processes are available. Perhaps the most common is calendering but here the cost of equipment is high, running to about $100,000 for an inverted L calender with a capacity of 30 yards per minute. An embossing roll alone might cost $5,000 and a Banbury mixer and compounder about $30,000.

Another method, as explained in Chapters 5 and 6, is extrusion. A 3½ in. extruder with full equipment for producing both film and sheeting might cost $20,000. A 2 in. extruder without additional equipment might cost from $7,000 to $8,000. If film alone is desired, casting on a stainless steel belt should be considered. The capital cost here, with the oven and other equipment is intermediate between extrusion and calendering. A new method of making film consists of casting on a paper carrier. This process is described briefly in Chapter 9.

For most all continuous forms of plastics, except films and sheeting, extrusion is the usual process. Non-continuous forms are customarily molded and the term molded is used even if the end product is to be a glass-fiber reinforced resin boat.

In the following tables the resins are listed with the lowest number usually the highest or most desirable of the properties being considered. Thus in Table 7.7 (Safe Top Operating Temperature) the number 1 listing covers mineral-filled phenolic and glass-filled melamine both of which have a top operating temperature of 400°F. This is the highest temperature given in the table. Some special resins, especially the fluorocarbons, have higher operating temperatures.

An attempt has been made in Table 7.1 to list some of the common materials in order of their over-all chemical resistance—in particular their resistance to acids, alkalies, and water. Lower numbers indicate higher resistance.

TABLE 7.1. CHEMICAL RESISTANCE

1. Fluorocarbons (trifluorochloroethylene and tetrafluoroethylene)
   Polyethylene
   Dichlorostyrene
2. Phenol formaldehyde (phenolics with various fillers)
3. Polyvinylidene chloride (saran)
   Polyamides (nylon)
4. Polyvinyl chloride
   Melamine
   Polyester
5. Urea
   Cold-molded
   Cellulose nitrate
6. Casein

TABLE 7.2. COMPARISON OF STRENGTH/WEIGHT PROPERTIES
OF PLASTICS AND METALS*

| Material | Specific Gravity | Tensile Strength | Tensile Strength divided by Specific Gravity |
|---|---|---|---|
| Magnesium alloy | 1.81 | 46,000 | 25,400 |
| Stainless steel | 7.85 | 185,000 | 23,600 |
| Pregwood | 1.30 | 30,000 | 23,000 |
| Chrome-moly steel | 7.85 | 180,000 | 22,900 |
| Aluminum alloy | 2.80 | 62,000 | 22,100 |
| Paper laminate | 1.33 | 12,500 | 9,400 |
| Glass fabric laminate | 1.50 | 14,000 | 9,300 |
| Canvas fabric laminate | 1.33 | 9,500 | 7,100 |
| Wood flour, phenolic, molded | 1.36 | 8,500 | 6,200 |
| Asbestos paper laminate | 1.80 | 10,000 | 5,500 |
| Impact phenolic molded | 1.38 | 7,500 | 5,400 |

* Some plastics fibers, such as nylon, having high tensile strength, are not shown in this table.

TABLE 7.3. SPECIFIC GRAVITY

Specific gravity is the ratio of the weight of the molded piece as compared to the weight of an equal volume of water.

| | |
|---|---|
| 1. Polyethylene | 0.92 |
| 2. Polyesters | 1.01 |
| 3. Polystyrene | 1.06 |
| 4. Ethyl cellulose | 1.14 |
| Polyamide (nylon) | 1.14 |
| 5. Acrylates | 1.18 |
| 6. Cellulose propionate | 1.20 |
| 7. Butyrate | 1.21 |
| 8. Molded phenolic | 1.28 |
| 9. Cellulose acetate | 1.30 |
| 10. Cast phenolic | 1.32 |
| 11. Casein | 1.35 |
| 12. Wood flour phenolic | 1.36 |
| 13. Fabric-filled phenolic | 1.38 |
| 14. Vinyl copolymer | 1.40 |
| Lignin | 1.40 |
| Cellulose nitrate | 1.40 |
| 15. Urea | 1.48 |
| 16. Melamine | 1.49 |
| 17. Hard rubber | 1.50 |
| Laminated phenolic | 1.50 |
| 18. Vinylidene chloride (saran) | 1.70 |
| 19. Shellac | 1.90 |
| 20. Mineral-filled phenolic | 1.90 |
| 21. Organic, cold-molded | 2.00 |
| 22. Inorganic, cold-molded | 2.20 |

TABLE 7.4. RELATIVE PRICES OF SOME COMMON PLASTICS

| | |
|---|---|
| 1. Phenolics | $.20 |
| 2. Polystyrene | .29 |
| 3. Polyvinyl chloride | .30 |
| 4. Acetates | .32 |
| 5. Ureas | .34 |
| 6. Polyesters | .37 |
| 7. Polyethylene | .38 |
| 8. Polyvinyl acetate | .42 |
| 9. Melamine | .47 |
| 10. Butyrates | .50 |

### TABLE 7.5. TENSILE STRENGTH

Tensile strength is the pulling force in pounds necessary to break a given sample, divided by the area of the cross section in square inches.

|  | Figures are in Thousands of Pounds |
|---|---|
| 1. Laminated phenolic | 17.5 |
| 2. Casein | 10.0 |
| Nylon | 10.0 |
| Melamine | 10.0 |
| 3. Urea | 9.5 |
| Lignin | 9.5 |
| 4. Wood flour phenolic | 8.5 |
| 5. Vinyl | 8.0 |
| Acrylates | 8.0 |
| 6. Clear phenolic molded | 7.5 |
| Cellulose nitrate | 7.5 |
| Cast phenolic | 7.5 |
| 7. Fabric-filled phenolic | 7.0 |
| Styrene | 7.0 |
| Hard rubber | 7.0 |
| 8. Mineral-filled phenolic | 5.0 |
| Ethyl cellulose | 5.0 |
| 9. Cellulose acetate | 4.3 |
| 10. Butyrate | 3.9 |
| 11. Organic, cold-molded | 2.0 |
| 12. Polyethylene | 1.9 |
| 13. Shellac | 1.5 |
| 14. Polyesters | 0.5 |

### TABLE 7.6. COMPRESSIVE STRENGTH

The compressive strength of a material is the crushing load at failure of a piece, divided by the number of square inches of resisting surface.

|  | Figures Given are Thousands of Pounds |
|---|---|
| 1. Casein | 40.0 |
| 2. Laminated phenolic | 34.0 |
| 3. Melamine, alpha-filled | 30.0 |
| Melamine, rag-filled | 30.0 |
| Melamine, asbestos-filled | 30.0 |
| Melamine, glass-filled | 30.0 |
| Lignin | 30.0 |
| 4. Wood flour phenolic | 27.5 |
| Flock-filled phenolic | 27.5 |
| 5. Urea | 27.0 |
| 6. Fabric-filled phenolic | 21.5 |

TABLE 7.6  (*Continued*)

| | Figures Given are Thousands of Pounds |
|---|---|
| 7. Polyester | 21.3 |
| 8. Cellulose acetate | 21.0 |
| 9. Mineral-filled phenolic | 20.0 |
| 10. Styrene | 15.0 |
| 11. Cast phenolic | 13.5 |
| 12. Shellac | 13.5 |
| 13. Nylon | 13.0 |
| 14. Acrylate | 11.0 |
| 15. Ethyl cellulose | 11.0 |
| Vinyl copolymer | 10.0 |
| Cellulose propionate | 10.0 |
| Hard rubber | 10.0 |

TABLE 7.7.  SAFE TOP OPERATING TEMPERATURE

| | °F |
|---|---|
| 1. Mineral-filled phenolic | 400 |
| Glass-filled melamine | 400 |
| 2. Flock-filled phenolic | 300 |
| Asbestos melamine | 300 |
| Nylon | 300 |
| 3. Wood flour phenolic | 280 |
| Mica-filled phenolic | 280 |
| 4. Laminated phenolic | 260 |
| 5. Resin-filled phenolic | 250 |
| Fabric-filled phenolic | 250 |
| 6. Fabric-filled melamine | 220 |
| 7. Alpha-filled melamine | 210 |
| 8. Polyester | 185 |
| Polyethylene | 185 |
| 9. Vinylidene chloride | 180 |
| Cellulose propionate | 180 |
| Styrene | 180 |
| 10. Lignin | 175 |
| Urea | 175 |
| 11. Butyrate | 170 |
| Shellac | 170 |
| 12. Acrylate | 160 |
| Ethyl cellulose | 160 |
| Cellulose acetate | 160 |
| Vinyl copolymer | 160 |
| Cast phenolic | 160 |
| 13. Cellulose nitrate | 130 |

TABLE 7.8. MODULUS OF ELASTICITY

The modulus of elasticity is the quotient obtained by dividing the stress per square inch by the elongation in one inch caused by this stress.

| | |
|---|---|
| 1. Mineral-filled phenolic | 14.5 |
| 2. Urea | 13.5 |
| Laminated phenolic | 13.5 |
| 3. Melamine | 13.0 |
| 4. Lignin | 12.5 |
| 5. Fabric-filled phenolic | 12.0 |
| 6. Flock-filled phenolic | 10.0 |
| Mineral-filled phenolic | 10.0 |
| 7. Wood flour-filled phenolic | 9.0 |
| 8. Molded resin phenolic | 8.5 |
| 9. Shellac | 5.5 |
| 10. Casein | 5.4 |
| 11. Hard rubber | 5.3 |
| 12. Cast phenolic | 5.0 |
| 13. Vinyl copolymer | 4.6 |
| 14. Acrylates | 4.5 |
| 15. Nylon | 4.0 |
| 16. Cellulose acetate | 2.5 |
| 17. Cellulose nitrate | 2.4 |
| 18. Ethyl cellulose | 2.0 |
| Cellulose propionate | 2.0 |
| 19. Butyrate | 1.5 |
| 20. Vinylidene chloride | 0.60 |
| 21. Polyester | 0.19 |
| 22. Polyethylene | 0.15 |

TABLE 7.9. THERMAL CONDUCTIVITY

Thermal conductivity is the time rate of the transfer of heat by conduction, through unit thickness, across unit area for unit difference in temperature.

| | |
|---|---|
| 1. Mineral-filled phenolic | 12.0 |
| 2. Polyethylene | 8.0 |
| Polyester | 8.0 |
| 3. Melamine | 7.5 |
| 4. Urea | 7.0 |
| 5. Laminated phenolic | 6.5 |
| 6. Cellulose acetate | 6.0 |
| Butyrate | 6.0 |
| 7. Nylon | 5.8 |

TABLE 7.9.  (*Continued*)

| | |
|---|---|
| 8. Cellulose nitrate | 5.5 |
| Wood flour phenolic | 5.5 |
| Flock-filled phenolic | 5.5 |
| Fabric-filled phenolic | 5.5 |
| Cellulose propionate | 5.5 |
| 9. Acrylate | 5.0 |
| Ethyl cellulose | 5.0 |
| 10. Resin-filled phenolic | 4.5 |
| 11. Cast phenolic | 4.0 |
| 12. Vinyl copolymer | 3.7 |
| 13. Hard rubber | 3.2 |
| 14. Vinylidene chloride | 3.0 |
| Styrene | 3.0 |

TABLE 7.10.  FLEXURAL STRENGTH

Flexural strength is the pressure in pounds necessary to break a given sample when applied to the center of the sample which has been supported at its end.

| | Figures in Thousands of Pounds |
|---|---|
| 1. Laminated phenolic | 28.0 |
| 2. Lignin | 18.0 |
| 3. Polyamides (nylon) | 14.6 |
| 4. Cast phenolic | 14.0 |
| Resin-filled phenolic | 14.0 |
| Casein | 14.0 |
| Melamine | 14.0 |
| 5. Vinyl copolymer | 13.0 |
| Acrylate | 13.0 |
| 6. Hard rubber | 12.5 |
| 7. Polystyrene | 12.0 |
| 8. Urea | 11.5 |
| 9. Fabric-filled phenolic | 10.8 |
| 10. Cellulose nitrate | 10.5 |
| 11. Flock-filled phenolic | 10.0 |
| Cellulose propionate | 10.0 |
| Wood flour phenolic | 10.0 |
| 12. Ethyl cellulose | 9.0 |
| 13. Polyester | 8.5 |
| 14. Cellulose acetate | 7.5 |
| 15. Butyrate | 6.8 |
| 16. Vinylidene chloride (saran) | 5.0 |
| 17. Polyethylene | 1.7 |

### TABLE 7.11. SPECIFIC HEAT*

The specific heat of a substance is the ratio of the heat required to raise the temperature of a gram of a substance one degree C. to that required to raise the temperature of a gram of water one degree C.

|  |  |
|---|---|
| 1. Vinyl copolymer | 0.23 |
| 2. Mineral-filled phenolic | 0.30 |
| 3. Vinylidene | 0.32 |
| Styrene | 0.32 |
| 4. Hard rubber | 0.33 |
| Fabric phenolic | 0.33 |
| 5. Acrylate | 0.35 |
| Butyrate | 0.35 |
| Laminated phenolic | 0.35 |
| Cast phenolic | 0.35 |
| Cellulose nitrate | 0.35 |
| 6. Wood flour phenolic | 0.38 |
| Flock-filled phenolic | 0.38 |
| 7. Cellulose acetate | 0.40 |
| Urea | 0.40 |
| Cellulose propionate | 0.40 |
| Nylon | 0.40 |
| 8. Ethyl cellulose | 0.58 |
| 9. Polyester | 0.55 |
| 10. Polyethylene | 0.53 |

\* The lower the specific heat, the lower the heating costs.

### TABLE 7.12. REFRACTIVE INDEX

The refractive index for any substance is the ratio of the velocity of light in a vacuum to its velocity in the substance. It is also the ratio of the sine of the angle of incidence to the sine of the angle of refraction.

|  |  |
|---|---|
| 1. Cellulose propionate | 1.47 |
| Ethyl cellulose | 1.47 |
| Butyrate | 1.47 |
| 2. Cellulose acetate | 1.48 |
| 3. Acrylates | 1.49 |
| 4. Cellulose nitrate | 1.50 |
| 5. Polyethylene | 1.52 |
| 6. Nylon | 1.53 |
| Vinyl copolymer | 1.53 |
| 7. Urea | 1.55 |
| 8. Melamine | 1.59 |
| Styrene | 1.59 |
| Cast phenolic | 1.59 |
| 9. Molded resin phenolic | 1.60 |
| 10. Vinylidene | 1.61 |

TABLE 7.13. IMPACT STRENGTH

Impact strength is the mechanical energy absorbed by a standard test piece during fracture by a blow from a pendulum hammer.

| | |
|---|---|
| 1. Cellulose nitrate | 6.0 |
| 2. Ethyl cellulose | 3.5 |
| Fabric-filled phenolic | 3.5 |
| 3. Glass-filled phenolic | 2.9 |
| 4. Shellac | 2.7 |
| 5. Cellulose acetate | 2.2 |
| 6. Butyrate | 1.5 |
| Nylon | 1.5 |
| 7. Cellulose propionate | 1.4 |
| 8. Casein | 1.0 |
| 9. Laminated phenolic | 0.90 |
| 10. Lignin | 0.70 |
| 11. Rag-filled melamine | 0.69 |
| 12. Hard rubber | 0.50 |
| Acrylate | 0.50 |
| 13. Flock-filled phenolic | 0.46 |
| 14. Cast phenolic | 0.35 |
| 15. Asbestos-filled melamine | 0.33 |
| 16. Wood flour phenolic | 0.32 |
| 17. Urea | 0.30 |
| Melamine | 0.30 |
| 18. Resin-filled phenolic | 0.28 |

TABLE 7.14. HARDNESS

Hardness as listed here is a comparison of the resistance to indentation, not of surface hardness or abrasion resistance. The difference between Brinell and Rockwell is mainly in the calculation. The Rockwell R scale is used for softer materials, M for harder.

|  *Brinell* | |
|---|---|
| 1. Urea | 51.0 |
| 2. Lignin | 40.0 |
| 3. Wood flour phenolic | 37.5 |
| Flock-filled phenolic | 37.5 |
| 4. Fabric-filled phenolic | 36.0 |
| 5. Laminated phenolic | 32.0 |
| 6. Hard rubber | 31.0 |
| 7. Styrene | 25.0 |
| 8. Casein | 23.0 |
| 9. Acrylate | 19.0 |
| Cast phenolic | 19.0 |

TABLE 7.14. (*Continued*)

*Brinell* (*Continued*)

| | |
|---|---|
| 10. Vinyl copolymer | 14.0 |
| 11. Cellulose nitrate | 9.5 |
| 12. Butyrate | 9.0 |
| 13. Ethyl cellulose | 6.0 |

*Rockwell M Series*

| | |
|---|---|
| 1. Resin-filled phenolic | 126 |
| 2. Alpha-filled melamine | 120 |
| 3. Wood flour phenolic | 115 |
| Fabric-filled phenolic | 115 |
| Urea | 115 |
| 4. Allyl resins cast | 110 |
| 5. Mineral-filled phenolic | 105 |
| Mica-filled phenolic | 105 |
| 6. Polyester | 100 |
| Acrylate | 100 |
| 7. Cast phenolic | 90 |
| 8. Casein | 85 |
| 9. Styrene | 78 |
| 10. Vinylidene | 58 |
| 11. Cold-molded organic | 50 |
| Cold-molded inorganic | 50 |

*Rockwell R Series*

| | |
|---|---|
| 1. Nylon | 118 |
| 2. Cellulose nitrate | 105 |
| 3. Cellulose acetate (high acetyl) | 100 |
| 4. Ethyl cellulose | 90 |
| Butyrate | 90 |
| Cellulose propionate | 90 |
| Cellulose acetate | 90 |

TABLE 7.15. THERMAL EXPANSIVITY

Thermal expansivity (coefficient of expansion) is the increase in length per unit length per degree centigrade rise in temperature.

| | |
|---|---|
| 1. Mineral-filled phenolic | 2.1 |
| 2. Lignin | 2.3 |
| 3. Laminated phenolic | 2.4 |
| 4. Urea | 2.8 |
| 5. Fabric-filled phenolic | 3.0 |
| 6. Wood flour phenolic | 3.3 |
| 7. Flock-filled phenolic | 3.5 |

TABLE 7.15.  (*Continued*)

| | |
|---|---|
| 8. Melamine | 4.0 |
| 9. Resin-filled phenolic | 4.1 |
| 10. Casein | 4.4 |
| 11. Vinyl copolymer | 7.0 |
| Styrene | 7.0 |
| Cast phenolic | 7.0 |
| 12. Shellac | 8.0 |
| 13. Acrylate | 9.0 |
| 14. Nylon | 10.0 |
| Cellulose nitrate | 10.0 |
| 15. Cellulose acetate | 12.0 |
| 16. Butyrate | 14.0 |
| 17. Cellulose propionate | 14.5 |
| 18. Ethyl cellulose | 15.0 |
| 19. Polyethylene | 18.0 |
| 20. Polyester | 18.0 |

TABLE 7.16.  DIELECTRIC STRENGTH

Dielectric strength is the voltage that will rupture or puncture the material in question when placed between electrodes of a given size. Dielectric tests are usually made at commercial frequencies, i.e., 60 cycles. The results will vary with the thickness tested. The thinner the section the higher the electrical gradient. Puncture voltage in volts per mil thickness is given below.

| | |
|---|---|
| 1. Styrene | 600 |
| Hard rubber | 600 |
| 2. Laminated phenolic | 550 |
| 3. Asbestos melamine | 535 |
| 4. Acrylate | 500 |
| 5. Mica-filled phenolic | 475 |
| 6. Glass melamine | 460 |
| Polyester | 460 |
| 7. Cellulose nitrate | 450 |
| 8. Polyethylene | 440 |
| 9. Vinyl copolymer | 430 |
| 10. Cellulose propionate | 425 |
| 11. Casein | 400 |
| Shellac | 400 |
| 12. Nylon | 385 |
| 13. Cast phenolic | 375 |

TABLE 7.16. (*Continued*)

| | |
|---|---|
| 14. Resin-filled phenolic | 350 |
| Vinylidene | 350 |
| Lignin | 350 |
| Wood flour phenolic | 350 |
| Urea | 350 |
| 15. Alpha melamine | 340 |
| 16. Flock phenolic | 325 |
| Butyrate | 325 |
| Mineral phenolic | 325 |
| 17. Fabric melamine | 270 |
| 18. Fabric phenolic | 250 |

TABLE 7.17. DIELECTRIC CONSTANT

Dielectric constant is the ratio between the capacity of a condenser with a given dielectric and the same capacity with a vacuum as a dielectric.

| | Dielectric Constant 60 Cycles |
|---|---|
| 1. Polyester | 2.3 |
| Polyethylene | 2.3 |
| 2. Styrene | 2.6 |
| 3. Hard rubber | 2.8 |
| 4. Vinyl copolymer | 3.2 |
| 5. Shellac | 3.5 |
| 6. Ethyl cellulose | 3.6 |
| 7. Acrylate | 4.0 |
| 8. Nylon | 4.1 |
| 9. Vinylidene | 5.0 |
| Butyrate | 5.0 |
| 10. Resin-filled phenolic | 5.5 |
| Mica-filled phenolic | 5.5 |
| Cellulose acetate | 5.5 |
| 11. Wood flour phenolic | 6.3 |
| 12. Cast phenolic | 7.0 |
| 13. Cellulose acetate | 7.2 |
| 14. Fabric melamine | 7.7 |
| 15. Alpha melamine | 7.9 |
| 16. Urea | 8.2 |
| 17. Asbestos melamine | 8.5 |
| Fabric phenolic | 8.5 |
| 18. Flock phenolic | 10.0 |

TABLE 7.18. COMPARATIVE VOLUME RESISTIVITY

Following is an abitrary listing to indicate the resistance in ohms between opposite faces of a centimeter cube of the material. Actual values are in the order of millions of ohms.

| | |
|---|---|
| 1. Styrene | 18.0 |
| 2. Vinyl copolymer | 16.0 |
| 3. Acrylate | 15.0 |
| 4. Hard rubber | 13.5 |
| 5. Vinylidene | 13.0 |
| Nylon | 13.0 |
| Ethyl cellulose | 13.0 |
| Polyethylene | 13.0 |
| Melamine | 13.0 |
| Polyester | 13.0 |
| Cellulose propionate | 13.0 |
| 6. Cast phenolic | 12.5 |
| 7. Resin-filled phenolic | 12.0 |
| 8. Urea | 12.0 |
| Fabric-filled phenolic | 11.5 |
| 9. Butyrate | 11.0 |
| Wood flour phenolic | 11.0 |
| Cellulose nitrate | 11.0 |
| Laminated phenolic | 11.0 |
| Mineral-filled phenolic | 11.0 |
| 10. Shellac | 9.0 |

TABLE 7.19. POWER FACTOR

In a perfect condenser the current leads the voltage by 90 degrees. When a loss takes place in the insulation the absorbed current, which produces heat throws the 90 degree relation out according to the proportion of current absorbed by the dielectric. The power factor is the cosine of the angle between voltage applied and the current resulting.

| | Power Factor 60 Cycles |
|---|---|
| 1. Styrene | 0.0001 |
| 2. Polyethylene | 0.0002 |
| 3. Polyester | 0.0005 |
| 4. Hard rubber | 0.0055 |
| 5. Vinyl copolymer | 0.0090 |
| 6. Nylon | 0.0140 |
| 7. Ethyl cellulose | 0.017 |
| 8. Shellac | 0.022 |
| 9. Mica-filled phenolic | 0.025 |
| Butyrate | 0.025 |

TABLE 7.19. *(Continued)*

| | Power Factor 60 Cycles |
|---|---|
| 10. Cellulose acetate | 0.035 |
| 11. Alpha melamine | 0.037 |
| 12. Vinylidene | 0.038 |
| 13. Urea | 0.040 |
| 14. Acrylate | 0.050 |
| 15. Resin-filled phenolic | 0.060 |
| 16. Glass-filled melamine | 0.070 |
| 17. Fabric melamine | 0.080 |
| Wood flour phenolic | 0.080 |
| 18. Cellulose nitrate | 0.110 |
| Asbestos melamine | 0.110 |
| 19. Cast phenolic | 0.125 |
| 20. Fabric phenolic | 0.160 |
| 21. Mineral phenolic | 0.250 |
| 22. Flock phenolic | 0.300 |

TABLE 7.20. MOISTURE ABSORPTION

The moisture absorption is the percentage by weight of water absorbed in 24 hrs. by a sample immersed in water. (Depends on area exposed.)

| | |
|---|---|
| 1. Polyester | 0.01 |
| 2. Polyethylene | 0.02 |
| Hard rubber | 0.02 |
| 3. Styrene | 0.04 |
| 4. Mica-filled phenolic | 0.07 |
| 5. Vinylidene | 0.10 |
| Shellac | 0.10 |
| Resin-filled phenolic | 0.10 |
| 6. Asbestos melamine | 0.13 |
| 7. Mineral phenolic | 0.18 |
| 8. Alpha melamine | 0.30 |
| 9. Cast phenolic | 0.35 |
| 10. Laminated phenolic | 0.50 |
| 11. Wood flour phenolic | 0.60 |
| Urea | 0.60 |
| 12. Fabric phenolic | 1.00 |
| Fabric melamine | 1.00 |
| 13. Ethyl cellulose | 1.50 |
| Nylon | 1.50 |
| Cellulose nitrate | 1.50 |
| Cellulose propionate | 1.50 |
| 14. Cellulose acetate | 3.80 |
| 15. Casein | 10.50 |

TABLE 7.21.  FLAMMABILITY

Flammability is based on the time a given piece will continue to support a flame after having been held in a Bunsen burner for a fixed period. The first material listed supports flame the least number of seconds.

1. Vinylidene chloride (saran)
2. Phenolic—heat resistant
3. Phenolic—low loss
4. Phenolic—acid and alkali resistant
5. Phenolic—wood flour
6. Phenolic—shock resistant
7. Urea
8. Polystyrene
9. Acetate

TABLE 7.22.  SPECIFIC GRAVITIES

For reference and comparison the specific gravities of some non-plastic materials are listed here together with those of a few of the common plastics.

| | |
|---|---|
| Acrylates | 1.18 |
| Aluminum | 2.70 |
| Aluminum, bronze | 7.70 |
| Amber | 1.1 |
| Asbestos | 3.0 |
| Applewood | 0.76 |
| Ashwood | 0.62 |
| Asphaltum | 1.1 - 1.5 |
| Beeswax | 0.97 |
| Bone | 1.8 - 2.0 |
| Brass | 8.5 |
| Brick, pressed | 2.2 - 2.3 |
| Basalt | 2.7 - 3.2 |
| Bronze | 8.85 |
| Beechwood | 0.7 - 0.9 |
| Briarwood | 0.81 |
| Birchwood | 0.65 |
| Boxwood | 0.97 |
| Casein | 1.35 |
| Cement, Portland | 3.10 |
| Cedar | 0.32 - 0.38 |
| Chestnut | 0.66 |
| Ceramics | 2.5 |
| Cold-molded, organic | 2.00 |
| Cold-molded, inorganic | 2.20 |
| Cellulose acetate | 1.28 - 1.34 |
| Cellulose nitrate | 1.35 - 1.40 |
| Concrete | 2.00 |

TABLE 7.22. (*Continued*)

| | |
|---|---|
| Copper | 8.93 |
| Ebony wood | 1.23 |
| Epoxies | 1.15 |
| Fir, Douglas spruce | 0.51 |
| Fir, Eastern | 0.40 |
| Glass, plate | 2.50 |
| Glass, crystal | 2.90 |
| Gutta Percha | 0.98 |
| Hickory | 0.74 - 0.84 |
| Hemlock | 0.42 - 0.52 |
| Ivory | 1.85 |
| Iron, cast white | 7.60 |
| Iron, cast gray | 7.00 |
| Iron, cast wrought | 7.70 |
| Lead | 11.37 |
| Leather | 0.86 - 1.02 |
| Lignum vitae | 1.14 |
| Locust | 0.73 |
| Limestone, marble | 2.5 - 2.8 |
| Marble | 2.5 - 2.8 |
| Mica | 2.85 |
| Maple | 0.68 |
| Manganese | 7.2 - 8.0 |
| Mercury | 13.6 |
| Phenolic, cast | 1.27 - 1.32 |
| Phenolic, wood flour | 1.34 - 1.52 |
| Phenolic, laminated | 1.34 - 1.55 |
| Phenolic, mineral | 1.70 - 2.09 |
| Phenolic, fabric | 1.37 - 1.40 |
| Plaster of Paris | 1.8 |
| Platinum | 21.1 -21.5 |
| Pine, white | 0.41 |
| Polyethylene | 0.92 |
| Poplar | 0.48 |
| Parphyry | 2.6 - 2.9 |
| Paraffin | 0.87 - 0.91 |
| Pitch | 1.07 - 1.15 |
| Quartz | 2.66 |
| Rubber, pure | 0.92 |
| Rubber, hard | 1.50 |
| Redwood | 0.42 |
| Silver | 10.5 |
| Steel, stainless | 7.78 |
| Steel, alleghany | 7.86 - 7.95 |
| Steel, cast | 7.81 |
| Spruce | 0.40 - 0.46 |
| Solder | 9.4 |
| Sulphur | 2.00 |

TABLE 7.22.  (*Continued*)

| | |
|---|---|
| Slate | 2.85 |
| Sandstone | 2.2 - 2.5 |
| Shellac | 1.10 - 2.70 |
| Soapstone | 2.6 - 2.8 |
| Styrene resin | 1.06 |
| Tin | 7.29 |
| Tar | 1.20 |
| Urea | 1.48 - 1.50 |
| Vinyl resin | 1.40 |
| Vinylidene | 1.70 |
| Walnut, black | 0.61 |
| Walnut, white | 0.41 |
| Zinc | 7.10 |

TABLE 7.23.  SPECIFIC GRAVITY INTO OUNCES AND GRAMS PER CU. IN.

| Specific Gravity | Ounces Per Cu. In. | Grams Per Cu. In. |
|---|---|---|
| 1.25 | 0.722 | 20.484 |
| 1.26 | 0.728 | 20.648 |
| 1.27 | 0.734 | 20.811 |
| 1.28 | 0.740 | 20.975 |
| 1.29 | 0.745 | 21.139 |
| 1.30 | 0.751 | 21.303 |
| 1.31 | 0.757 | 21.467 |
| 1.32 | 0.763 | 21.631 |
| 1.33 | 0.768 | 21.795 |
| 1.34 | 0.774 | 21.959 |
| 1.35 | 0.780 | 22.122 |
| 1.36 | 0.786 | 22.286 |
| 1.37 | 0.792 | 22.450 |
| 1.38 | 0.797 | 22.614 |
| 1.39 | 0.803 | 22.778 |
| 1.40 | 0.809 | 22.942 |
| 1.41 | 0.815 | 23.106 |
| 1.42 | 0.820 | 23.269 |
| 1.43 | 0.826 | 23.433 |
| 1.44 | 0.832 | 23.597 |
| 1.45 | 0.838 | 23.761 |
| 1.46 | 0.844 | 23.925 |
| 1.47 | 0.849 | 24.089 |
| 1.48 | 0.855 | 24.253 |
| 1.49 | 0.861 | 24.417 |
| 1.50 | 0.867 | 24.581 |
| 1.51 | 0.872 | 24.745 |

TABLE 7.23. (*Continued*)

| Specific Gravity | Ounces Per Cu. In. | Grams Per Cu. In. |
|---|---|---|
| 1.52 | 0.878 | 24.908 |
| 1.53 | 0.884 | 25.072 |
| 1.54 | 0.890 | 25.236 |
| 1.55 | 0.896 | 25.400 |
| 1.56 | 0.901 | 25.564 |
| 1.57 | 0.907 | 25.726 |
| 1.58 | 0.913 | 25.891 |
| 1.59 | 0.919 | 25.035 |
| 1.60 | 0.924 | 26.219 |
| 1.61 | 0.930 | 26.383 |
| 1.62 | 0.936 | 26.547 |
| 1.63 | 0.942 | 26.711 |
| 1.64 | 0.948 | 26.875 |
| 1.65 | 0.953 | 26.039 |
| 1.66 | 0.959 | 27.202 |
| 1.67 | 0.965 | 27.366 |
| 1.68 | 0.971 | 27.530 |
| 1.69 | 0.976 | 27.694 |
| 1.70 | 0.982 | 27.858 |
| 1.71 | 0.988 | 28.022 |
| 1.72 | 0.994 | 28.186 |
| 1.73 | 1.000 | 28.350 |
| 1.74 | 1.005 | 28.513 |
| 1.75 | 1.010 | 28.677 |

To find the specific gravity of a material multiply the pounds per cubic foot by 0.01604.

To find the pounds per cubic foot when you know the specific gravity multiply specific gravity by 62.4.

To find the pounds per cubic inch when you know the specific gravity multiply specific gravity by 0.0361.

# 8. MATERIAL MANUFACTURERS' STATEMENTS

About one hundred companies in the United States produce the raw materials of the plastics industry—the resins and molding powders. John Wetherby of The Society of the Plastics Industry said he thought the important manufacturers making plastics materials would not total more than thirty-five. From this came the thought "Why not list the thirty-five most important plastics materials manufacturers in this book?" As a result, requests for such a list were sent to the editors of *Modern Plastics, Plastics World* and *Plastics Technology*—the three leading journals in the plastics field. However, although many suggestions and many names were received no one wanted to sponsor such a list. Finally, Frank Carmen, Technical Director of The Manufacturing Chemists' Association, Inc., 1625 Eye Street, N. W., Washington 6, D. C., said that if the list could be expanded to forty-three, he would furnish and sponsor such a list. Accordingly, his list of the forty-three most important plastics materials manufacturers, together with their addresses, appears in the following pages.

With this list in hand another thought arose, "Wouldn't readers of this book like to know more about these forty-three companies?" This resulted in a request being sent to each of the companies, asking for a statement which would give a brief account of the company's history, a list of its plastics materials, a list of its trade names, and a statement of its sales and profits for the last five years. As a result forty-two statements have been received and appear in this chapter. Most of these are complete and they furnish some interesting statistical material as noted in Chapter 1.

THE CARMAN LIST OF THE 43 MOST IMPORTANT PLASTICS MATERIALS PRODUCERS
IN THE UNITED STATES

American Cyanamid Company
Plastics & Resins Division
30 Rockefeller Plaza
New York 20, N. Y.

American Viscose Corporation
1617 Pennsylvania Boulevard
Philadelphia 3, Pa.

Archer-Daniels-Midland Company
600 Roanoke Building
Minneapolis 2, Minn.

Bakelite Company
Div. of Union Carbide Corporation
30 East 42nd Street
New York, N. Y.

Barrett Division
Allied Chemical & Dye Corporation
40 Rector Street
New York 6, N. Y.

The Borden Company
Chemical Division
350 Madison Avenue
New York 17, N. Y.

Brea Chemicals, Inc.
714 West Olympic Boulevard
Los Angeles, Calif.

Catalin Corporation of America
1 Park Avenue
New York, N. Y.

Celanese Corporation of America
290 Ferry Street
Newark 5, N. J.

Ciba Co., Inc.
627 Greenwich Street
New York 14, N. Y.

Diamond Alkali Company
300 Union Commerce Building
Cleveland 14, Ohio

The Dow Chemical Company
Midland, Mich.

E. I. du Pont de Nemours & Co., Inc.
Polychemicals Department
Wilmington 98, Del.

Durez Plastics Division
Hooker Electrochemical Company
Walck Road
North Tonawanda, N. Y.

Eastman Chemical Products, Inc.
Kingsport, Tenn.

Escambia Chemical Corporation
70 Memorial Drive
Cambridge 42, Mass.

Firestone Plastics Company
P.O. Box 690
Pottstown, Pa.

Foster-Grant Company
289 Main Street North
Leominster, Mass.

General Electric Company
Chemical & Metallurgical Division
Pittsfield, Mass.

The General Tire & Rubber Company
1708 Englewood Avenue
Akron 9, Ohio

B. F. Goodrich Chemical Company
324 Rose Building
Cleveland 15, Ohio

The Goodyear Tire & Rubber Co., Inc.
1144 East Market Street
Akron 16, Ohio

W. R. Grace & Company
Polymer Chemicals Division
3 Hanover Square
New York 5, N. Y.

Hercules Powder Company
Delaware Trust Building
Wilmington, Del.

Interchemical Corporation
67 West 44th Street
New York 36, N. Y.

The M. W. Kellogg Company
Foot of Danforth Avenue
Jersey City 3, N. J.

Koppers Company, Inc.
Koppers Building
Pittsburgh 19, Pa.

Loven Chemical of California
244 South Pine Street
Newhall, Calif.

The Marblette Corporation
37-21 30th Street
Long Island City 1, N. Y.

Marbon Chemical Division
Borg-Warner Corporation
1926 West 10th Avenue
Gary, Ind.

Mobay Chemical Company
1900 South Second Street
St. Louis 4, Mo.

Monsanto Chemical Company
Plastics Division
Springfield 2, Mass.

Naugatuck Chemical
Division of United States Rubber Co.
Elm Street
Naugatuck, Conn.

Nixon Nitration Works
Nixon, N. J.

Ohio-Apex, Inc.
Division of Food Machinery Corp.
Nitro, W. Va.

Phillips Chemical Company
Bartlesville, Okla.

Pitt-Consol Chemical Company
191 Doremus Avenue
Newark 5, N. J.

Reichhold Chemicals, Inc.
525 North Broadway
White Plains, N. Y.

Rohm & Haas Company
222 West Washington Square
Philadelphia 5, Pa.

Rubber Corporation of America
274 Ten Eyck Street
Brooklyn 6, N. Y.

Shell Chemical Corporation
50 West 50th Street
New York, N. Y.

Spencer Chemical Company
610 Dwight Building
Kansas City 6, Mo.

U.S. Industrial Chemicals Company
Div. National Distillers Products Corp.
99 Park Avenue
New York 16, N. Y.

## AMERICAN CYANAMID COMPANY

*President:* K. C. Towe                                    *Home Office:* New York, N. Y.

American Cyanamid Company has grown from a one-product, one-plant corporation in 1907 to an organization with over 27,000 employees, more than 40 plants throughout the world and thousands of products for every industry that uses chemicals.

It has grown in three major steps: (1) early growth through product diversification based on calcium cyanamide 1907-1922; (2) rapid diversification through acquisitions and expansion 1922-1952; and (3) reorientation and consolidation based on research. This has brought Cyanamid to the point where it now has 12 divisions and two wholly-owned subsidiaries. The divisions are: Engineering and Construction, Farm and Home, Fibers, Fine Chemicals, Industrial Chemicals, Lederle Laboratories, Organic Chemicals, Phosphates and Nitrogen Products, Pigments, Plastics and Resins, Research, and Surgical Products. The subsidiaries are the Formica Corporation and North American Cyanamid Ltd.

*Principal Plastics Products:*

Alkyd resins
Melamines
Polymethylstyrenes
Ureas

*Plastics Trade Names:*

Beetle and Cymel—thermosetting molding materials
Cymac—thermoplastic molding material
Cycopol and Rezyl—coating resins
Laminac—polyester resin used with fibrous glass to make reinforced plastic
Urac and Melurac—resins for adhesives

*Operations:*

| Year | Net Sales | Net Profit |
|------|-----------|------------|
| 1951 | $388,717,000 | $34,778,000 |
| 1952 | 368,408,000 | 26,612,000 |
| 1953 | 380,393,000 | 27,473,000 |
| 1954 | 397,595,000 | 27,050,000 |
| 1955 | 451,088,000 | 38,714,000 |
| 1956 | 500,651,000 | 44,247,000 |

Percentage of plastic sales to total sales:

| | |
|------|------|
| 1950 | 11% |
| 1955 | 10% |
| 1956 | 9% (Estimated figure) |

## AMERICAN VISCOSE CORPORATION

*Chairman of Board and President:* Frank H. Reichel     *Home Office:* Philadelphia, Pa.
*Vice President:* Harry L. Dalton

The American Viscose Corporation was founded in 1910 and now has eight producing plants. It also has a 50% interest in the Chemstrand Corporation, the other 50% being held by Monsanto. The Chemstrand Corporation produces nylon and acrylics. The American Viscose Corporation produces urea-formaldehyde compounds under a wholly-owned subsidiary, Sylvan Plastics, Inc., operated by the Film Division.

The general sales office is in Philadelphia, and the plant is in Fredericksburg, Va.

*Plastics Products:*
Urea-formaldehyde molding compounds
Nylon
Acrylics

*Plastics Trade Names:*
Sylplast—urea-formaldehyde molding compounds used for such items as buttons, closures, and wiring devices
Acrilan—methyl methacrylate

*Operations:*
Plastic sales are a minor part of the Film Division's total activities. No percentage figures are available for publication.

## ARCHER-DANIELS-MIDLAND COMPANY

*President:* Thomas L. Daniels            *Home Office:* Minneapolis, Minn.
*Mgr. Vinyl Plasticizer Dept.:* Robert S. Mathews
*Mgr. Resin & Plastics Div.:* Walter G. Andrews

Starting in 1902 as a processor of agricultural crops, Archer-Daniels-Midland Company has grown amazingly in that field. It has recently entered the plastics field in an ambitious way.

Since marketing its first two Admex vinyl plasticizers in 1953, ADM has kept pace with this mushrooming industry by adding five or more Admex products to its line. Purchase of the Resin Division of U.S. Industrial Chemicals in 1954 placed ADM in the polyester field. Today its Aropol polyester line consists of 13 products. The Company's alkyd resin line, which stems back to 1950, was expanded substantially in 1956 with the purchase of a group of General Electric Company resins which ADM now markets under its Aroplaz trade name.

*Products for the Plastics Industry:*

Adhesives—phenolics
Coating resins—alkyds, copolymers, polyester, maleic ester gums, phenolic resins
Molding materials—polyesters

*Plastics Trade Names:*

Arofene—pure phenolics
Aroplaz—alkyd resins, vinyl plasticizers
Aropol—polyester resins

*Operations:*

| Year | Net Sales* | Net Profit |
|------|-----------|------------|
| 1952-53 | $219,696,649 | $3,853,319 |
| 1953-54 | 207,731,719 | 5,013,390 |
| 1954-55 | 221,024,386 | 5,749,888 |
| 1955-56 | 210,947,884 | 5,871,506 |

\* Grain Division transactions not included.

Chemicals represent approximately 19 per cent of total sales. It is estimated that plastics represent about 9 per cent of total sales.

## BAKELITE COMPANY

### Division of Union Carbide Corporation

*President, Union Carbide:* M. G. Dial                *Home Office:* New York, N. Y.
*President, Bakelite:* G. C. Miller

The corporation was formed in November 1917 and has expanded rapidly since then. It now has the following principal divisions in the plastics field: Bakelite Company, Silicones Division, and Visking Company. Other subsidiaries operate in Canada.

*Plastics Products:*

Bonding materials—pulverized and spray-dried phenolic resins; oil- and rosin-modified phenolic resins and solutions; polystyrene emulsions; cresol resins and solutions; resorcinol resins and solutions; urea, epoxy, and vinyl resins; chlorinated naphthalenes and resins.

Calendering materials—vinyl chloride and copolymer resins and compounds; polystyrene resins and compounds (including copolymers); polyethylene; chlorinated naphthalenes.

Extrusion materials—polyethylene resins and compounds; rigid and plasticized vinyl chloride and copolymer resins and compounds; fluorothene resins and compounds; polystyrene; polystyrene rubber compounds; styrene-acrylonitrile compounds; chlorinated naphthalenes and resins.

Film and sheeting materials—vinyl chloride and copolymer plasticized calendered film and sheeting; cast film; calendered rigid sheeting; planished elastomeric sheets; planished rigid sheets.

Flexible packaging materials—vinyl copolymer cast film and coated paper; polyethylene resins and compounds; polyethylene coated paper.

Laminating materials—phenolic, cresol, polyester, urea, epoxy, and silicone resins, chlorinated naphthalenes and resins.

Molding materials—rigid and plasticized vinyl chloride and copolymer resins and compounds; phenolic compounds; polystyrene rubber compounds; styrene-acrylonitrile compounds; fluorothene resins and compounds; polyethylene resins and compounds; silicone compounds.

Surface-coating materials—vinyl chloride and copolymer resins; vinyl acetate resins; solutions, and latices; vinyl butyral resins; vinyl ether resins; polyethylene resins and compounds; polystyrene latices; phenolic resins and solutions; modified phenolic resins and solutions; epoxy resins; chlorinated naphthalenes and compounds.

*Plastics Trade Names:*

Bakelite—resins and plastics
Krene—plastic products
Vinylite—resins and plastics
Visking—plastic products
Visqueen—plastic film

*Operations:*

| Year | Total Sales | Plastics | Net Profit |
|---|---|---|---|
| 1951 | $   928,000,000 | $149,000,000 | $103,800,000 |
| 1952 | 957,000,000 | 155,000,000 | 98,300,000 |
| 1953 | 1,026,000,000 | 173,000,000 | 102,700,000 |
| 1954 | 924,000,000 | 180,000,000 | 89,700,000 |
| 1955* | 1,231,000,000 | 262,000,000 | 145,800,000 |
| 1956** | 1,325,000,000 | 267,000,000 | 146,200,000 |

* Operations of the Visking Corporation (acquired by Union Carbide on December 31, 1956) are combined with the exception of intercompany sales, which have been eliminated.
** Operations of The Visking Corporation are consolidated.

Allied Chemical & Dye Corporation

*President:* Thomas J. Kinsella                    *Home Office:* New York, N. Y.
*Director, Plastics & Resins Sales:* H. W. DeVore

Founded in 1854, Barrett Division owns and operates 58 plants and 3 research laboratories in the United States. Barrett is one of the seven divisions of Allied Chemical & Dye Corporation. Other divisions include: General Chemical, International, National Aniline, Nitrogen, Semet-Solvay, and Solvay Process.

Barrett Division entered the plastics field in 1948 with phenolic varnishes. This was followed by plant expansions and the purchase of Synvar Southern in 1952, the former Plaskon Division of Libbey-Owens-Ford Glass Company in 1953, and Industrial Resins Corporation in 1956.

The Barrett Division manufactures and sells hundreds of plastic, resin, coal tar, chemical, roofing, and paving products.

*Plastic and Resin Products:*

Molding compounds—urea, melamine, nylon, alkyd

Coating resins—alkyds, ureas, melamines, silicone-alkyds, modified phenolics, maleics, ester gums, styrenated-alkyds

Industrial resins—polyester resins for laminates, pre-mix and poly-urethane foams, adhesives, paper treating resins, phenolic laminating varnishes, foundry resins, friction resins, phenolic molding resins, phenolic bonding resins

Lubricants—polyethylene mold release

*Plastics Trade Names:*

Plaskon—plastics and resins
Cumar—paracoumarone-indene resin
A-C—polyethylene lubricants

Operations not supplied.

## THE BORDEN COMPANY

*President:* H. W. Comfort                    *Home Office:* New York, N. Y.
*Chemical Div. President:* A. R. Marusi

The Borden Company has completed a hundred years of operation and has plants in all but two of the United States. The Chemical Division was organized in 1948, using as nucleus the former Casein Company of America (acquired in 1929) and Durite Plastics, Inc. (acquired in 1947). The following companies were added to the Chemical Division during the period 1953-1956, inclusive:

American Polymer Corp.                     American Monomer Corp.
Monomer-Polymer, Inc.                      Dajac Laboratories
American Resinous Chemicals Corp.          Reslac Chemicals, Inc.
Pioneer Latex and Chemical Co.             Resin Industries, Inc.
Grant Chemical Co.                         Resinite Sales Corp.

The Chemical Division has a central research laboratory at Philadelphia, Pa., and development laboratories at Peabody, Leominster (2), Bainbridge, Middlesex, Philadelphia, Chicago, Seattle, and Santa Barbara. Foreign affiliates are located in Argentine, Australia, Brazil, Canada, Colombia, England, France, Mexico, Philippine Islands, Spain, Sweden.

*Plastic Products of the Chemical Division are:*
Adhesives—acrylic, epoxy, phenolic, polyvinyl acetate, resorcinol, urea
Binders—phenolic, thermoplastic resin polymers and copolymers, urea
Esters—acrylic, allyl, fumaric, vinyl
Extruded products—polyvinyl chloride and copolymers
Molding powders—acrylic, phenolic
Plastisols—thermoplastic resins
Resins, thermoplastic—acrylic; acrylonitrile; butadiene copolymer; styrene and
    copolymers; vinyl acetate, vinyl alcohol, vinyl chloride and copolymers;
    vinylidene copolymers
Resins, thermosetting—epoxy, phenol formaldehyde, phenol furfural, resorcinol,
    urea

*Plastics Trade Names:*

Acrylon—synthetic rubber
Cascamite—synthetic thermosetting
    resin plastic adhesive
Cascolac—casein for inks; casein
    solutions for coating paper
Cascoloid—casein base binder,
    emulsifier, stabilizer, thickener
Cascophen—resin glues, thermosetting
Casco resin—thermosetting resins,
    adhesives
Compregnite—liquid phenol formal-
    dehyde solution
Durite—synthetic resins; phenolic
    molding powders

Epiphen—epoxide resins for glue
Lemac—polyvinyl acetate, solid form
Lemol—polyvinyl alcohol
Methac—methanol-methyl acetate
    mixture
MPL—acrylic monomer
Placcolock—vinyl tile adhesive
Protovac—solubulized caseins
Polyco—resin emulsions
Reslac—resinous lacquers
Stixall—casein glue
Thor—foundry core binders
Vinylac—organic tackifiers for poly-
    vinyl chloride emulsions

*Operations:*

| Year | Net Sales | Net Profit |
|------|-----------|------------|
| 1951 | $722,770,000 | $18,080,000 |
| 1952 | 768,019,000 | 17,667,000 |
| 1953 | 792,381,000 | 20,264,000 |
| 1954 | 776,838,000 | 22,724,000 |
| 1955 | 810,126,000 | 21,653,000 |

Plastics sales represent approximately 5% of the total sales.

## BREA CHEMICALS, INC.

### Subsidiary of Union Oil Company of California

*President:* Homer Reed                    *Home Office:* 714 West Olympic Blvd.
                                                          Los Angeles, Calif.


Brea Chemicals has postponed its plans to manufacture and market high-density polyethylene and so its statement is not included in this chapter.


## CATALIN CORPORATION OF AMERICA

*President:* Harry Krehbiel                    *Home Office:* New York, N. Y.


Incorporated in 1929, Catalin owns and operates three plants located at Fords, N. J.; Calumet City, Ill.; and Thomasville, N. C. Central Research Laboratories are at Fords, N. J.

*Plastics Products:*
    Urea, phenolic, cresylic, resorcinol and melamine resins for applications such as:
        Wood adhesives—for plywood, edge gluing, structural laminates, wood waste utilization
        Textile finishing resins—for crease resistance
        Laminating resins—for decorative and industrial laminates
        Bonding resins—for foundry cores and shell molding, glass and rock wool insulation, grinding wheels and sandpaper, cork, brake linings and clutch facings
        Impregnating resins—for filter and paper specialties

*Plastic Molding and Extrusion Compounds:*
    Polyethylene
    Polystyrene
    Nylon

*Plastics Trade Names:*
    Catalin Bonding Resins
    Catalin Impregnating Resins
    Catalin Laminating Resins
    Catalin Nylon
    Catalin Polyethylene
    Catalin Styrene
    Catalin Textile Finishing Resins
    Catalin Wood Adhesives

*Operations:*

| Year | Net Sales | Net Income |
|------|-----------|------------|
| 1951 | $13,411,844 | $448,898 |
| 1952 | 14,178,350 | 225,927 |
| 1953 | 15,396,924 | 116,562 |
| 1954 | 15,845,066 | 61,308 |
| 1955 | 20,492,951 | 593,580 |

CELANESE CORPORATION OP AMERICA

*President:* Harold Blancke

*Home Office:* 180 Madison Avenue
New York 16, N. Y.
*Plastics Div.:* 290 Ferry Street
Newark 5, N. J.

Incorporated in 1918, Celanese Corporation of America is a large producer of textiles, plastics, and chemicals. The principal business of the corporation is the manufacture and sale of cellulose acetate and rayon yarns and variations. Celanese is the world's largest producer of acetate yarns.

The Celanese Chemical Division, formed originally as a supplier of chemicals for other divisions of the company, has broadened its product base to develop external markets and achieve greater autonomy.

In December 1941, Celluloid Corporation, a pioneer in the plastics industry, merged with the company and became the Celanese Plastics Division. In 1948, Celanese halted production of cellulose nitrate, the principal plastic produced by Celluloid Corporation, because of its flammable characteristics and concentrated on making and marketing cellulose acetate. Since then, Celanese has expanded and diversified its plastics operation considerably.

*Plastics:*

Cellulose acetate film
Cellulose acetate sheeting
Celluose acetate molding compounds
Cellulose propionate molding compounds
Polyester resins
Polyethylene film
Polyolefin and polyolefin resins
Polyvinyl acetate emulsions

*Plastic Trade Names:*

Lumarith—cellulose acetate
Fortiflex—polyolefin resin
Forticel—cellulose propionate
Marco Resins—polyester resins
Marcothix—thixotropic liquid polyester resin

*Operations:*

These were not furnished.

Percentage of Plastics Sales to Total Sales: This was said to be small.

## CIBA COMPANY, INC.

*President:* Dr. H. B. Marshall                    *Home Office:* New York, N. Y.
*Executive Vice President:* Keith R. J. Horner

Ciba Limited, parent firm of Ciba Company, Inc., was founded at Basle, Switzerland, in 1884. At present the organization comprises 38 production and sales companies in Europe, North and South America, Asia, and Australia. In addition it has a controlling interest in three manufacturing companies located in North America, England, and Italy. A fourth plant in which Ciba has an interest is under construction in Brazil. Ciba's main fields of activities are dyestuffs, pharmaceuticals, textile auxiliary products, plastics, and chemicals for pest control.

In the United States Ciba's plastics interests are looked after by the Ciba Company, Inc. in New York, which has at its disposal a manufacturing installation of its own, the Ciba Products Corporation in Kimberton, Pa. This plant also has a research department.

*Products of the Plastics Department:*
   Adhesives—epoxy, melamine, urea, phenolic, resorcinol, polyvinyl
   Casting Resins—epoxy
   Coating Resins—epoxy, melamine, urea
   Laminating Resins—epoxy, melamine, aniline
   Molding Materials—urea, melamine, epoxy

*Plastic Trade Names:*
   Araldite—epoxy
   Cibanite—aniline-formaldehyde
   Melocol—polyamide-formaldehyde glue
   Melopas—polyamide-formaldehyde

*Operations:*
   Not given.

Plastics sales in United States represent more than 10% of Ciba's world sales, which amounted to some $183 million in 1955.

## DIAMOND ALKALI COMPANY

*President:* John A. Sargent                    *Home Office:* Cleveland, Ohio
*Vice Pres. & Gen. Mgr. Plastics Division:* A. L. Geisinger

Diamond Alkali Co. was founded in 1912 and now operates 14 plants in the United States producing a wide range of inorganic and organic chemicals.

In 1953, as part of a broad product diversification program, Diamond constructed a plant to produce vinyl chloride monomer and polymers at the site of its largest and then, newest, electrolytic caustic-chlorine producing facility in Deer Park, Tex.

*Products of the Plastic Division:*
Diamond PVC-50—for film, sheeting, profile extrusions and electrical applications
Diamond PVC-45—for heavy sheeting, molding, and non-electrical extrusions
Diamond Compound R4—for Type 1, chemical resistant, rigid PVC moldings and extrusions

*Operations:*

| Year | Net Sales | Net Profit |
|------|-----------|------------|
| 1951 | $ 80,749,000 | $ 6,674,000 |
| 1952 | 76,674,000 | 5,462,000 |
| 1953 | 86,734,000 | 5,939,000 |
| 1954 | 93,506,000 | 5,529,000 |
| 1955 | 110,292,000 | 8,443,000 |
| 1956 | 121,261,571 | 10,380,141 |

Plastics sales are currently less than 10 per cent of total sales.

## THE DOW CHEMICAL COMPANY

*President:* Dr. Leland I. Doan  *Home Office:* Midland, Mich.
*Executive Vice President:* Dr. Mark E. Putnam

The Dow Chemical Company was established in 1897 at Midland, Mich., under the leadership of Herbert H. Dow. The company has 14 manufacturing operations in 9 states and is constructing two new operations in two other states.

The company's subsidiaries include: Bay Pipe Line Corporation; Bay Refining Corporation; Cliffs Dow Chemical Company; Dow Chemical of Canada, Limited; Dowell Incorporated; Dow Chemical Inter-American Limited; Dow Chemical International Limited; LaDominica, S.A. de C.V.; Nederlandsche Dow Maatschappij N.V.; United Oilwell Service, S.A.

Associated companies in the United States are Dow Corning Corporation, Ethyl-Dow Chemical Company and The Saran Yarns Company. Foreign associated companies are located in Japan, Wales, India and Mexico.

The Dow Plastics Department has five manufacturing operations in as many states.

*Products of the Plastics Department:*

Molding materials—Dow polyvinyl chloride; ethocel plastic; polyethylene; saran fabricated products; saran molding materials

Coating materials—Dow 276 and 622 resins; Dow PS resins; ethocel bulk; saran resins; saran and vinyl latexes; styrene-butadiene latexes; styrene latex

Sheeting and film—ethocel sheeting; saran wrap-consumer products; saran wrap-industrial products

*Trade Names of Plastics Products:*

Ethocel—ethyl cellulose
Saraloy—an elastomeric copolymer based on vinylidene chloride
Saran Wrap—transparent plastic film
Styrex—styrene-acrylonitrile copolymer
Styrofoam—plastic foam
Styron—polystyrene plastic

*Operations:*

| Year | Net Sales | Net Profit |
|------|-----------|------------|
| 1951 | $339,600,000 | $40,500,000 |
| 1952 | 407,200,000 | 35,800,000 |
| 1953 | 430,400,000 | 35,900,000 |
| 1954 | 428,300,000 | 33,400,000 |
| 1955 | 470,700,000 | 37,400,000 |
| 1956 | 565,300,000 | 59,700,000 |

Plastics sales represented approximately 32 per cent of total Dow sales in the fiscal year ended May 31, 1956.

## E. I. du PONT de NEMOURS AND COMPANY, INC.

*President:* Crawford H. Greenewalt                *Home Office:* Wilmington, Del.
*Gen. Mgr. Polychemicals Dept.:* R. L. Hershey

Organized in 1802 as a manufacturer of black powder, E. I. du Pont de Nemours & Company, Inc. today ranks as the largest and most diversified of all the chemical producers. The company has grown from a single powder mill to an organization with plants in many states, with operations covering virtually the entire scope of the chemical industry. Du Pont is one of the largest producers of plastics. A wide range of solvents, catalysts, intermediates, plasticizers, adhesives, and other compounds is produced for the plastics industry. A smaller number of plastics ingredients is produced for use within the company itself. An outstanding material of du Pont is nylon, which has unusual properties as a plastic as well as a fiber. In 1935 du Pont began commercial production of urea.

*Principal Plastics Products:*

Acrylic resin—methacrylate polymers and molding powders
Cellulose acetate—semi-rigid sheets
Cellulose nitrate—semi-rigid sheets
Nylon monofilaments, molding powder and resins
Polyethylene resins—cube solids
Polyvinyl butyral resin—flake and sheeting
Tetrafluoroethylene resin

*Plastic Trade Names:*

Alathon—polyethylene resins
Butacite—polyvinyl butyral resin
Lucite—acrylic resin
Plastacele—cellulose acetate plastic
Pyralin—cellulose nitrate plastic
Rulan—flame-retardant plastic
Teflon—tetrafluoroethylene resin
Tynex—nylon filament
Zytel—nylon resin

*Operations:* (Company totals)

| Year | Net Sales | Net Profit |
|------|-----------|------------|
| 1951 | $1,531,100,000 | $220,700,000 |
| 1952 | 1,602,200,000 | 224,100,000 |
| 1953 | 1,749,600,000 | 235,600,000 |
| 1954 | 1,687,600,000 | 344,400,000 |
| 1955 | 1,909,200,000 | 431,600,000 |

## DUREZ PLASTICS DIVISION
### Hooker Electrochemical Company

*President:* Bjarne Klaussen
*Gen. Sales Mgr. Durez Plastics Div.:* Alfred W. Hanmer, Jr.

*Durez Plastics Div.:* No. Tonawanda, N. Y.
*Home Office:* Niagara Falls, N. Y.

Founded in 1903 as The Development and Funding Company, Hooker Electrochemical Company operates plants in seven localities in the United States and a Durez Plastics Division laboratory at LeRoy, N. Y. Also, Hooker Chemicals Limited, Canadian subsidiary, begins plant operation in 1957. Hooker manufactures more than 100 organic and inorganic chemicals, and several hundred synthetic resins and molding compounds.

Hooker's position in the plastics industry was relatively minor until Durez Plastics and Chemicals, Inc. was acquired in 1955. The leading producer of phenolic resins and phenolic molding compounds, Durez had been founded in 1921. Acquisition of Niagara Alkali Co., also in 1955, brought the plastics additive Niagathal, tetrachlorophthalic anhydride. Acquisition of Oldbury Electro-Chemical Co. in 1956 brought phosphorus oxychloride and trichloride, both used in the manufacture of phosphorus plasticizers, and alkyl acid phosphates-catalysts in resin curing and stabilizers for vinyl plastics.

Plants manufacturing plastic products exclusively are located at North Tonawanda, N. Y., and Kenton, Ohio. Chemical products for the plastics industry are made entirely at the Niagara Falls headquarters plants.

*Plastics, and Chemicals used in Plastics:*

Molding compounds—phenolic, polyester, diallylphthalate
Synthetic resins—phenolic, polyester
Plasticizer—MPS-500—a stabilized ester of a fatty acid
Epoxy hardening agent—HET anhydride (chlorendic anhydride)
Intermediates for phenolic manufacture—phenol and formaldehyde
Intermediate for polyester manufacture—HET acid (chlorendic acid)
Intermediates for plasticizer manufacture—phosphorus oxychloride, phosphorus trichloride
Lacquer—Hetrolac, a polyester
Catalysts in resin curing—alkyl acid phosphates
Stabilizers for vinyl plastics—alkyl acid phosphates
Additive—tetrachlorophthalic anhydride

*Plastics Trade Names:*

Durez—phenolic resins, and phenolic, diallylphthalate, and polyester molding compounds
Hetron—polyester resins
Hetrolac—polyester lacquer
MPS-500—stabilized chlorinated ester of a fatty acid, a plasticizer

*Operations of Consolidated Companies:*

| Year | Net Sales | Net Profit |
|------|-----------|------------|
| 1951 | $ 81,963,000 | $ 7,970,000 |
| 1952 | 72,998,000 | 6,084,000 |
| 1953 | 85,115,000 | 7,551,000 |
| 1954 | 85,898,000 | 8,768,000 |
| 1955 | 104,275,000 | 11,377,000 |
| 1956 | 109,980,000 | 11,497,000 |

Plastics sales were approximately one quarter of total sales for fiscal 1956.

## EASTMAN CHEMICAL PRODUCTS, INC.

*President:* W. S. Vaughn
*Vice President Plastics Div.:* S.E. Palmer

*Home Office:* Kingsport, Tenn.
*Plastics Div.:* Kingsport, Tenn.

Organized in 1952 to market all the products of Tennessee Eastman Company, Kingsport, Tenn., and Texas Eastman Company, Longview, Tex., both divisions of Eastman Kodak Company. Tennessee Eastman produces plastics, synthetic fibers, dyes, and industrial chemicals including cellulose esters, acids and anhydrides, solvents, plasticizers, amines, phenols, petroleum additives, and antioxidants. Texas Eastman produces primarily raw material for Tennessee Eastman and for the trade including alcohols, aldehydes, and polyethylene.

*Products of Plastics Division:*

Molding materials—cellulose acetate, cellulose acetate butyrate, polyethylene

*Plastic Trade Names:*

Tenite Acetate—cellulose acetate molding and extrusion composition
Tenite Butyrate—cellulose acetate butyrate molding and extrusion composition
Tenite Polyethylene—polyethylene molding and extrusion composition

*Operations:\**

| Year | Net Sales | Net Profit |
|------|-----------|------------|
| 1951 | $542,284,510 | $49,025,906 |
| 1952 | 575,022,750 | 45,803,851 |
| 1953 | 633,668,918 | 50,171,153 |
| 1954 | 633,457,838 | 69,821,719 |
| 1955 | 714,443,836 | 85,600,330 |

\* Figures shown are for Eastman Kodak Company and its United States subsidiaries. As a wholly owned subsidiary of Eastman Kodak Company, Eastman Chemical Products, Inc., does not publish separate financial statements. Sales of cellulose products, plastics and acetate film, however, are shown on a recent company report to total 29 per cent of total sales.

## ESCAMBIA CHEMICAL CORPORATION

*President:* R. U. Haslanger                    *Home Office:* New York, N. Y.

Escambia Chemical Corporation was organized in October, 1954, by United Gas Corporation, Shreveport, La.; Electric Bond and Share Company, N. Y., and National Research Corporation, Cambridge, Mass. In December, 1955, the first Escambia unit began production. This plant, which is located in Pensacola, Fla., produces anhydrous ammonia, nitric acid, ammonium nitrate (trade name Ammo-Nite) and nitrogen fertilizer solutions (trade name Bay-Sol). During 1956, a 30-million pound polyvinyl chloride resins plant was constructed in the same area and began commercial production of polyvinyl chloride resins in January, 1957. In addition to these units at the Pensacola, Fla. site, a large methanol plant is being constructed and will be in operation by the end of 1957. The research and technical service laboratories are in Newton Highlands, Mass.

*Principal Plastic Product:*
Polyvinyl chloride resins

*Plastics Trade Names:*
Escambia PVC 1250—high molecular weight PVC for extrusion of shapes and profiles and for calendered film
Escambia PVC 1225—intermediate molecular weight PVC for supported and unsupported sheeting
Escambia PVC 1200—lowest molecular weight in this series, designed for flexible and rigid sheeting.
Commercial production of vinyls started early in 1957.

## FIRESTONE PLASTICS COMPANY

### Division of The Firestone Tire & Rubber Company

*President:* Roger S. Firestone                    *Home Office:* Pottstown, Pa.

Firestone established its plastics division in 1937 with development work in the molding of plastics. Early development work led to extrusion of a vinylidene chloride monofilament named Velon suitable for woven fabrics. In 1946, facilities for mixing, milling, and calendering vinyl resins were installed at the Firestone plant in Pottstown, Pa., to produce vinyl film, semirigid and rigid sheeting—also called Velon. Meanwhile, the Company had begun the development of vinyl resins which it named Exon. In 1947, the Firestone Plastics Company was organized and a program of expansion was mapped out. That year, a resin plant was started at Pottstown and resin production was begun in it. Since that time, production facilities have been continuously expanded to meet demands for Exon (vinyl) resins, latices for rubber-base paints, and various types of synthetic rubber and latex. The Firestone Plastics Company has two sales divisions: the Chemical Sales Division which handles the sale of Exon vinyl resins and the Velon Products Division which handles the sale of Velon film, sheeting, and yarn. Divisional research laboratories are located in Pottstown.

*Plastics Products:*
   Vinyl molding, solution, plastisol, calendering, and extrusion resins
   Vinyl electrical grade compounds
   Vinyl film and sheeting (flexible, semirigid, rigid)
   Styrene-butadiene paint latex
   Polyethylene film

*Plastics Trade Names:*
   Butaprene—styrene-butadiene paint latices
   Exon—vinyl resins
   Velon—vinyl film, sheeting and vinylidene chloride monofilaments

## FOSTER GRANT COMPANY, INC.

*President:* Joseph C. Foster                    *Home Office:* Leominster, Mass.

Founded in 1919, Foster Grant owns and operates polymerization and molding plants in Leominster, Mass. and Manchester, N. H.; a monomer plant in Baton Rouge, La.; research laboratories and pilot plants in all locations; an affiliate company, Lamex Chemical Corporation.

*Principal Products:*

Raw materials—styrene monomer
Molding materials—polystyrene, polycaprolactam (Nylon 6)
Sheeting and film—modified styrene, polyethylene, nylon
Finished plastic products—sunglasses, combs, housewares, blow-molded bottles and containers for industry
Custom molded products—blow-molded bottles, containers, injection molded displays, packaging, housewares, hair accessories

*Plastic Trade Names:*

Fostarene—polystyrene
Fosta—sunglasses, combs, housewares
Grantly—sunglasses
Precision Ware—housewares

## GENERAL ELECTRIC COMPANY

*President:* Ralph J. Cordiner
*Vice Pres. & Gen. Mgr. Chemical & Metallurgical Div.:* Robert L. Gibson

*Home Office:* Schenectady, N. Y.
*Chemical & Metallurgical Div.:* Pittsfield, Mass.

General Electric Company, a large manufacturer of electrical equipment, grew out of the work of Thomas A. Edison and other pioneers in the electrical field. Edison's patent for the incandescent lamp injected a basic chemical problem into the business of the Edison Electric Company. Born, thus, of the application of chemistry to an electrical problem, chemical and electrical research within General Electric have since the start gone hand in hand. From this beginning, the General Electric Company has grown into an organization of 158 plants, employing a total of some 280,000 people, working in 123 cities in 34 states, territories, and provinces of the United States and Canada.

The Chemical and Metallurgical Division has plants operating in Anaheim, Calif., Chelsea, Mass., Coshocton, Ohio; Detroit and Edmore, Mich., Pittsfield, Mass., Schenectady, N. Y., Springfield and Taunton, Mass., and Waterford, N. Y.

*Some Division Products:*

Phenolic molding compounds
Shell resins for foundry use
Coating resins
Irradiated polyethylene
Wire enamels
Insulating varnishes and compounds
Decorative and industrial laminates
Alkyd resin

Injection, compression and transfer
  molding
G-E mycalex
Fabricated silicone rubber
Silicone fluids
Silicone rubber gums and compounds
Silicone resins, emulsions and chemical
  specialties

*Trade Names:*

Alkanex—wire enamels
Glyptal—alkyd resin
Irrathene—irradiated polyethylene
Methylon—coating resins
Textolite—decorative and industrial laminates
Velvasil ⎫
Viscasil ⎭ —silicone fluids

*Operations:*

| Year | Net Sales | Net Profit |
|------|-----------|------------|
| 1951 | $2,319,300,000 | $138,100,000 |
| 1952 | 2,623,800,000 | 151,700,000 |
| 1953 | 3,128,100,000 | 165,700,000 |
| 1954 | 2,959,000,000 | 198,900,000 |
| 1955 | 3,095,400,000 | 200,900,000 |

## THE GENERAL TIRE & RUBBER COMPANY

*President:* William F. O'Neil
*Vice Pres. in Charge of Plastics:* John E. Powers

*Home Office:* Akron, Ohio

Founded in 1915, General Tire now employs more than 24,000 people. Seventeen domestic manufacturing plants turn out products, ranging from tires and other rubber goods through plastics, chemicals, and rockets.

Comprising the General Plastics Division, with headquarters in Akron, are: Textileather Division, Toledo, Ohio; Bolta Division, Lawrence, Mass.; Pennsylvania Division, Jeannette, Pa.; Respro Division, Cranston, R. I., and Textileather's subsidiaries, Atkin Manufacturing Company in Toledo and Forrest Process Company in New York City. Another phase of plastics production is carried on at General's Marion, Ind., plant. Also an integral part of General's plastics operations, is the Ashtabula, Ohio, chemical plant where polyvinyl chloride resins are manufactured both for consumption by the company's own plastics plants and for sale to other firms. General acquired Bolta Corporation and Textileather Corporation in 1954, making it the world's largest producer of vinyl film and sheeting. This position was further enhanced by the merger into the company of Respro, Inc., in 1955.

*Products of Plastics Division:*

Sheeting and film—vinyl chloride
Extrusion materials—vinyl chloride
Foam—polyurethane, vinyl chloride
Molding materials*—vinyl chloride, modified polystyrene, laminating polyester
Coating resins*—vinyl resins, styrene latices

* Produced and sold by The General Tire & Rubber Company Chemical Division.

*Principal Plastics Trade Names and Products:*

Bolta—plastic film, sheeting, moldable compounds, coated and laminated materials made from vinyl resins
Boltaflex—vinyl upholstery material, vinyl sheeting and film
Bolta-Floor—vinyl floor covering
Bolta-Wall—vinyl wall covering
Fashion—vinyl film and sheeting
Nygen-Tolex—vinyl coated nylon fabric
Polyfoam—polyurethane foam
Respro—adhesively integrated fibrous materials
Sy-Loy—plastics reinforced polyester fiberglass material
Textileather—pyroxylin leathercloth
Tolex—vinyl plastic leathercloth

*Operations:*

| Year | Net Sales | Net Profit |
|------|-----------|------------|
| 1951 | $170,771,522 | $7,016,640 |
| 1952 | 185,914,247 | 6,147,918 |
| 1953 | 205,371,098 | 6,275,158 |
| 1954 | 216,986,110 | 4,502,645 |
| 1955 | 295,731,096 | 9,704,731 |
| 1956* | 385,000,000 | — |

* Estimated sales, estimated profit not available.

Plastics sales represent approximately 22 per cent of 1955 net sales.

### B. F. GOODRICH CHEMICAL COMPANY

*President:* John R. Hoover                    *Home Office:* Cleveland, Ohio

The B. F. Goodrich Chemical Compay was formed as a separate division with its own officers in April, 1945, although it had been operating as a department of the B. F. Goodrich Company since early in 1941. There are currently seven producing plants located at Akron, Ohio; Avon Lake, Ohio; Niagara Falls, N. Y.; Louisville and Calvert City, Ky.; Kearney and Haledon, N. J. Another plant in Henry, Ill., is scheduled to be built. There are also four Associated Companies manufacturing chemicals, plastics, and rubber. They are located in England, Japan, Canada, and Brazil. The products being manufactured by the Chemical Company and its allied units include polyvinyl chloride resins and plastics, various synthetic rubbers, and many specialty chemicals.

*Plastic Products:*

General-purpose resins—polyvinyl chloride, modified polyvinyl chlorides, and copolymers of vinyl chloride and vinylidene chloride
Plastic compounds—polyvinyl chloride, both flexible and rigid types; copolymers of vinyl chloride and vinylidene chloride
Solution resins—polyvinyl chloride, modified
Paste resins—polyvinyl chloride for plastisols and organosols
Polyblend—a blend of polyvinyl chloride and nitrile rubber
Latex—polyvinyl chloride

*Plastics Trade Names:*

Geon—all the above resins and compounds, including the latices
Good-rite—plasticizers
Hycar—the nitrile rubber plasticizer

*Operations:**

| Year | Net Sales | Net Income |
|------|-----------|------------|
| 1950 | $550,000,000 | $34,900,000 |
| 1951 | 650,000,000 | 34,900,000 |
| 1952 | 625,000,000 | 32,500,000 |
| 1953 | 666,000,000 | 34,000,000 |
| 1954 | 630,000,000 | 38,000,000 |
| 1955 | 750,000,000 | 47,000,000 |
| 1956 | 725,000,000 | 46,000,000 |

* The figures listed above are rounded off to the nearest million, and they represent the sales and income for the entire B. F. Goodrich Company. As a matter of policy there is no publication of figures for any of the divisions of the parent company.

## GOODYEAR TIRE AND RUBBER COMPANY

*President:* E. J. Thomas                                      *Home Office:* Akron, Ohio
*General Manager Chemical Div.:* H. R. Thies

The Goodyear Tire & Rubber Company started operations in the rubber industry in 1898 in a little pioneer factory in Akron, Ohio, with an original investment of $13,500. Today, Goodyear is a world wide organization with 27 plants in the United States and subsidiaries in 23 foreign countries. The present investment in plants, tools, and inventory totals about $12,000 for each Goodyear employee. Goodyear is one of America's top 20 largest industrial operations in sales and ranks ninth in number of employees. Among American corporations in total assets, Goodyear stands 28th and its securities are on the preferred list of big investment companies and mutual trusts.

Research dates back to the very beginning of the company and is one of the key phases of Goodyear's far-reaching operations. The research and development organization numbers more than 1,200 scientists.

*Product Categories:*

Adhesives—general purpose, high temperature, contact
Coating resins—cyclized natural rubber, styrene copolymer
Plastic resins—vinyl, modified styrene
Synthetic latices—nitrile, styrene copolymer, polybutadiene, vinyl
Synthetic rubbers—nitrile, styrene copolymer
Reinforcing resins—styrene copolymer, modified styrene
Rubber chemicals—antioxidants, short-stopping agents, accelerators

*Trade Names:*

Chemigum Rubber—nitrile polymers
Chemigum Latex—nitrile latices
Pliobond Series—adhesives
Plioflex Rubber—styrene type polymers
Pliolite Latex—styrene copolymer latices
Pliolite S-5 Series—protective coating resins
Pliolite S-6 Series—reinforcing resins
Pliolite S-7—paper coating resin
Pliolite NR Series—cyclized rubber resins
Pliovic Latex—vinyl copolymer latex
Pliovic Series—vinyl resins
Plio-Tuf Series—modified styrene resins
Pliotac—adhesive
Wing-Stay S—antioxidant
Wing-Stop Series—short-stopping agents

*Operations:*

| Year | Net Sales | Net Profit |
|------|-----------|------------|
| 1951 | $1,101,141,392 | $36,628,296 |
| 1952 | 1,138,403,608 | 39,009,866 |
| 1953 | 1,210,508,783 | 49,323,167 |
| 1954 | 1,090,094,050 | 48,055,196 |
| 1955 | 1,372,176,139 | 59,665,845 |

## W. R. GRACE & COMPANY

Polymer Chemicals Division
  *President:* T. T. Miller
  *Vice President:* E. E. Winne

*Home Office:* Clifton, N. J.
*Main Plant:* Baton Rouge, La.

Dewey and Almy Chemical Company Division:
  *President:* G. W. Blackwood
  *Vice President:* W. L. Taggart, Jr.

*Home Office:* Cambridge, Mass.
*Main Plant:* Cambridge, Mass.

Founded in 1854 in Lima, Peru, Grace has six chemical operation divisions in the United States at 32 locations. The current chemical operations started with establishment of Grace Chemical in 1952 and the acquisition of Thurston Chemical in 1953. Grace merged with the Davison Chemical Corporation and with Dewey and Almy Chemical Company in 1954. In 1955 Polymer Chemicals Division and Grace Chemical Research and Development Company were formed. Cryovac Company Division was formed in 1956. The Dewey and Almy Overseas Company Division was formed in 1955 with offices and plants in Argentina, Australia, Brazil, England, France, Germany, and Italy. Polymer Chemicals Division is building a low-pressure, linear polyethylene plant in Baton Rouge, La., and an applications, customer and technical service laboratory at its general offices in Clifton, N. J. Polyethylene sales offices are being established throughout the United States.

*Products:*
  Polymer Chemicals Division:
    Polyethylene resins (high density)
    Polyethylene resins formulated for irradiation
  Dewey and Almy Chemical Company Division:
    Resins latices—butadiene-styrene, styrene-butadiene, polyvinyl acetates, and copolymers
    Solid resins—high styrene copolymers

*Plastic Trade Names:*
  Polymer Chemicals Division:
    Grex—polyethylene resins
  Dewey and Almy Chemical Company Division:
    Darex products—high styrene copolymers

*Operations:*

| Year | Net Sales | Net Profit |
|------|-----------|------------|
| 1951 | $294,425,000 | $26,837,000 |
| 1952 | 315,588,000 | 21,064,000 |
| 1953 | 330,980,000 | 31,715,000 |
| 1954 | 413,402,000 | 41,721,000 |
| 1955 | 427,066,000 | 50,155,000 |

Chemical sales represented approximately 34 per cent of total sales in 1955.

## HERCULES POWDER COMPANY

*President:* A. E. Forster                    *Home Office:* Wilmington, Del.

Incorporated in 1912, Hercules Powder Company owns and operates 25 plants in the United States, and has 26 sales offices. In 1956, the company further broadened its interest in plastics with the announcement that Hercules and Imperial Chemical Industries Limited of England, were forming a company known as Hawthorn Chemical Corporation, which will build and operate a new plant at Louisiana, Mo., for the production of methyl methacrylate, monomer, and polymer.

Hercules also will bring on stream the second quarter of 1957 a new multimillion dollar plant for the production of linear polyethylene.

In addition to extensive research facilities devoted to plastics at its Research Center near Wilmington, the company also has a plastics development laboratory at its Parlin, N. J., plant site.

*Products for the Plastics Industries:*

Acetone
Alpha-methylstyrene
Cellulose acetate
Ethyl cellulose
Nitrocellulose
Phenol
Molding powders—cellulose acetate, ethyl cellulose, high acetyl cellulose acetate, linear polyethylene, chlorine-containing polyether
Vinyl plasticizers

*Plastics Trade Names:*

Hercocel A—cellulose acetate molding powders
Hercocel E—ethyl cellulose molding powders
Hercocel W—high acetyl cellulose acetate molding powders
Hercoflex—liquid plasticizers for vinyl resins
Hi-fax—linear polyethylene molding powders
Penton—chlorine-containing polyether molding powders

*Operations:*

| Year | Net Sales | Net Income |
|------|-----------|------------|
| 1951 | $216,849,000 | $13,565,000 |
| 1952 | 181,517,000 | 11,218,000 |
| 1953 | 190,202,000 | 11,681,000 |
| 1954 | 157,548,000 | 14,140,000 |
| 1955 | 226,651,000 | 19,012,000 |

Approximately 8 per cent of sales are to plastics industries.

## INTERCHEMICAL CORPORATION

| | |
|---|---|
| *President:* Herbert B. Woodman | *Home Office:* New York, N. Y. |
| *President, Finishes Div.:* Charles W. Scott | *Finishes:* Newark, N. J. |
| *President, R-B-H Dispersions Div.:* Harold D. Craft | *R-B-H:* Bound Brook, N. J. |

Interchemical Corporation was organized in 1928 as a consolidation of three important printing ink companies. Through the development of products, and by acquisition, it has expanded into industrial finishes, textile colors, pigment dispersion, industrial adhesives, carbon paper and inked ribbon, coated fabric, and other chemical coatings activities. It has over a hundred factories, branches, and sales offices across the United States.

Interchemical's Finishes Division, with headquarters in Newark, N. J., has the largest volume of Interchemical sales in the plastics industry, while the R-B-H Dispersions Division has a position through the sale of pigment dispersions as color bases. Interchemical's central research laboratories are in New York.

*Products of the Finishes Division:*

IC Polyester Resins for molding, casting or laminating re-enforced plastics
Organosols and plastisols for application to metal, fabric or plastic film

*Products of the R-B-H Dispersions Division:*

Vinyl resin dry blends, nylon extrusion and molding compounds, polyethylene extrusion compounds, plastisols and organosols, and polystyrene compounds

*Plastics Trade Names:*

IC Polyester Resins—polyester resins
Polyprene—vinyl organosol finish
Protektol—protective strippable coating
Valtex—plastisol colors for print-embossing textiles
Vynafoam—expandable vinyl plastisol

*Operations:*

| Year | Net Sales | Net Profit |
|---|---|---|
| 1951 | $ 88,586,000 | $2,349,000 |
| 1952 | 88,188,000 | 2,283,000 |
| 1953 | 90,827,000 | 2,727,000 |
| 1954 | 89,803,000 | 3,770,000 |
| 1955 | 100,489,000 | 4,747,000 |
| 1956* | 110,000,000 | — |

* Estimated.

Sales of plastic materials are estimated to be about 4 per cent of total sales.

## M. W. KELLOGG COMPANY

*General Offices and Works:* Jersey City 3, N. J.
*New York Office:* 711 Third Avenue, New York 17, N. Y.

This company after first agreeing to include a statement in this chapter finally decided not to do so.

*The Principal Trade Names are:*
Kel-F—high polymer, trifluorochlorethylene
Kel-Flo—low polymer, trifluorochlorethylene

## KOPPERS COMPANY, INC.

*President:* Fred C. Foy                    *Home Office:* Pittsburgh, Pa.
*Vice Pres. & Gen. Mgr. Chemical Div.:* B. J. C. van der Hoeven

The origin of Koppers Company, Inc., goes back to 1907 when a group of Pittsburgh executives asked the H. Koppers Company of Essen, Germany, to come to this country and build a chemical recovery coke oven in Joliet, Ill. The H. Koppers Company maintained offices in Chicago until 1912 when a controlling interest in its American operations was purchased by a group of Pittsburghers, and headquarters of the company moved to Pittsburgh. Later the remaining interest of H. Koppers was purchased and the company has since been operated completely as an American concern. During World War II Koppers Engineering and Construction Division built a $70,000,000 styrene-butadiene plant at Kobuta, Pa., for the government and operated it for the nation's synthetic rubber program. Following the war, Koppers purchased the facilities at this plant and began producing polystyrene. Thus was formed Koppers Chemical Division, which now has the following plants for producing plastics or plastics materials: Kobuta, Pa., Berkeley Heights, N. J., and Port Arthur, Tex.

Currently Koppers is building a large plant at Woodbridge, N. J., to make Ziegler Process polyethylene and also has entered into an agreement with Brea Chemicals, chemical subsidiary of Union Oil Company of California, for a joint venture plant of the same kind on the West Coast.

*Plastic Products:*

Adhesives—resorcinol and resorcinol modified; polystyrene
Molding materials—polystyrene, polyethylene (regular and low pressure), expandable polystyrene
Coating resins—styrene and styrene-butadiene latices
Film—polyethylene

*Plastic Trade Names:*

Dylan—polyethylene
Super Dylan—low-pressure polyethylene
Dylene—polystyrene
Dylite—expandable polystyrene
Dylex—styrene-butadiene latices
Durethene—polyethylene film
Penacolite—resorcinol adhesives

*Operations:*

| Year | Net Sales | Net Profit |
|---|---|---|
| 1951 | $284,312,815 | $10,818,217 |
| 1952 | 319,303,903 | 8,612,822 |
| 1953 | 266,484,959 | 9,025,981 |
| 1954 | 188,305,241 | 6,125,329 |
| 1955 | 230,261,130 | 10,414,877 |

In 1955 about 37 per cent of all Koppers sales were to the chemical, plastics, rubber and dye industries.

## LOVEN CHEMICAL OF CALIFORNIA

*President:* Raymond B. Seymour                    *Home Office & Plant:* Newhall, Calif.
*Technical Director:* Harry A. Fedderson

This company was founded in 1948 in order to manufacture plastics for the growing western plastics industry. The company produced its first salable products in 1950. Its growth has been slow and no profits were earned until recent years. It is the only producer of phenolic molding powders, west of the Mississippi.

The present management joined the firm in 1955. The firm is now operating on a profitable basis and is expanding to meet the requirements of the industry.

*Plastics Products:*

   Adhesives—urea, phenolic
   Coating resins—phenolic
   Industrial resins—phenolic
   Molding materials—phenolic

*Operations:*

| Year (ending July 31) | Net Sales | Net Profit |
|---|---|---|
| 1952 | $558,000 | — |
| 1953 | 620,000 | — |
| 1954 | 566,000 | — |
| 1955 | 684,000 | $33,000 |
| 1956 | 778,000 | 35,000 |

## THE MARBLETTE CORPORATION

*President:* Samuel Glickstein                 *Home Office:* Long Island City, N. Y.

The Marblette Corporation was founded in 1929. Its headquarters and its research and product development laboratories are situated at its Long Island City plant. In 1951, Marblette acquired the cast resins department of the Catalin Corporation of America. Marblette has since occupied a position as the world's leading supplier of cast phenolic resins. These are provided in a virtually unlimited range of shapes, sizes, degrees of transparency, colors, jewel-like and other special effects. They are used in the fabrication of a wide number of industrial and consumer products, parts, and components. Apart from cast phenolics, Marblette has operated as a basic supplier of liquid phenolic formulations. It subsequently broadened its line to include liquid epoxy resins. Its liquid resins are used for many industrial applications, including plastic tooling for metal-forming and plastic-forming, reinforced plastic fabrication, vacuum forming, latex dipping, and foundry practice. In addition to offering technical collaboration to foster the uses of standard compounds, Marblette has frequently developed special-purpose resins to meet specific needs. The line also includes catalysts and mold preparation materials.

*Principal Products:*

Castings—phenolic
Casting, laminating, foaming, coating, surfacing, trowelling, splining, gasketing,
   bonding, sealing, potting, and encapsulating resins—epoxy, phenolic
Catalysts—hardeners for epoxy and phenolic resins
Mold preparation materials—sealers, part coats, wax coats, mold releases

*Plastic Trade Names:*

Marblette—phenolic lines
Maraset—epoxy lines

## MARBON CHEMICAL DIVISION

### Borg-Warner Corporation

*President:* R. Shattuck　　　　　　　　　　　　　*Home Office:* Gary, Ind.

Marbon Chemical began operations in 1934 in Gary, Ind. Originally the business was limited to the manufacture of resins and adhesives with crude rubber being the raw material. Research work over a period of years developed a line of synthetic resins that became the principal products when the crude rubber producing areas in the Orient were lost in World War II. These resins, together with a line of rubber-to-metal vulcanizing adhesives, are sold to the rubber and paint industries. As a result of continuing research, Cycolac, a high-impact, tough, versatile thermoplastic resin was developed. Cycolac resin is the principal product to be produced at the new Woodmar Plant now under construction in Washington, W. Va.

*Plastics Products:*

Adhesives—rubber-to-metal vulcanizing type
Molding materials—acrylonitrile-butadiene-styrene multipolymer. Grades suitable for injection molding, extruding, and calendering
Paint resins—styrene-butadiene copolymers
Rubber reinforcing resins—styrene-butadiene copolymers

*Plastics Trade Names:*

Cycolac—ABS high-impact thermoplastic resin
Marbon 8000—rubber reinforcing resins, styrene-butadiene copolymers
Marbon 9200—paint resins, styrene-butadiene copolymers
Ty-Ply—rubber-to-metal vulcanizing adhesives

*Operations:* (for Borg-Warner Corporation)

| Year | Net Sales |
|------|-----------|
| 1951 | $369,166,000 |
| 1952 | 353,948,000 |
| 1953 | 407,379,000 |
| 1954 | 380,317,000 |
| 1955 | 552,192,000 |

## MOBAY CHEMICAL COMPANY

*President:* David L. Eynon, Jr.                    *Home Office:* St. Louis, Mo.

Mobay was created in May of 1954 as a joint affiliate of Monsanto Chemical Company of St. Louis, Mo. and Farbenfabriken Bayer A.G. of Leverkusen, Germany. The company was formed for the purpose of manufacturing and selling isocyanate, polyesters, and other chemicals required in the production of flexible and rigid polyurethane foams, urethane surface coatings, adhesives, wire enamels, and solid rubber-like elastomers.

The general offices and a customer service laboratory were established in St. Louis in 1954 and a plant for the production of polyesters and isocyanates along with a research laboratory were constructed at New Martinsville, W. Va., in 1955. The laboratories were occupied in the latter part of 1955 and the plant went into operation at the end of 1955 and early in 1956.

Mobay does not manufacture plastics or end-use products, but supplies basic urethane chemicals to a group of licensed firms which convert them into flexible and rigid urethane foams and elastomers. These materials, in turn, are converted into industrial applications and end-use items by the licensees' fabricating customers.

*Plastics Products:*

Polyesters and isocyanates, catalysts and additives for the manufacture of polyurethane products.

*Plastics Trade Names:*

Mondur—isocyanates
Multron—polyesters

## MONSANTO CHEMICAL COMPANY

*President:* Charles Allen Thomas          *Home Office:* St. Louis, Mo.
*V. Pres. & Gen. Mgr. Plastics Div.:* Robert K. Mueller     *Plastics Div.:* Springfield, Mass.

Founded in 1901, Monsanto owns and operates 24 plants and 12 research laboratories in the United States. The company also has 50 per cent interests in three other U.S. companies: The Chemstrand Corporation, Shawinigan Resins Corporation and Mobay Chemical Company. Its eight subsidiaries include Monsanto Chemicals Limited (England) and Monsanto Canada Limited. The company manufactures hundreds of plastics, chemicals and petroleum products.

Monsanto acquired Fiberloid Corporation in 1938 and purchased the Resinox Corporation in 1939. It bought I. F. Laucks, Incorporated, in 1944. Headquarters for the firm's Plastics Division is located at the site of Fiberloid's plant in Springfield, Mass. Other Plastics Division plants are in Seattle, Wash.; Texas City, Tex.; Santa Clara, Calif.; Long Beach, Calif.; Trenton, Mich.; and Addyston, Ohio. Divisional research laboratories are at Springfield, Texas City, Seattle, and Santa Clara.

*Products of Plastics Division:*

  Adhesives—urea, phenolic, melamine, resorcinol, casein, soybean
  Molding materials—polyethylene, phenolic, melamine, vinyl chloride, polystyrene
  Coating resins—melamine, urea, phenolic, melamine laminating materials, poly-
    electrolyte resins, styrene latices
  Sheeting and film—cellulose acetate, cellulose nitrate, vinyl chloride, vinyl butyral

*Plastic Trade Names:*

  Lauxein—protein adhesives
  Lauxite—resin adhesives
  Lustrex—styrene molding materials
  Lytron—synthetic resins
  Monsanto Polyethylene—polyethylene
    resins
  Nitron—cellulose nitrate sheets
  Opalon—vinyl chloride resins
    and compounds
  Resimene—melamine resins

  Resinox—phenolic resins and molding
    compounds
  Resloom—textile finishes
  Saflex—vinyl butyral film
  Scriptite—paper finishes
  Stymer—sizes
  Ultron—vinyl film and sheeting
  Vuepak—cellulose acetate rolls
    and sheets

*Operations:*

| Year | Net Sales | Net Profit |
|---|---|---|
| 1951 | $310,549,000 | $24,227,000 |
| 1952 | 306,669,000 | 22,292,000 |
| 1953 | 383,170,000 | 25,615,000 |
| 1954 | 410,104,000 | 25,195,000 |
| 1955 | 632,978,000 | 50,303,000 |
| 1956* | 545,000,000 | 38,600,000 |

* Approximate figures based on 9 months operations.

Plastics sales represent approximately 20 per cent of total sales.

## NAUGATUCK CHEMICAL DIVISION

### United States Rubber Company

*President:* H. E. Humphreys, Jr.                    *Home Office:* New York, N. Y.
*Vice Pres. & Gen. Mgr. Chemical Div.:* George R. Vila

Since its inception in 1904 as the Naugatuck Chemical Company, Naugatuck Chemical Division of United States Rubber Company has been a manufacturer of basic, intermediate, and finished chemical materials.

In 1911, United States Rubber Company purchased the Naugatuck Chemical Company. In 1950 the chemical and plastics division of Glenn L. Martin Company was acquired, and in 1951, the nitrile rubber interests of the Enjay Corp. were purchased. The products of the Naugatuck Chemical Division may be broadly classified in three main fields, rubber, plastics and chemicals.

In the field of plastics, Naugatuck Chemical is one of the principal producers of vinyl chloride resins and a major producer of polyester resins and high-impact resin-rubber blends for molding and extrusion. Naugatuck owns and operates seven plants in the United States and Canada. Sales of the Chemical Division have increased over 800% in the last 25 years.

*Plastics Products of the Chemical Division:*

Molding materials—vinyl chloride resins and compounds; polyester resins, resin-rubber blends
Coating resins—high styrene latices, vinyl acetate latices
Calendering resins—vinyl chloride, resin-rubber blends

*Trade Names:*

Acetex—synthetic resin latices
Celogen—blowing agents for rubber and plastics
Dispersite—aqueous dispersions of resins and rubbers
Kotol—solvent solutions of synthetic resins
Kralac—styrene copolymers
Kralastic—resin-rubber blends for molding, extrusion and calendering
Marvibond—vinyl-metal laminates
Marvinol—vinyl chloride resins and compounds
Naugatex—styrene-copolymer latices
Polygard—stabilizer for rubber and plastics
Tonox—hardener for epoxy resins
Vibramix—polyester molding compounds
Vibrathane—polyurethane

*Operations* (United States Rubber Company):

| Year | Net Sales | Net Profit |
|------|-----------|------------|
| 1950 | $695,756,000 | $24,658,000 |
| 1951 | 837,222,000 | 30,366,000 |
| 1952 | 850,152,000 | 28,170,000 |
| 1953 | 838,451,000 | 32,732,000 |
| 1954 | 781,574,000 | 27,959,000 |
| 1955 | 925,539,000 | 33,559,000 |
| 1956 | 901,260,000 | 31,870,000 |

## NIXON NITRATION WORKS

*Chairman of Board:* Stanhope Nixon          *Home Office:* Nixon, N. J.
*President:* Morris Breitkopf

Nixon Nitration Works was founded in 1916. The plant is located at Nixon, N. J. The first plastic produced was cellulose nitrate. Later, the company produced cellulose acetate, cellulose acetate butyrate, styrene, and rigid vinyl sheeting. The company also manufactures rods and tubes in cellulose nitrate, cellulose acetate, and cellulose acetate butyrate.

All of the plastics manufactured by Nixon Nitration Works belong in the thermoplastic group.

*Plastics Trade Names:*

C/N—cellulose nitrate
C/A—cellulose acetate
C/A/B—cellulose acetate butyrate
V/L—copolymer rigid vinyl
V/L H—high impact copolymer rigid vinyl
V/P—PVC rigid vinyl
V/P H—high impact PVC rigid vinyl
Styco—styrene copolymer

## OHIO-APEX DIVISION

### Food Machinery and Chemical Corporation

*President:* Ernest Hart                    *Home Office:* San Jose, Calif.

*Div. Mgr., Ohio-Apex:* Bert S. Taylor              *Div. Office:* Nitro, W. Va.

Food Machinery and Chemical Corporation is a widely diversified organization with mechanical plants making equipment to serve the agricultural and food processing and packaging industries; an ordnance division making amphibious army vehicles; and chemical plants producing insecticides, heavy chemicals, organic chemicals, hydrogen peroxide, phosphorus chemicals, plasticizers and resins.

What is now the Ohio-Apex Division was originally founded in 1928 as Kavalco Products Company. Later reorganized as Ohio-Apex, Inc., the product line gradually changed as the company began developing a complete line of plasticizers. These early efforts resulted in Ohio-Apex being the first manufacturer to produce DOP (di-2-ethylhexyl phthalate) on a commercial scale. The line of products grew until today Ohio-Apex is one of the major producers of plasticizers.

With the steady growth of the organization it was acquired by Food Machinery and Chemical Corporation in 1951 and made a division of the corporation. A recent change in organization combined Ohio-Apex with other chemical activities in the new Food Machinery and Chemical Corporation Organic Chemicals Division.

After several years of research, the Ohio-Apex Division recently expanded its position as a supplier of plastics materials to include thermosetting resins and reactive monomers. Although still relatively new, the solid prepolymer of diallyl phthalate, Dapon resin, has been well received for use in molded electrical components and a variety of laminates.

*Products of Ohio-Apex Division:*

Plasticizers—adipates, phthalates, phosphates, fatty acid esters, specialties
Resins—dapon resin (diallyl phthalate prepolymer)
Monomers—diallyl adipate, diallyl diglycollate, diallyl maleate, diallyl phthalate

*Trade-Marks of Ohio-Apex Division:*

Adipol—plasticizers (adipate)
Dapon—thermosetting resin
Dinopol—plasticizers (phthalate)
Kapsol—plasticizer (oleate)
Kronisol—plasticizer (phthalate)
Kronitex—plasticizers (phosphate)

*Operations* (Food Machinery and Chemical Corporation):

| Year | Gross Income | Net Profit |
| --- | --- | --- |
| 1951 | $151,849,843 | $ 9,745,779 |
| 1952 | 223,438,333 | 10,701,323 |
| 1953 | 229,054,708 | 11,520,584 |
| 1954 | 233,401,699 | 12,122,125 |
| 1955 | 264,619,766 | 14,881,575 |
| 1956* | 228,213,000 | 12,065,000 |

* Total for 9 months.

Ohio-Apex gross sales represent approximately 4½% of the gross income of the corporation.

### PHILLIPS CHEMICAL COMPANY

*Chairman of the Board:* K. S. Adams               *Home Office:* Bartlesville, Okla.
*Vice Pres. & Gen. Mgr.:* T. L. Cubbage

Phillips Chemical Company was formed in 1948 as a wholly owned subsidiary of Phillips Petroleum Company to operate and expand the company's principal chemical manufacturing activities.

Since its formation, Phillips Chemical Company has expanded its carbon black manufacturing facilities; has become one of the largest nitrogen fertilizer producers and has added to its line of fertilizer; has entered the manufacture of raw materials for synthetic fibers; has acquired the synthetic rubber facilities formerly operated by Phillips for the Government, and has built a plant to make the company's superior polyethylene plastics.

*Products of Plastics Division:*
New catalytic type of polyethylene resin

*Plastics Trade Mark:*
Marlex—family of olefin polymers

*Operations:*
Commercial olefin polymer plant on Houston Ship Channel at Pasadena, Texas, began operation late in 1956. No information available on sales and earnings.

### PITT-CONSOL CHEMICAL COMPANY

*Address:* 191 Doremus Avenue, Newark 5, N. J.

Pitt-Consol Chemical Company is a wholly owned subsidiary of Pittsburgh Consolidation Coal Company. The subsidiary, formed in the summer of 1955, operates its modern plant in Newark, N. J., at a site purchased from Reilly Tar & Chemical Corporation.

Another plant now under construction at Cresap, W. Va., is scheduled to produce a range of refined acids by 1959-1960. Already one of the nation's top producers of cresylics, Pitt-Consol by 1960 expects a combined plant output of 60 million pounds. Approximately 60% of total sales to date is derived from the plastics industry.

In addition to its balanced line of refined acids for the plastics industries Pitt-Consol also upgrades many products from its refinery to comprise a line of one- and two-stage molding compounds. The line of molding compounds, identified by the trade name "INDUR" is available in assorted colors in general purpose, heat resistant, modified impact, non-bleeding and electrical types.

## REICHHOLD CHEMICALS, INC.

*President:* Henry H. Reichhold                    *Home Office:* White Plains, N. Y.

Founded originally in 1927 to produce, through the use of synthetic resins, faster drying and more durable automobile finishes, Reichhold Chemicals, Inc., has become one of the world's largest producers of synthetic resins and basic chemicals for the plastics and surface coatings industries.

RCI owns and operates thirteen plants in the United States stretching from Brooklyn, N. Y. to Seattle, Wash. Throughout the world, in Canada and sixteen nations, there are 22 plants, either subsidiaries or firms in which RCI owns stock and with which it has license agreements, manufacturing RCI products.

*Principal Products:*

Alkyd resins—for surface coating applications

Melamine resins—for laminating and surface coating applications and adhesives

Phenol-formaldehyde resins—used as fibrous glass and rock wool insulation binders; bonding agents for brake linings, grinding wheels and abrasive papers; varnishes for decorative and industrial laminates; surface coating vehicles; adhesives

Polyester and epoxy resins—for adhesive, casting, laminating, molding and surface coating applications

Polyvinyl acetate—emulsions for surface coating applications and adhesives

Urea-formaldehyde resins—for foundry core binders, paper, textile and surface coating applications

*Plastic Trade Names:*

Beckamine—urea-formaldehyde resins

Beckopol—high melt point modified phenolic resins

Beckosol—alkyd resins

Fabrez—urea-formaldehyde textile resins

Foundrez—urea-formaldehyde and phenol-formaldehyde foundry resins

Plyamine—urea-formaldehyde adhesives

Plyamul—polyvinyl acetate adhesives

Plyophen—phenol-formaldehyde resins, adhesives and varnishes

Polylite—polyester resins

Polyox—epoxy resins

Polytool—polyester, epoxy, phenolic and poly-urethane tooling compounds

Styresol—styrenated alkyd resins

Super-Beckacite—pure phenolic resins

Super-Beckamine—melamine-formaldehyde resins

Super-Beckosol—isophthalic acid alkyd resins

*Operations:*

| Year | Net Sales | Net Profit |
|------|-----------|------------|
| 1951 | $56,394,000 | $1,466,000 |
| 1952 | 45,181,000 | 824,000 |
| 1953 | 47,805,000 | 656,000 |
| 1954 | 47,029,000 | 285,000 |
| 1955 | 53,573,000 | 2,075,000 |

According to Henry H. Reichhold, about three quarters of the company's output is devoted to the plastics industry.

## ROHM & HAAS COMPANY

*President:* Otto Haas
*Home Office:* Philadelphia, Pa.

Rohm & Haas Company was established in 1909 and incorporated in 1917 as an independent American business. The company's first product was an enzymatic bate for preparing leather for tanning. Activities expanded in the years immediately following, both in development of additional chemicals for leather manufacture and of chemicals useful in a wide range of other industries. The company entered the plastics field in 1926 with a urea formaldehyde molding powder. In 1929 the company introduced Plexigum, the first laminating medium for safety glass to give a "flexible break" on impact. In 1936 the company pioneered in the introduction of cast acrylic plastic sheets and has remained an important producer of acrylic raw materials including molding powders. Rohm & Haas polyester resins were introduced in 1945. In 1947 Charles Lennig & Company, a wholly owned subsidiary purchased in 1920, was liquidated and dissolved; and in 1948 an associate firm, The Resinous Products & Chemical Company, a pioneer producer of oil soluble resins for paints and varnishes, was merged with Rohm & Haas Company. The company operates manufacturing plants in Philadelphia and Bristol, Pa., Knoxville, Tenn., and Houston, Tex.

*Plastics Products:*

Acrylic resin emulsions—aqueous dispersions of acrylic resins for coatings for leather and paper, textile finishing and for manufacture of water base paints
Adhesives—nitrogenous, phenol formaldehyde powder and film, and resorcinol resins for plywood bonding
Coating resins—acrylic resin solutions in organic solvents; drying oil and nondrying oil modified alkyd resins; nitrogenous resins thermosetting components in baked protective coatings; oil-soluble phenol formaldehyde and maleic resins; resin modified oxidizing type phthalic alkyd resins
Ion exchange resins—cross-linked polyelectrolytes for industrial and domestic water conditioning. Metal recovery, processing of pharmaceuticals, etc.
Molding materials—acrylic resin molding powders for compression injection and extrusion; styrene solutions of unsaturated polyester resins
Polyester resins—solutions of unsaturated polyester resins in monomeric styrene
Sheets—cast acrylic resin (methyl methacrylate)

*Plastics Trade Names:*

| | | |
|---|---|---|
| Acryloid | Duraplex | Rhonite |
| Acrysol | Monoplex | Rhoplex |
| Amberlac | Paraplex | Plexiglas |
| Amberol | Plexigum | Uformite |
| Amberlite | Primal | |

*Operations:*

| Year | Net Sales | Net Profit |
|---|---|---|
| 1951 | $106,896,000 | $ 6,721,000 |
| 1952 | 105,772,000 | 5,402,000 |
| 1953 | 120,676,000 | 6,540,000 |
| 1954 | 132,615,000 | 12,431,000 |
| 1955 | 161,644,000 | 17,687,000 |

## RUBBER CORPORATION OF AMERICA

*President:* William A. Merton                    *Home Office:* New York, N. Y.
*Vice President & Secretary:* Richard G. Merton

Rubber Corporation of America was founded in 1930. It originally was an importer of natural rubber latex and rubber latex concentrates. These activities and the importation of crude rubber are continued in addition to the expanding activities in the plastic field. Rubber Corporation's plant is maintained at Hicksville, Long Island, N. Y.

*A Summary of the Plastic Products:*
Film and sheeting—polyvinyl chloride
Coating and molding materials—plastisol and rigidsol compounds
Laminates—polyvinyl chloride with other materials
Polyesters—for polyurethane polymers
Synthetic resins—polyvinyl chloride and copolymers

*Plastics Trade Names:*
Rucoam—polyvinyl chloride film and sheeting

Plastic sales constitute a substantial part of the sales of Rubber Corporation of America.

## SHELL CHEMICAL CORPORATION

*President:* R. C. McCurdy                    *Home Office:* New York, N. Y.

Shell Chemical Corporation was organized as a wholly owned subsidiary of Shell Oil Company in 1929. The company operates 8 chemical plants, all in the United States, from which it produces plastics, chemicals for industry and agriculture, fertilizers, and synthetic rubber. Research on its products is conducted at 7 laboratories at various locations across the nation.

Shell Chemical's epoxy resins—trade marked Epon—are manufactured at its Houston, Tex., plant. Eleven field offices handle the sales of Epon resins. They are located in Los Angeles and San Francisco, Calif.; Houston, Tex.; St. Louis, Mo.; Chicago, Ill.; Detroit, Mich.; Cleveland, Ohio; Atlanta, Ga.; Newark, N. J.; New York, N. Y.; and Boston, Mass.

*End Uses of Epon Resins:*

    Surface coatings—bake, air dry, catalysed; industrial production; industrial maintenance; trade sales

    Structural—adhesives, electrical encapsulation, printed circuits, aircraft laminates, marine construction, foams, non-skid road and floor coatings, automotive and marine patch kits, resin solder and repair compounds, plastic pipe and tankage, and tooling (jigs, fixtures, metal and plastic forming)

    Miscellaneous—textile treateement and finishing

*Operations:* Shell Chemical Corporation does not publish an annual report. Its sales figures and profits are reflected in Shell Oil Company's report, the net sales and profit of which are shown below, along with the chemical sales figures.

| Year | Net Sales | Net Profit | Sales of Chemical Products |
|---|---|---|---|
| 1951 | $1,072,434,000 | $ 97,020,000 | $ 97,522,000 |
| 1952 | 1,142,632,000 | 90,873,000 | 97,763,000 |
| 1953 | 1,269,551,000 | 115,407,000 | 125,811,000 |
| 1954 | 1,312,060,000 | 121,127,000 | 138,809,000 |
| 1955 | 1,484,069,000 | 125,532,000 | 193,860,000 |
| 1956 | Not yet available | 135,800,000* | Not yet available |

    * Estimated.

## SPENCER CHEMICAL COMPANY

*President:* Kenneth A. Spencer                    *Home Office:* Kansas City, Mo.
*Gen. Mgr.-Industrial Chemical Sales:* Harold R. Dinges

Organized in 1941 as a wholly owned subsidiary of The Pittsburg & Midway Coal Mining Company, the company became financially independent in 1946. The first production facility was the Jayhawk Ordnance Works, which in 1946 was leased and later purchased from the government to produce ammonia and related nitrogen products. Today Spencer operates six plants in six states, producing a complete line of nitrogen chemicals as well as a diverse group of industrial and plastic chemical products. In 1955, Spencer commenced production of polyethylene at Orange, Tex., under license agreements with Imperial Chemical Industries, Ltd. Since that date the company has pioneered in the development of high density polyethylenes from the high-pressure type process. The company is also a licensee of the Standard Oil (Indiana) process for the low pressure synthesis of polymers of ethylene and propylene. In 1957, Spencer will commence production of nylon-6 (polycaprolactam) at Henderson, Ky., under licenses with Algemene Kunstzijde Unie N.V. and affiliates.

*Principal Plastic Products:*
   Polyethylene resins
   Nylon resins
   Formaldehyde
   Hexamine

*Plastic Trade Names:*
   Poly-Eth—conventional density polyethylene resins
   Poly-Eth Hi-D—high density polyethylene from high pressure process
   Spencer Nylon—nylon-6 molding resins

*Operations:*

| Year | Net Sales | Net Profit |
|------|-----------|------------|
| 1951 | $23,736,000 | $4,562,000 |
| 1952 | 28,772,000 | 4,223,000 |
| 1953 | 30,837,000 | 4,661,000 |
| 1954 | 34,104,000 | 5,287,000 |
| 1955 | 36,155,000 | 5,118,000 |
| 1956 | 45,625,000 | 5,924,000 |

## U.S. INDUSTRIAL CHEMICALS COMPANY

### Division of National Distillers Products Corporation

*President (National Distillers):* John E. Bierwirth          *Home Office:* New York, N. Y.
*V. Pres. & Gen. Mgr. U.S.I. Div.:* Dr. Robert E. Hulse

The company was founded in 1906 as U.S. Industrial Alcohol Co., to make industrial alcohol. Later it changed its name to U.S. Industrial Chemicals Co., and was merged in 1951 with National Distillers Products Corporation. Products are industrial alcohol, solvents, polyethylene resins, intermediates for plastics and plasticizer manufacture, plasticizers, chemicals, feed supplements, pharmaceuticals, and reactive metals. The polyethylene plant is in Tuscola, Ill., and other solvents and intermediate plants are located in Anaheim, Calif. and New Orleans, La. Another alcohol denaturing plant is located in Newark, N. J. National Petro-Chemicals Corporation, Tuscola, Ill., a plastics plant, is a 60% owned subsidiary company managed by U.S.I. Division, but jointly owned by Panhandle Eastern Pipeline Corporation. Output is sold through U.S.I.

*Plastics Products:*

Molding materials—polyethylene
Solvents—ethyl alcohol, butyl alcohol, diethyl carbonate, ethyl acetate, acetone
Plasticizers—dibutyl phthalate
Plastics and plasticizer intermediates—sebacic acid, sebacic acid isomers

*Plastics Trade Names:*

Ansol[R]—anhydrous denatured alcohol, special solvent blend for lacquers, resins, etc.
Diatol[R]—diethyl carbonate solvent for special purpose lacquers
Petrothene[R]—polyethylene resin

*Operations:*

| Year | Net Sales | Net Profit |
|------|-----------|------------|
| 1951 | $466,881,000 | $25,018,000 |
| 1952 | 470,127,000 | 11,745,000 |
| 1953 | 488,711,000 | 12,133,000 |
| 1954 | 487,333,000 | 13,713,000 |
| 1955 | 500,192,000 | 15,514,000 |
| 1956 | 543,100,000 | 20,104,000 |

Figures are for parent corporation, National Distillers Products Corporation. U.S.I. Division sales have not been separated.

# 9. THE FUTURE OF PLASTICS

If someone in 1939 had given an estimate covering the future of plastics with as extravagant an increase as has actually taken place, few, if any, would have believed him. In 1939 the total annual production of all plastics stood at about 213 million pounds while in 1957 it stands at over 4 billion pounds, or an increase of nearly 1900 per cent in seventeen years. This same rate of increase projected forward would give an almost astronomical figure for the year seventeen years ahead, or 1974. If sights are lowered, say to a five-year interval the results are still impressive. The same rate of increase from 1957 to 1962 as occurred from 1952 to 1957 gives the total plastics production in 1962 as about 7,000,000,000 pounds.

When one notes that a plastics hard top is to appear on one model of a Ford car and a plastics hood overlay on a Studebaker model to mention but two recent developments, the 7 billion pound figure may not seem too extravagant a prediction.

Most producers are reluctant to say much about their plans for future new materials. However, some have given information about the future of existing materials and this has been interpreted in the following accounts covering most of the widely used plastics and resins. The materials of two or three producers are included because they seem to have general trend value.

The chemical industry expects that 15 per cent of the large future increase in plastics production will be in materials not even commercially available today.

**Research in Plastics**

In 1954 *Fortune Magazine* gave the following figures for the research budgets of the four most important research companies in this field:

| | |
|---|---|
| du Pont | $57,000,000 |
| Union Carbide & Chemical | 34,000,000 |
| American Cyanamid | 20,000,000 |
| Allied Chemical | 15,000,000 |

This is the first time Allied has appeared in this impressive list. It is assumed that all of the budgets have been substantially increased in recent years but details are not available.

### Cellulosics

A variety of new applications including heels for women's shoes and an increased activity in packaging helped boost the cellulosics to an all-time high in 1956. The commercial production of cellulose propionate was started. With its short molding cycle and its application in the production of fountain pens and appliance housings it is expected that this will help keep the cellulosics on an upward trend in the future.

### Thermosetting Resins

The thermosetting resins appeared to move sideways in 1956. While there were shifts within the individual categories, year-end totals for phenolics, melamine, and urea plastics were about the same as in 1955. Shell molding, which uses phenolic resins, continues to make satisfactory progress, particularly among automobile manufacturers.

Phenolic molding powder sales were about 200 million pounds in 1956 and are expected to stay at this level for some time in the future. Ureas and melamines, on the other hand, are expected to move forward slowly, partly due to their demand in dishware and adhesives.

### Polyethylene

On a statistical basis polyethylene's sales increase of from 346,000,000 to 500,000,000 pounds was the outstanding feature of the year. Use of polyethylene as insulation and jacketing for communication wire and cable has increased markedly. This new type of cable has been going largely into the expansion and modernization of telephone systems. This expansion is expected to continue in the future.

Polyethylene pipe received a significant boost during 1956 with approval by the National Sanitation Foundation for its use with potable water. Additionally, broad gains are expected in practically all other polyethylene uses, including molded housewares, packaging, and various construction and agricultural applications.

One source estimates that sales of polyethylene may reach a billion pounds annually by 1960 or 1961.

The new capacity of some 300,000,000 pounds of so-called "high-pressure process" polyethylene will have been completed by 1958 bringing the total industry capacity to some 850,000,000 to 900,000,000 pounds per year. Furthermore, new plants to produce "low-pressure process" polyethylene have been announced to a total capacity of about 430,000,000 pounds per year, with all of such capacity due to be in operation by 1960. Thus a total polyethylene capacity of some 1,300,000,000 pounds per year is likely within the next three years.

The major factor in the future according to Mr. Miller of Bakelite will not be pounds of productive capacity, as this alone will not earn an important place in the polyethylene picture. Markets must be widened by superior and special properties better suited to current fields of application, with new types of polyethylene for a still broader field of use. This means more and more emphasis on research and development in the markets as well as in the laboratories. The same may be said of other major types of plastic materials. Those with a solid background of research and development, with ample and modern scientific facilities and a willingness to invest large sums in these areas, will be the leaders in the plastic industry of the future.

By 1960 the low-pressure material is expected to account for about 46 per cent of the total.

The two types have somewhat different markets due to different properties but an end-use overlap of about 20 per cent is thought probable.

The demand for polyethylene continues to grow more rapidly than that for the other two big production plastics—the vinyls and polystyrene. One authoritative estimate places the 1965 world production of both high-pressure and low-pressure polyethylene at the amazing figure of 3,000,000,000 pounds with about 40 per cent being the so-called low-pressure type. An English authority suggests calling the original type of polyethylene in the United States "low-density" polyethylene and the later type, which generally has been called the low-pressure type, "high-density" polyethylene. This is to avoid confusion when high pressures are used in the production of the second type. When the newer type of polyethylene was first introduced some producers thought it would displace the first type. However, experience has shown that there is no basis for this assumption.

## Polyesters

A bright future is predicted for polyesters. Early in 1957 the annual production of polyesters for 1956 was placed at around 66,000,000 pounds and estimates covering the 1957 production ran as high as 86,000,000 pounds. Some authorities expect this rate of increase to continue for many years ahead, basing their estimates to a large extent on the increased use of polyesters in boats, airplanes, furniture, and auto-mobiles.

An entirely new type of polyester molding powder was recently an-nounced by Durez Division. Experimental quantities have been sold and commercial production is scheduled for late 1957 delivery. The new material as yet is without a name but is said to be a new family of resins which can be molded in standard phenolic molding equipment. It has good dimensional stability and heat resistance and can be furnished in light colors. The price is expected to be about 50¢ a lb.

### Polystyrene

The styrene category, second largest of the plastic family groups with sales of an estimated 590,000,000 pounds in 1956, showed very little change in over-all totals from 1955. But there were shifts within the category. Polystyrene has lost some ground to polyethylene in the house-wares market, but there have been compensating increases in the high-impact category, for example, refrigerator liners, toys, radio cabinets, power lawn mower wheels.

Polystyrene is expected to stay close to an annual production of 600,000,000 pounds for several years unless some new applications or new developments are found.

### Melamine Resins*

The basic properties of cured melamine-formaldehyde resins include surface hardness, nonflammability, heat-resistance, freedom from initial color and resistance to discoloration, freedom from odor and taste, good dielectric properties, and resistance to tracking under the electric arc.

This unique combination of useful properties, combined with moderate cost, assures a steady expansion of fields of profitable use for melamine-formaldehyde resins.

Molded dinnerware is the application of melamine resin molding com-pounds best known to the general public. Appearance, light-weight and utility created the initial sales appeal, but now, after years of experience, the public is also aware of serviceability. Break-resistance is established as a reality. Successful trials, running more than a year in one of New York's largest hotels, have demonstrated long-term serviceability under severe restaurant conditions, emphasizing low replacement costs. The

---

* Prepared in cooperation with American Cyanamid Co.

introduction of decorative patterns through the use of molded-in overlays has added esthetic appeal to melamine dinnerware.

These factors insure a continued growth in the use of molded melamine resin dinnerware. Actually a recent survey indicates the possibility of a threefold increase in ultimate demand.

New applications are continually developing for alpha-filled molding material. In general, one may expect a steady substantial growth in the demand for this material.

The potential value of glass-fiber filled melamine resins has long been realized, but only recently have practical molding compounds become available to industry. The reinforcing effect of glass fiber combines with the basic properties of melamine resin to create the added advantages of impact, flexural, and compressive strength. These new materials are rapidly gaining acceptance and an increasing demand may be expected for critical industrial and military applications.

Laminated melamine resin has gained broad acceptance in the home, hotel, and cafeteria for durable table-tops and furniture surfaces. Continued use may be expected in this area as well as wider use for durable, fireproof wall surfaces.

In other fields such as wet strength paper wood-bonding and textile finishing, an increasingly quality-conscious industry will demand greater usage of melamine-formaldehyde resins. They will be used more and more to upgrade urea-formaldehyde adhesives and to improve the properties of cotton and woolen goods.

The increasingly popular multi-tone automobiles demand finishes resistant to color-change during the baking operation. Melamine resins have proved ideal for this purpose and will be used in increasing quantities.

## Silicones in Plastics

Whereas silicones have been adapted to a wide variety of applications in the relatively short span that they have been commercially available, it seems logical that their use will continue to increase.

The chemistry of silicones has been but scratched, and as research progresses, the flow of new and improved silicone products continues. New applications and new techniques are constantly being developed.

It is foreseeable that, the combination of continuing research and development work, plus the unusual and unique characteristics of these materials, will result in more extensive use of silicones to produce more heat-stable, durable plastic items for industrial, military, and domestic applications.

Table 9.1. Future Sales of Plastics

(pounds)*

| Type | 1949 | 1955 | 1960** |
|---|---|---|---|
| Vinyls (includes vinylidene chloride) | 205,000,000 | 600,000,000 | 900,000,000 |
| Styrene (polymers and copolymers) | 240,000,000 | 572,000,000 | 800,000,000 |
| Phenolics | 290,000,000 | 489,000,000 | 600,000,000 |
| Alkyds | 316,000,000 | 450,000,000 | 500,000,000 |
| Polyethylene | 30,000,000 | 400,000,000 | 950,000,000 |
| Urea and melamine | 134,000,000 | 302,000,000 | 400,000,000 |
| Cellulosics | 90,000,000 | 142,000,000 | 200,000,000 |
| Acrylics | 25,000,000 | 51,000,000 | 100,000,000 |
| Polyesters (film and reinforced) | — | 50,000,000 | 100,000,000 |
| Silicones | — | 30,000,000 | 100,000,000 |
| Polyamides | — | 25,000,000 | 50,000,000 |
| Epoxy | — | 22,000,000 | 100,000,000 |
| Polyurethane | — | 5,000,000 | 125,000,000 |
| Fluorocarbons | — | 2,000,000 | 10,000,000 |
| Others | — | 460,000,000 | — |
| Totals | 1,330,000,000 | 3,600,000,000 | 4,935,000,000 |

*Note*: Values in this table are approximate only.

　* Arranged in order of 1955 Totals.

　** Estimated. Based in part on a Modern Plastics projection.

## Vinyls*

At this time, the family of vinyls has no volume competitor other than polyethylene. It is generally believed that despite the tremendous growth of polyethylene, the vinyls will continue to outstrip its competitor. Many figures are given to estimate the future of vinyl resins. Conservative beliefs indicate that consumption in this country of the leading vinyl, polyvinyl chloride, will reach approximately 800,000,000 pounds by 1960. The sale of polyvinyl chloride in 1956 was about 600,000,000 pounds.

Processed polyvinyl chloride has a multitude of uses. The material is made by two different techniques. One involves a suspension polymeriza-

　* This section prepared in cooperation with Dr. W. Mayo Smith of Escambia Bay Chemical Corporation.

tion which is characterized by a rapid separation of the polymer after agitation is stopped.

Emulsion polymers do not separate and require spray-drying to recover the polymer. This latter type polymer is used in plastisol and organosol applications.

Polymer made by suspension methods is used in the production of calendered film and sheeting. The consumption of film alone in 1956 is estimated at 120,000,000 pounds. Further growth in this market may reach 150,000,000 pounds by 1960. Vinyl films find many uses, with draperies, bedspreads and curtains comprising one of the larger markets. Other large volume outlets are in rainwear, laminations, industrial tapes, shower curtains, adhesive-backed film, yard goods, nursery goods and appliance, furniture, and table covers.

Polyvinyl chloride, in addition to the great versatility of film, is also used in somewhat lesser amounts for sheeting. The greatest use for the unsupported sheeting is in upholstery material, luggage, handbags and inflatables. The plasticized sheeting industry has reached a fairly stable state, and it is expected that in 1960 this figure will not greatly exceed today's usage of about 65,000,000 pounds.

Molding and extrusions are directed toward such applications as electrical wire and cable coverings, extruded profiles, garden hose, phonograph records, and slush moldings, which combined represent a production figure today of perhaps 200,000,000 pounds. The anticipated production by 1960 has been estimated at between 275,000,000 and 375,000,000 pounds. The greatest usage in this category is for electrical wire and cable. By far the largest majority of house wiring is now vinyl coated. This has greatly reduced the use of rubber in this application. It is possible that electrical usage will reach 150,000,000 pounds by 1960.

Profile extrusions which consist of various weltings such as those used in automobile and window channeling, shoe welting and gasket materials, may amount to as much as 50,000,000 pounds. Polyvinyl chloride is finding accelerated use in garden hose and a conservative estimate by 1960 is 25,000,000 pounds. Phonograph records are made from a copolymer of vinyl chloride and vinyl acetate. The constantly increasing interest in records makes this estimate quite difficult; it is possible that use in 1960 will be in the order of 20-25,000,000 pounds.

Rigid applications represent a good prospect for future growth. PVC in piping and fittings is quite definitely beginning a major growth prospect, as indicated by several major producers of metal pipe turning to the production of rigid polyvinyl chloride. These non-plasticized pipes and fittings have marked chemical and solvent resistance and also are non-flammable. Rigid extruded sheets, both clear and opaque, rigid extruded film, and injection moldings are also believed to face good future growth. It is possible that rigid applications alone will be used in a minimum amount of 50,000,000 pounds, with a figure several times this amount entirely possible. Resin rubber blends which give higher impact strength than true rigids also have an accelerated growth prospect. These are less stable chemically, but have much higher impact strength than the rigid materials.

Vinyl flooring may exceed 100,000,000 pounds by 1960, which would then represent approximately 25 per cent of the total market. The largest volume type of vinyl used today is vinyl asbestos tile containing 16 per cent resin and 4 per cent plasticizer. Flexible vinyl tiles and vinyl coated flooring comparable to linoleum also are used. Textile and paper coatings are currenly used at the rate of about 70,000,000 pounds per year, and gradual increases are indicated.

One of the most difficult future markets to predict is vinyl foams. Resilient foams of latex, urethane, and vinyl will battle for future markets. It has been estimated by some that 1960 usage of vinyl foam will comprise as much as 125,000,000 pounds of a possible total market of over 500,000,000 pounds. If this is to be realized, a most rapid growth must result in that 1956 vinyl foam usage was possibly no greater than 5,000,000 pounds.

Polyvinyl chloride finds applications in the field of protective coatings. To date these have consisted mainly of coatings for metal and industrial finishings, tank linings, and can linings. By 1960 this use level may be in the realm of 30-40,000,000 pounds.

Polyvinyl acetate and polyvinyl alcohol are also used in large quantities. Vinyl acetate polymers in latex form have replaced starch and dextrin in many textile and adhesive applications. Polyvinyl alcohol is used in sizing paper to give greater wet and dry strength as well as grease resistance. Polyvinyl acetate is an intermediate in preparing polyvinyl butyral for use in safety glass. Future growth is expected for the acetate in the paint market.

Copolymers of vinylidene chloride and minor amounts of vinyl chloride have good chemical and heat resistance and find application in packing, filaments, films, and moldings. Although in general these materials are more costly than vinyl chloride homopolymer, certain physical properties justify this higher cost.

Sound recordings showed a sharp increase in 1956 continuing the trend to 33⅓ and 45 rpm records made of vinyl as the industry reached an all-time high in dollar volume.

A new vinyl plastic, developed by Air Reduction Chemical Co., is scheduled for early production. It is a vinyl stearate and may be copolymerized with vinyl acetate and with vinyl chloride. The acetate copolymer gives a tough flexible film with high water resistance. Suggested applications include adhesives, emulsion paints, paper coatings, and textile finishes. The chloride copolymer gives a stable coating material which does not "bleed" and which has excellent retention of its protective characteristics.

### Alkyds and Coumarone-indenes

The alkyd and coumarone-indene categories in 1956 were down slightly from 1955. The alkyds actually are polyester resins but they retain their separate identity and are limited to saturated types. They are used mostly in the manufacture of coatings where they face heavy competition from the newer materials. Their future is mixed but most authorities expect them to hold their own. The coumarone-indene resins also are used largely in coatings where they add water resistance to vehicles in which they are incorporated. Their future is expected to be similar to that of the alkyds.

### Polyurethane

A bright future for polyurethane is predicted by Dr. Richard B. Green of Barrett Division. He states, "The advent of commercial volumes of diisocyanates offers to polymer chemists a source of a new resin-former of great potential. Right now we are reacting almost entirely with linear polyesters. What the future holds I do not know, but it will be interesting. Here, for almost the first time, we have in our hands a means of tailoring resins. Since different reactivity is a characteristic of the groups of unsymmetrical diisocyanates, we can control the polymer generation by stages. Final products of urethane resin research will probably have little in common with the materials we now make."

Polyurethane gained much in prominence during 1956. While production probably did not reach 10,000,000 pounds, the great number of companies beginning to produce isocyanate materials would indicate considerable activity in the next few years.

### Plastics in Building

U. S. Rubber Co. has stated that the 500 million pounds of plastics now sold each year to the building industry represents only 3 per cent of the potential market for plastics in construction. If anything like the successful cultivation of the 97 per cent remaining takes place the increase in plastics sales in buildings during the years ahead will be far greater than anyone heretofore has ventured to predict.

If 500,000,000 pounds is but 3 per cent of possible plastics sales in building construction then 5,000,000,000 pounds is but 30 per cent, a conservative amount. Yet 5,000,000,000 pounds is more than an optimist's figure for total plastics sales in 1960. Estimates for total sales during the years ahead must be revised sharply upward or U. S. Rubber's 3 per cent figure will have to be discounted.

Homes constructed of plastic materials funnelled from helicopters hovering over a building site will become a reality soon, according to Henry H. Reichhold, president of Reichhold Chemicals, Inc. Walls and foundations of plastics will be poured through hoses from aircraft fitted with the type of equipment ordinarily used for cement mixing, Mr. Reichhold said. He added that not only the homes, but the driveways would be of plastics which, inherently, offer an unlimited range of color. The driveways might be sprayed on by slow flying aircraft. This may seem fantastic but so did spraying of crops from the air when it was originally suggested.

The new plastic homes—much more durable than those of the past—are just one more development that will expand the plastics and chemical industries from 15 to 25 per cent during the next few years and it may triple the volume in the next five, Mr. Reichhold maintained.

### Reinforced Plastics

Reinforced plastics are penetrating volume markets formerly held exclusively by die cast aluminum, porcelainized steel, and molded plywood, according to The Society of The Plastics Industry's forecast for 1957. Reinforced plastics combine plastic resins with fibrous reinforcements to make a wide variety of products from boat hulls and building panels to fishing rods and furniture.

The industry recorded a 30 per cent gain in sales in 1956 as compared with 1955 and predicts an equal percentage growth in the year ahead. More important than volume, though, in the opinion of industry leaders, is the entry into solid new markets and the growing number of structural and semi-structural components in building and in all forms of transportation. Equal importance is assigned to the widening manufacturing base for reinforced plastics due to the entrance into the field by compression molders and by old established manufacturers, many of whom are investing substantial sums in reinforced plastics development and research.

In reporting on the growth of the industry, Clare E. Bacon of Owens-

Corning Fiberglas Corp. credited advances in processing which have brought the reinforced industry closer to the goal of "parts per minute" rather than "minutes per part." Improvements in finish to a point where surfaces suitable for appliance parts are now possible and better understanding among designers and engineers and use flexibility of these materials are two other important growth factors.

The advances in processing involve faster curing resins, new types of compounds and better materials handling methods. For example, the development of premix compounds, combining resins and short chopped reinforcing materials, has made possible the injection and compression molding of reinforced plastics. New and improved preforming equipment and processing have also been developed that substitute mechanical for hand labor, thus more nearly approaching the automation of injection molding. As a result, many established compression and some injection molders are now entering the reinforced plastics field—on the one hand using their injection and compression presses to mold reinforced plastics and, on the other, adding preform equipment and departments.

Some fertile fields for reinforced plastics in the year ahead are the whole transportation industry (including passenger cars and trucks, airplanes, boats and railcars), household appliances, furniture and seating, containers, construction and electrical components.

Production of reinforced plastics automobile bodies continues at an increased rate and tooling for the next model of the Chevrolet Corvette was underway at the beginning of 1957, but the volume growth will be in components—for heater and air conditioner housings, instrument panels, fender fins, trim panels and "hardtops."

## Marblette Corporation Resins

Many expected future developments are based on experimental work leading to better applications of existing resins, as well as collaboration with users of present materials thus improving resins and bringing out formulations "tailored" to specific uses.

Plastic tooling work that has made recent strides and seems to offer big potentials for future progress includes the use of epoxy resins for tools and dies in automobile protype programs, where frequent design changes favor castings that can be quickly and easily revised or refaced; the use of epoxies to fabricate hand hammer forms, face drop hammer punches, and to efficiently replace other materials in other types of tools. An application still being explored by one user is the development of plastic tools for finishing heat-treated steel gears.

The use of gravel aggregate as a filler is widening the uses of tooling resins by making it practicable at low cost to employ large quantities of material for creating large-scale tools for large-size parts.

Efficient fabrication of big laminated parts is also being advanced by reinforced plastic firms, as in the use of resins together with fibrous glass to make what are said to be some of the largest plastic castings. These are used in the manufacture of sectional swimming pools.

Makers of electronic and electrical items and components are giving increasing attention to the use of newly developed resins for encapsulation, impregnation, potting and imbedment.

TABLE 9.2. ACRYLONITRILE-STYRENE COPOLYMER (BAKELITE C-11)*

| | |
|---|---|
| Specific gravity | 1.075 |
| Refractive index | 1.57 |
| Tensile strength, psi | 11,700 |
| Flexural strength, psi | 15,700 |
| Impact strength, lbs in. notch | 0.40 |
| Hardness Rockwell M | 82 |
| Thermal-expansion, $10^{-5}$ per °C | 6 |
| Heat distortion temperature, °F | 200 |
| Volume resistivity, ohms-cm | 10 |
| Dielectric strength, short time | 400 |
| Dielectric strength, step by step | 300 |
| Dielectric constant, 60 cycles | 3.4 |
| Loss factor, 60 cycles | 0.034 |

* Some explanation about property tables used in this book may be in order. Manufacturers are always glad to supply complete and lengthy tables of properties of their products but the republishing of such tables did not seem warranted in a condensed book such as this. Accordingly short tables have been used for comparative purposes and to indicate general characteristics. Large spreads in values such as:
tensile strength, psi          2000-7000
are not considered informative to most readers and thus average values, such as 5500 in the above case, have been adopted in most instances.

Pattern duplicates cast from resins are being used by companies utilizing the latex-dip process. New coating resins are finding additional use in this field. They strengthen the surface of dipping mandrels made of aluminum and other materials, fill in imperfections in the surfaces, and make them more resistant to abrasion and to the deterioration caused by repeated immersion in a latex bath.

Vacuum forming success is being accelerated by the use of dimensionally stable epoxy resins for cast and laminated forming dies.

In all these and other present and predictable developments of resin applications, plastics utilization progress is being assisted by a program of furnishing technical assistance to resin users, frequently in the form of personal on-the-spot cooperation by company technicians.

The early difficulties in eliminating the factors that caused dermatitic reactions in some individuals allergically sensitive to epoxy resins have been largely overcome. Low-toxic and nontoxic formulations are now offered.

TABLE 9.3. PROPERTIES OF A NEW ACRYLONITRILE, BUTADIENE, STYRENE MATERIAL*

| Physical | | Outdoor Burial, 9 mo. | | |
| --- | --- | --- | --- | --- |
| | | | Tensile, psi | Elongation, % |
| Specific gravity | 1.01 | Initial | 4480 | 170 |
| Izod (ft-lb/¼ in. of notch) | 5.0 | Indiana clay | 4570 | 140 |
| Hardness, Rockwell | R90 | Indiana loam | 4260 | 140 |
| Tensile, psi | 4500 | Florida inland | 4680 | 120 |
| Elongation, % | 100 | Florida beach | 4770 | 150 |
| Tensile modulus, psi | 196,000 | Florida sea | | |
| Compression set under constant load: 22 hr at 158°F, % | 0.00 | water | 4730 | 100* |
| Shear strength, psi | 4100 | * Damaged by sharp barnacles. | | |

| Thermal | | Chemical Resistance, 9 mo. | | |
| --- | --- | --- | --- | --- |
| | | | Tensile, psi | Elongation, % |
| Heat-distortion temperature, °F | 200 | Initial | 4480 | 170 |
| Flammability, in./min. | 1.30 | Shelf | 4800 | 130 |
| Brittleness temperature, °F | —45 | Tap water | 4300 | 170 |
| Thermal conductivity, Btu/hr/ft/°F/in. | 1.3 | Salt, 10% | 4500 | 150 |
| Coefficient of expansion, °C | $9.98 \times 10^{-5}$ | Sulfuric acid, 10% | 4260 | 150 |
| Specific heat, cal/°C/g | 0.006 | Nitric acid, 10% | 4310 | 150 |
| Mold shrinkage, in./in. | 0.006 | Caustic soda, 10% | 4530 | 150 |
| Demolding temperature, °F | 212 to 220 | Ammonia, 10% | 3930* | 160 |
| | | Sinclair 10W | 4680 | 150 |
| | | W. Kansas sour crude | 4540 | 150 |
| | | * No loss after 3 months. | | |

* Marbon's Cycolac.

Protection for surfaces and finishes of wood, metal, concrete, paper, plaster, and plastics exposed to corrosion and to adverse weather and atmosphere conditions is afforded by new coating resins, including a gray enamel epoxy maintenance paint and a clear epoxy varnish. These are being used by builders and in the chemicals, petroleum, automotive, maritime and other industries—applied to pipes, automobile bodies, marine and oilfield equipment, gasoline pumps, tank interiors, outdoor furniture, concrete floors, steel and masonry structures, and various kinds of machinery. Other surfacing resins are being readied for release.

A rubber-like epoxy, with an ability to produce sheets of varying thicknesses and a range of hardnesses from vinyl-like flexibility to hard-rubber toughness, is being employed in place of rubber and plastisol in gasketing and other applications. Other new synthetic rubbers are predicted.

Impregnating and encapsulating resins with high dielectric strength, heat and shock resistance, high fluidity and low surface tension, and resistance to contaminants and chemicals have recently been perfected, and additional resins for use in the electrical and electronic fields are emerging.

Resins with combinations of rigid and resilient properties are being developed, with the first of these already in industrial use.

Still in the laboratory stage but envisioned for early release are many formulations to meet various industrial needs, including: Two carvable materials for making models; an epoxy resin suitable for the manufacture of injection molds; an epoxy extrusion component; an epoxy compound with heat resistance as high as and higher than 700°F; epoxy encapsulating resins with a coefficient of expansion similar to metal; and a plastic solder in paste and stick form for metal-soldering purposes on cars, boats, body repair work, and other applications.

### Other Resins and Resin Prospects

For years research men have sought to hitch together propylene molecules, which are found in petroleum and natural gas, to form long chains for a new form of plastic. Recently they have succeeded and now both du Pont and Phillips announce production plans for new materials based on this development.

American Cyanamid places much importance on its new methylstyrene, Cymac 400, which is to be priced to compare with general-purpose polystyrene but which is said to have higher heat resistance. It is intended for items which have to be repeatedly washed in hot water such as trays and picnic ware. It may be frequently heated to 212°F with less than 0.3 per cent shrinkage.

General Aniline & Film Corporation expects much from their polyvinyl isobutyl ether. Its form is either as rubbery sheets or as liquid and its applications include adhesive tapes, fabric coating, and rubber-like products.

A new tough plastic is called Cycolac. Marbon Chemical Division was looking for a high-impact thermoplastic resin with some unique properties. The answer was found in a new polymer with uniform molecular structure based on Union Carbide's acrylonitrile, butadiene, and styrene. Some of the properties of Cycolac are: resistance to most chemicals, oils, and solvents; high impact and high heat-distortion strength and good electrical and low temperature properties. (See Table 9.3)

Ohio-Apex and Durez have demonstrated the merits of diallyl phthalates over polyesters in some cases and expect more activity with this material in the future. Allied Chemical has hopes for its ethanolamines in the future plastics picture. Owens-Corning expects to further promote its fiber glass reinforced polyester molding compound in the future. One company producing this compound is Thermaflow Chemical Corporation, Tunkhannock, Pa. Hercules Powder Company's chlorinated polyether resin, Penton, is said to have chemical resistance similar to that of the fluorocarbons. It is still in pilot plant production but future hopes for it are bright.

One of the potentially important materials is acrylonitrile and although not of itself a plastic its combining possibilities are so interesting that some description of it here seems warranted. It came into prominence in World War II for copolymerization with butadiene in the production of oil-resistant synthetic rubber. Polyvinyl chloride is plasticized with acrylonitrile to make a packaging film. A copolymer of acrylonitrile with styrene compounded with acrylonitrile-butadiene rubber gives a plastic material with much promise. It is tough and has good heat and chemical resistance; its trade names include Kralastic and Royalite. Some established synthetic fibers are copolymers with acrylonitrile as one of the monomers. Names for some of these fibers include Orlon, Dynel and Acrilan.

Bakelite is putting high hopes in its acrylonitrile-styrene copolymer which has both better heat resistance and better strength than the un-modified styrene.

The General Electric Co. is evaluating a new polycarbonate resin called Lexan which can be molded to form parts which are reported to be strong enough to withstand blows from a carpenter's hammer. Lexan molding compound is a thermoplastic resin with a heat distortion point of 280 to

290°F which combined with low water absorption gives good dimensional stability. It may be injection molded or extruded in conventional equipment.

## Plastics and Metals

One of the chief fields of plastics application in the future is in combination with metals. Plastics are in an excellent position to add to metals many characteristics which they lack. Quick drying plastics finishes did much to make today's automobile a commercial success. Zinc die castings become serviceable door handles covered with a molded thermoplastic which gives warmth, color and durability. Metal business machine mechanisms have plastics housings which not only are cheaper than metals when the design is complicated, but which also greatly increase sales appeal.

In a contrary direction plastics parts—especially buttons and jewelry—often are coated with metal. Successful processes have been developed for this and future expansion of such coatings looks promising. Metal powder is mixed with resins to give unique properties to molding compounds. Metal electrical circuits are printed on plastics and there are many other cases where the conductivity of metal and the insulating properties of plastics are combined to advantage.

## Polyethylene Foams

Adding to the already bright future of polyethylene comes the recent announcement that this material is being successfully foamed. Foams are available in closed-cell flexible forms. The cells are small and uniform and contain a harmless, inert gas. These foams in general retain all the basic desirable properties of polyethylene—its toughness, chemical resistance, moisture resistance, and its flexibility. The foam density can be varied from 10 to 50 pounds per cubic foot. Common wood and metal working tools can be used in fabricating these foams. They can be heat sealed and hot-gas welded.

## Vinyl Cast on a Paper Carrier

While casting on steel belts is the prevailing method of producing cast film, a revival of interest in the casting of vinyl film on a paper carrier has recently taken place and this method seems destined for a much more prominent place in the industry in the future. The casting of organosols and plastisols on a paper carrier is claimed by one of its leading advocates

—S. D. Warren Co., Boston—to be the most versatile process for manufacturing film. The paper used is a special product. It must have dimensional stability and easy release of the cured film. The equipment for this process, consisting of a casting head—usually a reverse roll coater—a curing oven, and unwind and rewind stands, is said to be relatively low priced. In addition suitable fly rolls for supporting and controlling the paper will be needed.

The paper can be reused from six to eight times. In fact, one user says that with proper care he has been able to reuse it for fifteen or more cycles, bringing his paper cost down to a little over a cent a yard for 54-in. film casting.

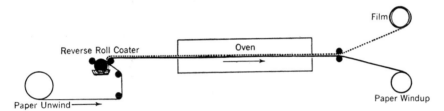

Figure 9.1. Paper taken from the unwind stand at the left, is carried by positioning rolls to the reverse roll coater where a vinyl film is cast upon it. From there paper and film together pass through an oven held at a temperature of about 400° F with travel at a rate of 75 to 100 yards per minute. After curing the paper and film are separated as shown, each being wound on its particular windup roll.

Printing on film in color is easily accomplished by this method of casting. The paper is prepared to accept special vinyl inks prior to casting, then when the film is separated from the paper after curing, the design is transferred from paper to film where it becomes a permanent part of the latter. Government maps in color have been made in this manner.

Thicker films may be built up with successive passes or different formulations may be cast layer upon layer to create special types of laminates. A feature of this method of casting is that exceptionally thin films (as low as 1 mil) may be combined with light weight fabrics. Vinyl cast on fabric in this way stays on the surface instead of soaking in as with usual fabric coating.

Curing is at about 400°F and oven temperatures should be carefully controlled. Casting rates as high as 130 yards per minute have been reported with this process.

# 10. TRADE NAMES

The purpose here is to present as complete and up-to-date as possible, a list of plastics trade names together with the materials they represent and the companies which produce such materials. In this connection the cooperation of The Manufacturing Chemists' Association and of The Society of the Plastics Industry has been gratefully received and the plan of presentation used in their "Retailers' Plastics Manual" has been used. In order to reduce the length of the list an attempt has been made to include only true plastics, that is to exclude plasticizers, gums, and similar materials. Also names which refer to products rather than to materials such as those referring to film or plywood have been eliminated as far as possible.

For Chapter 8, forty-two of the principal American plastics producers contributed statements which in most cases included up-to-date lists of their trade names. All these trade names have been included in the following trade name list. Many sources of information have been checked in an attempt to eliminate as far as possible obsolete terms. For the field covered, it is thought to be the most complete and up-to-date list* published.

United States Plastics Trade Names

| Trade Name | Material | Manufacturer |
|---|---|---|
| A-C polyethylene | polyethylene molding materials | Semet-Solvay, Petrochemical Div., Allied Chemical & Dye Corp. |
| Acetex | synthetic resin latices | Naugatuck Chemical Div., U.S. Rubber Co. |
| Acrilan | methyl methacrylate | American Viscose Corporation |

* Prepared by Mrs. Kathleen A. Schweitzer.

UNITED STATES PLASTICS TRADE NAMES (*Continued*)

| Trade Name | Material | Manufacturer |
|---|---|---|
| Acrylic: | | |
|   Acrilan | | American Viscose Corporation |
|   Cadco | | Cadillac Plastic Co. |
|   Crystalex | | Rohm & Haas Co. |
|   Gala | | George Morrell Corp. |
|   Joda Acrylic | | Joseph Davis Plastics Co. |
|   Lucite | | E. I. du Pont de Nemours & Co., Inc. |
|   Midlon M | | Midwest Plastic Products Co. |
|   Plexiglas | | Rohm & Haas Co. |
| Acrylon | synthetic rubber | The Borden Company |
| Aeroflex | polyethylene extruded sheeting, rods, tubing | Anchor Plastics Co. |
| Aeroglas | thermosetting resins | American Cyanamid Co. |
| Aeromold | plywood bonding resin | Timm Aircraft |
| Agilene | polyethylene molding compound, flexible sheeting, rigid sheets, rods, tubes | American Agile Corp. |
| Agipon | epoxy rigid sheets, rods, tubes, laminates, reinforcing materials | American Agile Corp. |
| Aico | cold-molded plastics | American Insulator Co. |
| Alathon | polyethylene resins | E. I. du Pont de Nemours & Co., Inc., Polychemicals Div. |
| Alkanex | wire enamels | General Electric Co. |
| Alphide | cold-molded plastics | Standard Plastics Co. |
| Alsynite | reinforced polyesters sheets, rigid reinforced material | Alsynite Company of America |
| Amerith | cellulose nitrate | Celanese Corp. of America |
| Ameroid | casein discs, sheet, rod and tube | American Plastics Corp. |
| Ampacet | cellulose acetate and ethyl cellulose molding compound | American Molding Powder & Chemical Corp. |
| Ampacet | polystyrene molding compound | American Molding Powder & Chemical Corp. |
| Amphenol | polystyrene | American Phenolic Co. |
| Apex | reinforced polyesters | Apex Electrical Manufacturing Co. |

UNITED STATES PLASTICS TRADE NAMES (*Continued*)

| Trade Name | Material | Manufacturer |
|---|---|---|
| Aqua-glass | reinforced polyester | Hawley Products Co. |
| Aqualite | phenolic laminate | National Vulcanized Fibre Co. |
| Aquapearl | pearly cast phenolic | Catalin Corp. of America |
| Aquaplex | alkyd-resin emulsions | Rohm & Haas Co. |
| Araldite | epoxy resins | Ciba Company, Inc. |
| Arcolite | phenolic | Consolidated Molded Products |
| Arochems | modified phenolics, maleics | U.S. Industrial Chemicals, Div. National Distillers Prod. Corp. |
| Arodures | ureas | U.S. Industrial Chemicals, Div. National Distillers Prod. Corp. |
| Arofene | pure phenolics | Archer-Daniels-Midland Co. |
| Aroplaz | alkyd resins, vinyl plasticizers; alkyd coatings | Archer-Daniels-Midland Co. |
| Aropol | polyester resins | Archer-Daniels-Midland Co. |
| Atlac | polyester resins (in solid state) | Atlas Powder Co. |
| Bakelite phenolic | phenolic molding compound | Bakelite Co., Div. of Union Carbide Corporation |
| Bakelite polyester | polyester resin | Bakelite Co., Div. of Union Carbide Corporation |
| Bakelite polyethylene | polyethylene molding compound | Bakelite Co., Div. of Union Carbide Corporation |
| Bakelite polystyrene | polystyrene molding compound | Bakelite Co., Div. of Union Carbide Corporation |
| Bakelite vinyl | vinyl molding compound, film, flexible sheeting, rigid sheeting | Bakelite Co., Div. of Union Carbide Corporation |
| Beckamine | urea-formaldehyde resins for laminates, adhesives, coating | Reichhold Chemicals, Inc. |
| Beckopol | high melt point modified phenolic resin | Reichhold Chemicals, Inc. |
| Beetle | urea molding materials | American Cyanamid Co., Plastics & Resins Div. |

| Trade Name | Material | Manufacturer |
|---|---|---|
| Bolta | plastic film, sheeting, moldable compounds, coated and laminated materials made from vinyl resins | General Tire & Rubber Co. |
| Boltaflex | vinyl upholstery material, vinyl sheeting and film, coated materials | General Tire & Rubber Co. |
| Bolta-Floor | vinyl floor covering | General Tire & Rubber Co. |
| Bolta-Quilt | vinyl flexible sheeting | General Tire & Rubber Co. |
| Boltaron | polystyrene laminates | General Tire & Rubber Co. |
| Bolta-Saran | saran filaments | General Tire & Rubber Co. |
| Bolta-Wall | vinyl wall covering | General Tire & Rubber Co. |
| Borinal | polyethylene-boron compounds, rigid and flexible sheets, rods and tubes | Allied Resinous Products, Inc. |
| Brasslyfe | vinyl, cellulose lacquers | Bee Chemical Co. |
| Brea | polyethylene | Brea Chemicals, Inc. |
| Bubblefil | regenerated cellulose | E. I. du Pont de Nemours & Co., Inc., Polychemicals Div. |
| Butacite | polyvinyl butyral resin | E. I. du Pont de Nemours & Co., Inc., Polychemicals Div. |
| Butaprene | styrene-butadiene paint latices; nitrile rubber | Firestone Plastics Co. |
| Butvar | polyvinyl butyral | Shawinigan Products |
| C-8 epoxy | epoxy resins | Bakelite Co., Div. of Union Carbide Corporation |
| Cadco | acrylic rod and tubing | Cadillac Plastic Co. |
| Caffelite | coffee-bean molding compound | Caffelite Corp. |
| Calresin and Calresin CPC | vinyl molding materials | Calresin Corp. |
| Camargo | vinyl impregnated fabric | Breneman-Hartshorn Inc. |
| Campco | ethyl cellulose flexible sheeting, film | Chicago Molded Products Corp. |

UNITED STATES PLASTICS TRADE NAMES (*Continued*)

| Trade Name | Material | Manufacturer |
|---|---|---|
| Campco | polystyrene (rubber-modified) rigid sheets | Chicago Molded Products Corp. |
| Cardolite | phenol-aldehyde resins | Irvington Varnish Co. |
| Cascamite | synthetic thermosetting resin plastic adhesive | The Borden Co. |
| Cascolac | casein for inks, casein solutions for coating paper | The Borden Co. |
| Cascoloid | casein base binder, emulsifier, stabilizer, thickener | The Borden Company |
| Cascophen | resin glues, thermosetting | The Borden Company |
| Casco Resin | thermosetting resins, adhesives | The Borden Company |
| Cascorez | vinyl adhesive | Casein Company |
| Casein: | | |
| Ameroid | American Plastic Corp. | |
| Cascolac | The Borden Co. | |
| Cascoloid | The Borden Co. | |
| Coronation | George Morrell Corp. | |
| Gala | George Morrell Corp. | |
| Galorn | George Morrell Corp. | |
| Kasolid | Synthetic Plastics Co. | |
| Protovac | The Borden Co. | |
| Stixall | The Borden Co. | |
| Catabond | phenolic resins | Catalin Corp. of America |
| Cataform | thermoplastic tooling resin | Catalin Corp. of America |
| Catalin | cast phenolic | Catalin Corp. of America |
| Catalin Bonding Resins | bonding resins | Catalin Corp. of America |
| Catalin Impregnating Resins | impregnating resins | Catalin Corp. of America |
| Catalin Laminating Resins | laminating resins | Catalin Corp. of America |
| Catalin Nylon | nylon | Catalin Corp. of America |
| Catalin Phenolic | phenolic resin | Catalin Corp. of America |
| Catalin Polyethylene | polyethylene | Catalin Corp. of America |
| Catalin Polystyrene | polystyrene molding materials | Catalin Corp. of America |
| Catalin Styrene | styrene | Catalin Corp. of America |
| Catalin Urea | urea resins | Catalin Corp. of America |

UNITED STATES PLASTICS TRADE NAMES (*Continued*)

| Trade Name | Material | Manufacturer |
|---|---|---|
| Catalin Wood Adhesives | wood adhesives | Catalin Corp. of America |
| Catavar | laminating phenolic | Catalin Corp. of America |
| Celanese Polyethylene | polyethylene film | Celanese Corp. of America |
| Cellothene | polyethylene-cellophane laminate | Chester Packaging Products Corp. |

Cellulose Acetate:

| | |
|---|---|
| Ampacet | American Molding Powder & Chemical Corp. |
| Cinelin | Cinelin Co. |
| Clearsite | Celluplastic Corp. |
| Fibestos | Monsanto Chemical Co. |
| Hercocel A | Hercules Powder Co., Inc. |
| Joda C/A | Joseph Davis Plastics Co. |
| Jodapac C/A | Joseph Davis Plastics Co. |
| Kodapak I | Eastman Kodak Co. |
| Lumarith | Celanese Corp. of America |
| Midlon A | Midwest Plastic Products Co. |
| Nixon C/A | Nixon Nitration Works |
| Plastacele | E. I. du Pont de Nemours & Co., Inc. |
| Pyra-Shell | Shoeform Co. |
| Strux | Aircraft Specialties Co. |
| TEC | Tennessee Eastman Co. |
| Tenite Acetate | Eastman Chemical Products, Inc. |
| Vuepak | Monsanto Chemical Co. |

Cellulose Acetate Butyrate:

| | |
|---|---|
| Clearsite | Celluplastic Corp. |
| Clearstream | Yardley Plastics Co. |
| General Plastics | General Plastics Corp. |
| Kodapak II | Eastman Kodak Co. |
| Nixon C/A/B | Nixon Nitration Works |
| Tenite Butyrate | Eastman Chemical Products, Inc. |

Cellulose Nitrate:

| | |
|---|---|
| Cinelin | Cinelin Co. |
| Duralin | Respro, Inc. |
| Fabrikoid | E. I. du Pont de Nemours & Co., Inc. |
| Herculoid | Hercules Powder Co., Inc. |
| Keratol | Textileather Corp. |
| Multipruf | Elm Coated Fabrics Co., Inc. |
| Nitrol | Monsanto Chemical Co. |
| Nitron | Monsanto Chemical Co. |
| Nixon C/N | Nixon Nitration Works |
| Pyralin | E. I. du Pont de Nemours & Co., Inc. |
| Textileather | Textileather Corp. |
| Textiloid | Textileather Corp. |

| Trade Name | Material | Manufacturer |
|---|---|---|
| Cellulose Triacetate:<br>  Kodapak IV | | Eastman Kodak Co. |
| Celogen | blowing agents for rubber<br>and plastics | Naugatuck Chemical Div.,<br>United States Rubber Co. |
| Celoron | phenolic-fabric laminate | Continental-Diamond Co. |
| Charmour | acetate sheets | Celanese Corp. of America |
| Chemigum Latex | nitrile latices | Goodyear Tire & Rubber Co. |
| Chemigum Rubber | nitrile polymers | Goodyear Tire & Rubber Co. |
| Chem-O-Glas | reinforced polyesters | Chemold Company |
| Chemold | reinforced polyesters | Chemold Company |
| Chemstrand | nylon filament | Chemstrand Corp. |
| Chesfoil | polyethylene-foil laminate | Chester Packaging Products<br>Corp. |
| Cheslene | polyethylene film, tubing,<br>sheeting | Chester Packaging Products<br>Corp. |
| Chespak | polyethylene-glassine laminate | Chester Packaging Products<br>Corp. |
| Cibanite | aniline-formaldehyde | Ciba Products Co. |
| Cinelin | cellulose acetate, nitrate | Cinelin Company |
| Clearsite | cellulose acetate and cellulose<br>acetate butyrate rods and<br>tubes | Celluplastic Corp. |
| Clearsite | polyethylene rods and tubes | Celluplastic Corp. |
| Clearstream | polyethylene flexible pipe | Yardley Plastics Co. |
| Cliderite | ethyl-cellulose potting<br>compound | Ernst Bischoff |
| Colloresin | methyl cellulose | General Dyestuff Co. |
| Coltrock | phenolic | Colt's Plastics Co. |
| Coltwood | high-impact phenolic | Colt's Plastics Co. |
| Compregnite | liquid phenol formaldehyde<br>solution | The Borden Company |
| Condurok | conductive plastic | Richardson Company |
| Conolon | reinforced plastic laminate | Narmco Resins & Coating Co. |

UNITED STATES PLASTICS TRADE NAMES (*Continued*)

| Trade Name | Material | Manufacturer |
|---|---|---|
| Consoweld | melamine decorative laminates | Consolidated Water Power & Paper Company |
| Copene | terpene copolymer | Neville Company |
| Cordopreg | polyester molding compounds, impregnated fabrics | Cordo Molding Products, Inc. |
| Coronation | casein | George Morrell Corp. |
| Corrulux | reinforced plastic sheets | Corrulux Div. of Libbey-Owens-Ford Glass Co. |
| CP-1 | polystyrene cast sheets | Cast Optics Corp. |
| Cresline | plastic pipe and tubing | Crescent Plastics, Inc. |
| Crystalex | acrylic | Rohm & Haas Co. |
| Crystle | clear phenolic | Marblette Corp. |
| Crystolex | acrylic denture | Kerr Dental Co. |
| Cumar | paracoumarone-indene resins | Barrett Div., Allied Chemical & Dye Corp. |
| Curtiss-Wright polyester foams | polyester foams | Curtiss-Wright Corp. |
| Cycolac | ABS high-impact thermo-plastic resin | Marbon Chemical Div., Borg-Warner Corp. |
| Cycolac | polystyrene (copolymers) compounds | Marbon Chemical Div., Borg-Warner Corp. |
| Cycopol | coating resins | American Cyanamid Company |
| Cymac | thermoplastic molding material | American Cyanamid Company |
| Cymel | melamine | American Cyanamid Company |
| Daka-Ware | urea plastics | Harry Davies Molding Co. |
| Dapon | diallyl phthalate prepolymer | Ohio-Apex Div., Food Machinery Corp. |
| Darex | high-styrene copolymer | Dewey & Almy Chemical Co., Div. W. R. Grace & Co. |
| Denflex | vinyl | Dennis Chemicals |
| Devran | epoxy resins | Devoe & Raynolds |

UNITED STATES PLASTICS TRADE NAMES (*Continued*)

| Trade Name | Material | Manufacturer |
|---|---|---|
| Diall | polyester reinforced molding compounds | Mesa Plastics Co. |
| Diamond PVC | vinyl molding materials | Diamond Alkali Co., Plastics Division |
| Diamond PVC-50 | for film, sheeting, profile extrusions and electrical applications | Diamond Alkali Co., Plastics Division |
| Diamond PVC-45 | for heavy sheeting, molding and non-electrical extrusions | Diamond Alkali Company |
| Diamond Compound R4 | for Type 1, chemical resistance, rigid PVC moldings and extrusions | Diamond Alkali Company |
| Diana Fyrban | vinyl coated and impregnated fabrics | Breneman-Hartshorn, Inc. |
| Dilecto | phenolic, melamine laminates | Continental-Diamond Fibre Div. |
| Dispersite | aqueous dispersions of resins and rubbers | Naugatuck Chemical Div., United States Rubber Co. |
| Dow Polyethylene | polyethylene molding compound | The Dow Chemical Company, Plastics Dept. |
| Dow PVC | vinyl molding compound | The Dow Chemical Company, Plastics Dept. |
| Dow Saran | saran molding compound | The Dow Chemical Company, Plastics Dept. |
| Dulux | alkyd coatings | E. I. du Pont de Nemours & Co., Inc., Polychemicals Div. |
| Duolite Polyesters | polyester resins | Chemical Process Co. |
| Duplacryl | acrylic denture | Coralite Dental Co. |
| Dura-Clear | polyethylene film | Harwid Co. |
| Duralon | furane resin | U.S. Stoneware Co. |
| Duran | vinyl sheeting, fabric backed material | The Masland Duraleather Co. |
| Duraplex | modified alkyd | Rohm & Haas |
| Durasol | vinyl coated materials | The Masland Duraleather Co. |
| Durez | phenolic resins and phenolic, diallylphthalate, and polyester molding compounds | Durez Plastics Div., Hooker Electrochemical Company |

| Trade Name | Material | Manufacturer |
|---|---|---|
| Durethene | polyethylene film | Koppers Company, Inc. |
| Durite | synthetic resins; phenolic molding powders | The Borden Company |
| Durolux | reinforced plastics | Depew Manufacturing Corp. |
| Dyal | alkyd solutions | Sherwin-Williams |
| Dylan | polyethylene | Koppers Company, Inc. |
| Dylene | polystyrene | Koppers Company, Inc. |
| Dylite | expandable polystyrene | Koppers Company, Inc. |
| Dylex | styrene-butadiene latices | Koppers Company, Inc. |
| Duxkin | vinyl sheeting | Harte & Co., Inc. |
| Ecolac | plastic lacquer, adhesive | Maas & Waldstein Co. |
| Edge-Glow | fluorescent acetate | Monsanto Chemical Co., Plastics Div. |
| Elasti-glass | vinyl copolymer | S. Buchsbaum |
| Elastofoam | vinyl foamed plastic | Elastomer Chemical Corp. |
| Elfolite | maleic resin | Ellis-Foster |
| Elvacet | polyvinyl acetate | E. I. du Pont de Nemours & Co., Inc., Polychemicals Div. |
| Elvanol | polyvinyl alcohol | E. I. du Pont de Nemours & Co., Inc., Polychemicals Div. |
| Enrup | thermosetting resin | United States Rubber Company |
| Epiphen | epoxide resins for glue | The Borden Company |
| Epoglas | epoxy reinforced laminate | Plastilight, Inc. |
| Epon | epoxy resins | Shell Chemical Company |

Epoxy:

| | |
|---|---|
| Agipon | American Agile Corp. |
| Araldite | Ciba Company, Inc. |
| Bakelite Epoxy | Bakelite Co., Div. of Union Carbide Corporation |
| Cordopreg | Cordo Molding Products, Inc. |
| Devran | Devoe & Raynolds |
| Epon | Shell Chemical Company |
| Polyox | Reichhold Chemicals, Inc. |

UNITED STATES PLASTICS TRADE NAMES (*Continued*)

| Trade Name | Material | Manufacturer |
|---|---|---|
| Escambia PVC 1250 | high molecular weight PVC for extrusion of shapes and profiles and for calendered film | Escambia Chemical Corp. |
| Escambia PVC 1225 | intermediate molecular weight PVC for supported and unsupported sheeting | Escambia Chemical Corp. |
| Escambia PVC 1200 | lowest molecular weight in this series, designed for flexible and rigid sheeting | Escambia Chemical Corp. |
| Esterol | alkyd resin | Paramet Chemical Co. |
| Estoglas | reinforced polyester laminate | Plastilight, Inc. |
| Ethocel | ethyl cellulose molding compound, flexible sheeting | The Dow Chemical Company, Plastics Dept. |
| Ethomulsion | ethyl-cellulose lacquer emulsion | The Dow Chemical Company, Plastics Dept. |
| Ethyl Cellulose: | | |
| Ampacet | American Molding Powder & Chemical Corp. | |
| Campco | Chicago Molded Products Corp. | |
| Cliderite | Ernst Bischoff | |
| Ethocel | The Dow Chemical Co. | |
| Ethomulsion | The Dow Chemical Co. | |
| Hercocel E | Hercules Powder Co., Inc. | |
| Jodapac E/C | Joseph Davis Plastics Co. | |
| Midlon E | Midwest Plastic Products Co. | |
| Nixon E/C | Nixon Nitration Works | |
| Evenglo | polystyrene | Koppers Company, Inc. |
| Exon | polystyrene (modified) molding compound | Firestone Plastics Company |
| Exon | vinyl molding materials | Chemical Sales Div., Firestone Plastics Company, Div. of Firestone Tire & Rubber Co. |
| Fabrez | urea-formaldehyde textile resins | Reichhold Chemicals, Inc. |
| Fabrikoid | pyroxylin (nitrate) coated material | E. I. du Pont de Nemours & Co., Inc., Polychemicals Div. |
| Falkaloid | modified alkyds | Falk Company |

UNITED STATES PLASTICS TRADE NAMES (*Continued*)

| Trade Name | Material | Manufacturer |
|---|---|---|
| Fashon | vinyl film and sheeting | General Tire & Rubber Co. |
| Fiberite | melamine molding compounds | The Fiberite Corp. |
| Fiberlac | cellulose nitrate lacquer | Monsanto Chemical Co., Plastics Div. |
| Fibestos | cellulose acetate | Monsanto Chemical Co., Plastics Div. |
| Fibertuff | polystyrene (modified with glass fibers) | Koppers Company, Inc. |
| Firestone Polyethylene | polyethylene film | Firestone Plastics Company |
| Flamenol | polyvinyl chloride | General Electric Co., Chemical & Metallurgical Div. |
| Flexiplast | polyvinyl acetate | Foster-Grant Company |
| Fluorescent Plastics: Edge-Glow | | Monsanto Chemical Co. |
| Globalite | | Luminous Resins, Inc. |
| Paulite | | Luminous Resins, Inc. |
| Fluorothene | trifluorochloroethylene film | Plax Corp. |
| Foamex | foamed latex, plastic | Firestone Plastics |
| Formex | polyvinyl formal-phenolic wire-coating | General Electric Co., Chemical & Metallurgical Div. |
| Formica | high-pressure laminates phenolic laminates | The Formica Company |
| Formrite | casting resin | Anacostic Tile |
| Formvar | polyvinyl acetal | Shawinigan Products |
| Forticel | cellulose propionate | Celanese Corp. of America |
| Fortiflex | polyolefin resin | Celanese Corp. of America |
| Fortisan | saponified acetate-rayon yarn | Celanese Corp. of America |
| Fostarene | polystyrene molding powder | Foster Grant Company, Inc. |
| Foundrez | urea-formaldehyde and phenol-formaldehyde foundry resins | Reichhold Chemicals, Inc. |
| Frostone | vinylidene chloride | President Suspender Co. |
| Furetone | furane resin | Irvington Varnish & Insulator Div. |

UNITED STATES PLASTICS TRADE NAMES (*Continued*)

| Trade Name | Material | Manufacturer |
|---|---|---|
| Gala | acrylic molding compound, rigid sheeting, rods | George Morrell Corp. |
| Gala | casein plastics | George Morrell Corp. |
| Gala | melamine and urea molding compounds | George Morrell Corp. |
| Gala | polyester molding compound, rigid sheeting reinforced | George Morrell Corp. |
| Galorn | casein plastics | George Morrell Corp. |
| G.E. Phenolic | phenolic molding compound | General Electric Co., Chemical & Metallurgical Div. |
| G.E. Polyester | polyester resin | General Electric Co., Chemical & Metallurgical Div. |
| Gelva | polyvinyl acetate | Shawinigan Products |
| Gem-Flex | vinyl | Gemloid Corp. |
| Gemstone | phenolic casting resin | A. Knoedler |
| General Plastics | polystyrene, modified and foamed | General Plastics Corp. |
| Geon | polyvinyl chloride | B. F. Goodrich Chemical Co. |
| Glasfloss | phenolic-impregnated glass fibers | Durez Plastics Div., Hooker Electrochemical Company |
| Glastrusions | reinforced polyester materials | Glastrusions, Inc. |
| Globalite | fluorescent plastics | Luminous Resins, Inc. |
| Glyptal | alkyd resin | General Electric Co., Chemical & Metallurgical Div. |
| Good-rite | plasticizers | B. F. Goodrich Chemical Co. |
| Grex | polyethylene resins | W. R. Grace Co., Polymer Chemicals Div. |
| GR-I | butyl rubber | Office of Rubber Reserve |
| GR-S | butadiene-styrene rubber | Office of Rubber Reserve |
| Harvel | resins, coatings | Irvington Varnish & Insulator Div. |
| Haveg | asbestos-filled phenolic | Haveg Corp. |
| Haveg 43 | graphite-filled phenolic | Haveg Corp. |
| Haveg 48 | cast phenolic | Haveg Corp. |

UNITED STATES PLASTICS TRADE NAMES (*Continued*)

| Trade Name | Material | Manufacturer |
|---|---|---|
| Haveg 60 | asbestos-filled furane resins | Haveg Corp. |
| Hercocel A | cellulose acetate molding compounds | Hercules Powder Company |
| Hercocel E | ethyl cellulose molding powders | Hercules Powder Company |
| Hercocel W | high acetyl cellulose acetate molding powders | Hercules Powder Company |
| Hercose AP | cellulose acetate-propionate | Hercules Powder Company |
| Herculoid | cellulose nitrate | Hercules Powder Company |
| Heresite | phenolic resins, coatings | Heresite & Chemical Co. |
| Heroprene | neoprene | Hewitt Rubber Div. |
| Hetrolac | polyester lacquer | Durez Plastics Div., Hooker Electrochemical Company |
| Hetron | polyester resins | Durez Plastics Div., Hooker Electrochemical Company |
| Hexcel | reinforced material | California Reinforced Plastics Company |
| Hi-fax | linear polyethylene molding powders | Hercules Powder Company |
| Homalite | cast polyester | Homalite Corp. |
| Horco X | polyvinyl butyral | Hodgman Rubber Co. |
| Hycar-Phenolic | phenolic resin plus Hycar compound | General Electric Co., Chemical & Metallurgical Div. |
| Hycoloid | cellulose nitrate | Hygienic Tube & Container Co. |
| IC Polyester Resins | polyester resins | Interchemical Corp. |
| Indur | phenolic molding materials | Reilly Tar & Chemical Corp. |
| Indurite | phenolic | Indurite Molding Co. |
| Insurok | phenolic; urea | Richardson Co. |
| Interchemical Polyester | polyester resin | Interchemical Co. |
| Irrathene | irradiated polyethylene | General Electric Co., Chemical & Metallurgical Div. |
| Irv-o-thin | vinyl coated | Irvington Varnish & Insulator Div. |

UNITED STATES PLASTICS TRADE NAMES (*Continued*)

| Trade Name | Material | Manufacturer |
|---|---|---|
| Isoflex | polyethylene tubing | Keystone Plastics, Inc. |
| Ivithene | polyethylene film and flexible sheeting | Irvington Varnish & Insulator Div. |
| Jet-Kote | furan coating | Furane Plastics, Inc. |
| Joda C/A | cellulose acetate molding compound, rigid sheets, rods, tubes | Joseph Davis Plastics Co. |
| Joda E/C | ethyl cellulose molding compound, rigid sheets, rods, tubes | Joseph Davis Plastics Co. |
| Kalwood | reinforced plastics rigid sheets, laminates | Keller Products, Inc. |
| Kasolid | casein plastics | Synthetic Plastics Co. |
| Kaurite | impregnant, laminant | Plaskon Div., Libbey-Owens-Ford |
| Kel-F | high polymer, trifluoro-chlorethylene | M. W. Kellogg Co. |
| Kel-Flo | low polymer, trifluoro-chlorethylene | M. W. Kellogg Co. |
| Kelon-E | polyethylene | W. S. Shamban & Co. |
| Kelon-Y | nylon | W. S. Shamban & Co. |
| Kodapak I | cellulose acetate sheeting | Eastman Kodak Co. |
| Kodapak II | cellulose acetate butyrate sheeting | Eastman Kodak Co. |
| Kodapak IV | cellulose triacetate sheeting | Eastman Kodak Co. |
| Kogene | rubberlike resin | Goodrich Chemical |
| Koppers Polyethylene | polyethylene molding compound | Koppers Co., Inc., Chemical Div. |
| Koppers Polystyrene | polystyrene molding compound, rubberized, expandable or foamed | Koppers Co., Inc. |
| Korogel | plasticized Koroseal | Goodrich Chemical |

## UNITED STATES PLASTICS TRADE NAMES (Continued)

| Trade Name | Material | Manufacturer |
|---|---|---|
| Korolac | Koroseal solutions | Goodrich Chemical |
| Koroplate | resin coating solutions | Goodrich Chemical |
| Koroseal | vinyl film, sheeting, coated materials; polyvinyl chloride products | B. F. Goodrich Co. |
| Kotol | solvent solutions of synthetic resins | Naugatuck Chemical Co., Div. United States Rubber Co. |
| Kralac | styrene copolymers | Naugatuck Chemical Co., Div. United States Rubber Co. |
| Kralac A | styrene (high styrene) butadiene copolymer | United States Rubber Co. |
| Kralac Latex | styrene-butadiene copolymer | United States Rubber Co. |
| Kralastic | butadiene-styrene and acrylonitrile materials | Naugatuck Chemical Div., United States Rubber Co. |
| Krene | vinyl film, flexible sheeting | Bakelite Company, Div. Union Carbide Corporation |
| Kriston | allyl ester casting resins | Goodrich Chemical |
| Lamicoid | urea, phenolic laminates | Mico Insulator |
| Laminac | polyester resin used with fibrous glass to make reinforced plastic | American Cyanamid Co. |

Laminates:

| | |
|---|---|
| Aqualite | National Vulcanized Fiber Co. |
| Boltaron | General Tire & Rubber Co. |
| Catavar | Catalin Corp. of America |
| Celoron | Continental-Diamond |
| Conolon | Narmco Resins & Coating Co. |
| Consoweld | Consolidated Water Power & Paper Co. |
| Decarlite | Decar Plastic Corp. |
| Dilecto | Continental-Diamond |
| Epoglas | Plastilight, Inc. |
| Estogral | Plastilight, Inc. |
| Formica | The Formica Company |
| Kalwood | Keller Products, Inc. |
| Lamicoid | Mico Insulator |
| Lamorok | Rogers Corp. |
| Marvibond | Naugatuck Chemical Div., United States Rubber Co. |
| Micarta | Westinghouse |

UNITED STATES PLASTICS TRADE NAMES (*Continued*)

| Trade Name | Material | Manufacturer |
|---|---|---|
| Laminates: (*Continued*) | | |
| Micoid | Mica Insulator Co. | |
| Naugatop | United States Rubber Co. | |
| Neopress | Loven Chemical of California | |
| Nevamar | National Plastic Products Co. | |
| Phenolite | National Vulcanized Fibre | |
| Phenocel | Plastilight, Inc. | |
| Plastaloy | The Atlas Mineral Products Co. | |
| Plyon | Swedlow Plastics | |
| Structoglas | International Plastic, Inc. | |
| Synthane | Synthane Corp. | |
| Taylor Laminated Phenolic | Taylor Fibre Co. | |
| Tempreg | U.S. Plywood | |
| Textolite | General Electric Co. | |
| Lamorok | phenolic laminate | Rogers Corp. |
| Lauxein | protein adhesives | Monsanto Chemical Co., Plastics Div. |
| Lauxite | resin adhesives; urea adhesives | Monsanto Chemical Co., Plastics Div. |
| Lemac | polyvinyl acetate, solid form | The Borden Company |
| Lemol | polyvinyl alcohol | The Borden Company |
| Loavar | polystyrene coating | Catalin Corp. of America |
| Lucite | acrylic resin molding powder | E. I. du Pont de Nemours & Co., Inc., Polychemicals Div. |
| Lumarith | cellulose acetate molding compound film, rigid sheets | Celanese Corp. of America |
| Lumite | saran filaments | Chicopee Mfg. |
| Lustrex | polystyrene molding compound, industrial and coating resins; styrene molding materials | Monsanto Chemical Co., Plastics Div. |
| Lustrex LX | heat-resistant polystyrene | Monsanto Chemical Co., Plastics Div. |
| Lustrex Q-3022 | polystyrene-glass compound | Monsanto Chemical Co., Plastics Div. |
| Lutrex | polyvinyl acetate | Foster Grant Company |
| Lytron | synthetic resins | |

UNITED STATES PLASTICS TRADE NAMES (*Continued*)

| Trade Name | Material | Manufacturer |
|---|---|---|
| Macoid | cellulosic dip coatings | Detroit Macoid Corp. |
| Macolite | vinyl extruded and foam | Detroit Macoid Corp. |
| Macoprene | vinyl extruded and foam | Detroit Macoid Corp. |
| Maraset | epoxy lines | Marblette Corporation |
| Marblette | cast phenolic | Marblette Corporation |
| Marblette | phenolic rigid sheets, foamed plastic, rods, tubes | Marblette Corporation |
| Marblette Foam Resin | expanded plastic | Marblette Corporation |
| Marbon 8000 | rubber reinforcing resins, styrene-butadiene copolymers | Marbon Chemical Div., Borg-Warner Corp. |
| Marbon 9200 | paint resins, styrene-butadiene copolymers | Marbon Chemical Div., Borg-Warner Corp. |
| Marco | polyester resins | Celanese Corp. of America |
| Marcothix | thixotropic liquid polyester resin | Celanese Corp. of America |
| Marlex | family of olefin polymers | Phillips Chemical |
| Marvibond | vinyl-metal laminates | Naugatuck Chemical Div., United States Rubber Co. |
| Marvinol | vinyl chloride resins and compounds | Naugatuck Chemical Div., United States Rubber Co. |

Melamine:

| | |
|---|---|
| Actone | Sun Chemical Corp. |
| Consoweld | Consolidated Water Power & Paper Co. |
| Cymel | American Cyanamid Co. |
| Fiberite | The Fiberite Corp. |
| Gala | George Morrell Corp. |
| Melantine | Ciba Company, Inc. |
| Melmac | American Cyanamid Co. |
| Melurac | American Cyanamid Co. |
| Nevamar | National Plastic Products Co. |
| Plaskon Melamine | Barrett Div., Allied Chemical & Dye Corp. |
| Resimene | Monsanto Chemical Co. |
| Super-Beckamine | Reichhold Chemicals, Inc. |
| Synthane | Synthane Corp. |
| Taylor Melamine | Taylor Fibre Co. |

UNITED STATES PLASTICS TRADE NAMES (*Continued*)

| Trade Name | Material | Manufacturer |
|---|---|---|
| Melantine | melamine resin | Ciba Company, Inc. |
| Melmac | melamine molding materials; resin | American Cyanamid Co. |
| Melocol | polyamide-formaldehyde glue | Ciba Company, Inc. |
| Melopas | polyamide formaldehyde | Ciba Company, Inc. |
| Melurac | melamine-urea resins; resins for adhesives | American Cyanamid Co. |
| Methac | methanol-methyl acetate mixture | The Borden Company |
| Methacrol | acrylic emulsion | E. I. du Pont de Nemours & Co., Inc., Polychemicals Div. |
| Methocel | methyl cellulose | The Dow Chemical Company, Plastics Dept. |
| Methylon | coating resins | General Electric Co., Chemical & Metallurgical Div. |
| Micabond | resin-bonded mica | Continental-Diamond |
| Micarta | phenolic laminate | Westinghouse |
| Micoid | phenolic laminate | Mica Insulator Co. |
| Midlon P | polyethylene sheet | Midwest Plastic Products Co. |
| Mirasol | alkyd | Carbogen Chemical |

Modified Styrene:

| | |
|---|---|
| Campco | Chicago Molded Products Corp. |
| Exon | Firestone Plastics Co. |
| Fibertuff | Koppers Company, Inc. |
| Joda Styrene H.I. | Joseph Davis Plastics Co. |
| Koppers Polystyrene | Koppers Company, Inc. |
| Kralac A | United States Rubber Co. |
| Kralac Latex | United States Rubber Co. |
| Kralastic | Naugatuck Chemical |
| Lustrex LX | Monsanto Chemical Co. |
| Lustrex Q-3022 | Monsanto Chemical Co. |
| Nixon Polystyrene | Nixon Nitration Works |
| Plexene | Rohm & Haas Co. |
| Plio-Tuf Series | Goodyear Tire & Rubber Co. |

| | | |
|---|---|---|
| Mondur | isocyanates | Mobay Chemical Company |
| Monolite | phenolic | Monowatt Electric |
| Monoplast | reinforced materials | Mastercraft Plastics Co. |

| Trade Name | Material | Manufacturer |
| --- | --- | --- |
| Monsanto Polyethylene | polyethylene resins | Monsanto Chemical Company, Plastics Div. |
| MPL | acrylic monomer | The Borden Company |
| MR Resin | polyester resins | Celanese Corp. of America |
| Multipruf | vinyl coated materials | Elm Coated Fabrics Co., Inc. |
| Multron | polyesters | Mobay Chemical Company |
| Mylar | polyester film | E. I. du Pont de Nemours & Co., Inc., Polychemicals Div. |
| Nacara | pyroxylin | Monsanto Chemical Co., Plastics Div. |
| Naugatex | styrene-copolymer latices | Naugatuck Chemical Div., United States Rubber Co. |
| Naugatop | plastic laminates | United States Rubber Co. |
| Neillite | phenolic | Watertown Mfg. |
| Nevillac | modified coumarone-indene | Neville Co. |
| Neville | coumarone-indene resins | Neville Co. |
| Nitrol | cellulose nitrate | Monsanto Chemical Co., Plastics Div. |
| Nitron | cellulose nitrate | Monsanto Chemical Co., Plastics Div. |
| Neopress | phenolic molding compounds, laminates, impregnated fabrics | Loven Chemical of California |
| Nevamar | melamine laminates | National Plastic Products Co. |
| 91-LD | phenolic resin for reinforced molding, laminating | American Reinforced Plastics Company |
| Nixon C/A | cellulose acetate rigid sheets, rods, tubing | Nixon Nitration Works, Inc. |
| Nixon Polystyrene | polystyrene (modified) rigid sheets | Nixon Nitration Works, Inc. |
| Nygen-Tolex | vinyl coated nylon fabric | General Tire & Rubber Co. |
| Nylasint | nylon molding powder | The Polymer Corporation of Pennsylvania |

## UNITED STATES PLASTICS TRADE NAMES (*Continued*)

| Trade Name | Material | Manufacturer |
|---|---|---|
| Nylatron | nylon molding powder | The Polymer Corporation of Pennsylvania |
| Nylon: | | |
| | Allied Chemical & Dye Corp. | |
| Catalin Nylon | Catalin Corp. of America | |
| Chemstrand | Chemstrand Corp. | |
| Kelon-Y | W. S. Shamban & Co. | |
| Nylatron | The Polymer Corp. of Pennsylvania | |
| Nyltite | Keystone Plastics, Inc. | |
| Spencer Nylon | Spencer Chemical | |
| Tynex | E. I. du Pont de Nemours & Co., Inc. | |
| Zytel | E. I. du Pont de Nemours & Co., Inc. | |
| Nymphwrap | moistureproof cellophane | Sylvania Ind. |
| Nypene | polystyrene resin | Neville Co. |
| Oil-Stop | cashew nutshell polymer | Irvington Varnish |
| Opalon | vinyl chloride compounds, industrial and coating resins | Monsanto Chemical Co., Plastics Div. |
| Pantasote | vinyl sheeting and coated material | The Pantasote Co. |
| Paracon | polyester rubber | Bell Telephone Laboratories |
| Paradene | coumarone-indene | Neville Co. |
| Paradura | phenolic | Paramet Chem. |
| Paraplex | alkyds; polyester resins | Rohm & Haas |
| Paraplex X-100 | polyester elastomer | Rohm & Haas |
| Paulite | phosphorescent plastics | Luminous Resins, Inc. |
| Pearlon | polyethylene film | Visking Corp. (Bakelite) |
| Penacolite | resorcinol adhesives | Koppers Co., Inc. |
| Penton | chlorine-containing polyether molding powders | Hercules Powder Co. |
| Petrex | alkyd | Hercules Powder Co. |
| Petrothene (R) | polyethylene resin | U.S. Industrial Chemicals Co., Div. National Distillers Products Corp. |

UNITED STATES PLASTICS TRADE NAMES (*Continued*)

| Trade Name | Material | Manufacturer |
|---|---|---|
| Phenolite | phenolic laminates | National Vulcanized Fibre Co. |
| Phenocel | phenolic laminate | Plastilight, Inc. |

Phenolic:

| | |
|---|---|
| Aqualite | National Vulcanized Fibre Co. |
| Arcolite | Consolidated Molded Products Co. |
| Arochems | U. S. Industrial Chemicals |
| Arofene | Archer-Daniels-Midland Co. |
| Bakelite Phenolic | Bakelite Co. |
| Beckopol | Reichhold Chemicals, Inc. |
| Catabond | Catalin Corp. of America |
| Catalin Phenolic | Catalin Corp. of America |
| Celoron | Continental-Diamond |
| Coltrock | Colt's Plastics Co. |
| Coltwood | Colt's Plastics Co. |
| Consoweld | Consolidated Water Power & Paper Co. |
| Crystle | Marbelette Corp. |
| Dilecto | Continental-Diamond |
| Durez | Durez Plastics & Chemicals, Inc. |
| Durite | The Borden Co. |
| Fiberite | The Fiberite Corp. |
| Formica | The Formica Co. |
| Gala | George Morrell Corp. |
| G.E. Phenolic | General Electric Co. |
| Gemstone | Knoedler Chemical Co. |
| Haveg | Haveg Corp. |
| Haveg 43 | Haveg Corp. |
| Heresite | Heresite & Chemical Co. |
| Hi-Den | Parkwood Laminates, Inc. |
| Hycar-Phenolic | General Electric Co. |
| Indur | Reilly Tar & Chemical Corp. |
| Indurite | Indurite Molding Co. |
| Insurok | Richardson Co. |
| Lamorok | Rogers Corp. |
| Marblette | Marblette Corp. |
| Micarta | Westinghouse Electric Corp. |
| Micoid | Mica Insulator Co. |
| Monolite | Monowatt Electric Co. |
| Neillite | Watertown Mfg. Co. |
| Neopress | Loven Chemical of California |
| 91-LD | American Reinforced Plastics Co. |
| Phenolite | National Vulcanized Fibre Co. |
| Phenocel | Plastilight, Inc. |
| Plaskon Phenolic | Barrett Div., Allied Chemical & Die Co. |
| Plastitool | Calresin Corp. |
| Plastone | National Plastics, Inc. |
| Plenco | Plastics Engineering Co. |

UNITED STATES PLASTICS TRADE NAMES (*Continued*)

| Trade Name | Material | Manufacturer |
|---|---|---|
| **Phenolic: (*Continued*)** | | |
| Plyophen | Reichhold Chemicals, Inc. | |
| Raycolite | Rayon Processing Co. | |
| Resinox | Monsanto Chemical Co. | |
| R-4200 | Monsanto Chemical Co. | |
| Rogers Board | Rogers Corp. | |
| Richelain | Richardson Co. | |
| Ryercite | J. T. Ryerson & Son, Inc. | |
| Spraymask | Adhere, Inc. | |
| Super-Beckacite | Reichhold Chemicals, Inc. | |
| Synthane | Synthane Corp. | |
| Synvar-Ite P | Synvar Corp. | |
| Taylor Laminated Phenolic | Taylor Fibre Co. | |
| Tego | Rohm & Haas Co. | |
| Trevarno F92 Series | Coast Mfg. & Supply Co. | |
| Tuffite | S. R. Browne | |
| Uniplast | Universal Plastics Co. | |
| Varcum | Varcum Chemical Corp. | |
| Vulcoid | Continental-Diamond Co. | |
| **Phenolic (Cast):** | | |
| Aquapearl | Catalin Corp. of America | |
| Haveg 48 | Haveg Corp. | |
| Marbelette | Marblette Corp. | |
| Plyophen | Reichhold Chemicals, Inc. | |
| Piccolyte | polyterpene resin | Pennsylvania Industrial Chemical Corp. |
| Placcolock | vinyl tile adhesive | The Borden Co. |
| Plaskon | plastics and resins | Barrett Div., Allied Chemical & Dye Corp. |
| Plaskon Melamine | melamine molding compound and resins | Barrett Div., Allied Chemical & Dye Corp. |
| Plaskon Phenolic | phenolic molding, coating, bonding resins | Barrett Div., Allied Chemical & Dye Corp. |
| Plaskon Polyester | polyester resins | Barrett Div., Allied Chemical & Dye Corp. |
| Plaskon Urea | urea molding compounds and resins | Barrett Div., Allied Chemical & Dye Corp. |
| Plaspreg | resin-plaster of Paris | Furane Plastics, Inc. |
| Plastacele | cellulose acetate sheets | E. I. du Pont de Nemours & Co., Inc., Polychemicals Div. |

UNITED STATES PLASTICS TRADE NAMES (*Continued*)

| Trade Name | Material | Manufacturer |
|---|---|---|
| Plastaloy | reinforced polyester laminate | The Atlas Mineral Products Co. |
| Plastiflex | vinyl mold materials | Calresin Corp. |
| Plastilock | adhesive for metal | B. F. Goodrich Chem. Co. |
| Plastitool | phenolic casting resin | Calresin Corp. |
| Plastone | phenolic | National Plastics, Inc. |
| Plastrong | reinforced polyesters | Bassons Industries Corp. |
| Plastylite | vinyl | Plastylite Corp. |
| Plaxpak | polyethylene products, film | Plax Corporation |
| Plenco | phenolic resins and molding compounds | Plastics Engineering Co. |
| Plexene | modified polystyrenes | Rohm & Haas Co. |
| Plexiglas | acrylic molding powders, resin, rigid sheets | Rohm & Haas Co. |
| Plexigum | acrylic adhesive | Rohm & Haas Co. |
| Plexton | reinforced polyester | G. B. Lewis Co. |
| Pliobond Series | adhesives | The Goodyear Tire & Rubber Co. |
| Plioflex | polyvinyl chloride | The Goodyear Tire & Rubber Co. |
| Plioflex Rubber | nitrile polymers | The Goodyear Tire & Rubber Co. |
| Pliofoam | expanded urea resin | The Goodyear Tire & Rubber Co. |
| Pliolite Latex | styrene copolymer latices | The Goodyear Tire & Rubber Co. |
| Pliolite S-5 Series | protective coating resins | The Goodyear Tire & Rubber Co. |
| Pliolite S-6 Series | reinforcing resins | The Goodyear Tire & Rubber Co. |
| Pliolite S-7 | paper coating resin | The Goodyear Tire & Rubber Co. |
| Pliolite NR Series | cyclized rubber resins | The Goodyear Tire & Rubber Co. |
| Pliotac | adhesive | The Goodyear Tire & Rubber Co. |
| Plio-Tuf | polystyrene (high styrene copolymer) | The Goodyear Tire & Rubber Co. |
| Plio-Tuf Series | modified styrene resins | The Goodyear Tire & Rubber Co. |
| Pliovic | vinyl molding materials | The Goodyear Tire & Rubber Co. |
| Pliovic Latex | vinyl copolymer latex | The Goodyear Tire & Rubber Co. |
| Pliovic Series | vinyl resins | The Goodyear Tire & Rubber Co. |

UNITED STATES PLASTICS TRADE NAMES (*Continued*)

| Trade Name | Material | Manufacturer |
|---|---|---|
| Plyamine | urea-formaldehyde adhesives; urea bonding material | Reichhold Chemicals, Inc. |
| Plyamul | polyvinyl acetate adhesives | Reichhold Chemicals, Inc. |
| Plyon | low-pressure laminate | Swedlow Plastics Co. |
| Plyophen | cast phenolic resins | Reichhold Chemicals, Inc. |
| Plyophen | phenol-formaldehyde resins, adhesives and varnishes | Reichhold Chemicals, Inc. |
| Plyophen | phenolic resins for laminates, rods, tubes | Reichhold Chemicals, Inc. |
| Polectron | vinyl carbazole | General Aniline & Film Corp. |
| Polyco | resin emulsions | The Borden Company |

Polyester:

| | |
|---|---|
| Aropol | Archer-Daniels-Midland Co. |
| Atlac | Atlas Powder Co. |
| Bakelite Polyester | Bakelite Co. |
| Cordopreg | Cordo Molding Products, Inc. |
| Curtiss-Wright Polyester Foams | Curtiss-Wright Corp. |
| Duolite Polyesters | Chemical Process Co. |
| Gala | George Morrell Co. |
| G. E. Polyester | General Electric Co. |
| Hetron | Durez Plastics Div. |
| IC Polyester Resins | Interchemical Corp. |
| Laminac | American Cyanamid Co. |
| Marco | Celanese Corp. of America |
| MR Resin | Celanese Corp. of America |
| Multron | Mobay Chemical Company |
| Mylar | E. I. du Pont de Nemours & Co., Inc. |
| Paracon | Bell Telephone Laboratories |
| Paraplex X-100 | Rohm & Haas Co. |
| Plaskon Polyester | Barrett Div., Allied Chemical & Dye Corp. |
| Polylite | Reichhold Chemicals, Inc. |
| Selectron | Columbia Chem. Div. |
| Vibrin | Naugatuck Chemical Div. |

| Trade Name | Material | Manufacturer |
|---|---|---|
| Poly-Eth | conventional density poylethylene resins, molding compound | Spencer Chemical Co. |
| Poly-Eth Hi-D | high density polyethylene from high pressure process | Spencer Chemical Co. |

UNITED STATES PLASTICS TRADE NAMES (*Continued*)

| Trade Name | Material | Manufacturer |
|---|---|---|
| Polyethylene: | | |
| A-C Polyethylene | Allied Chemical & Dye Corp. | |
| Aeroflex | Anchor Plastics Co. | |
| Agilene | American Agile Corp. | |
| Alathon | E. I. du Pont de Nemours & Co., Inc. | |
| Bakelite Polyethylene | Bakelite Co. | |
| Borinal | Allied Resinous Products, Inc. | |
| Brea | Brea Chemicals, Inc. | |
| Catalin Polyethylene | Catalin Corp. of America | |
| Celanese Polyethylene | Celanese Corp. of America | |
| Cellothene | Chester Packaging Products Corp. | |
| Clearsite | Celluplastic Corp. | |
| Clearstream | Yardley Plastics Co. | |
| Dow Polyethylene | The Dow Chemical Co. | |
| Dura-Clear | Harwid Co. | |
| Durethene | Koppers Company, Inc. | |
| Dylan | Koppers Company, Inc. | |
| Firestone Polyethylene | Firestone Plastics Co. | |
| General Plastics | General Plastics Corp. | |
| Grex | W. R. Grace Co., Polymer Chemicals Div. | |
| Hi-fax | Hercules Powder Co. | |
| Irrathene | General Electric Co. | |
| Isoflex | Keystone Plastics, Inc. | |
| Ivithene | Irvington Varnish & Insulator Co. | |
| Joda P/E | Joseph Davis Plastics Co. | |
| Jodapac P/E | Joseph Davis Plastics Co. | |
| Kelon-E | W. S. Shamban & Co. | |
| Koppers Polyethylene | Koppers Company, Inc. | |
| Midlon P | Midwest Plastic Products Co. | |
| Monsanto Polyethylene | Monsanto Chemical Co. | |
| National Polyethylene | National Petra-Chemical Corp. | |
| Pearlon | Visking Corp. (Bakelite) | |
| Petrothene (R) | U. S. Industrial Chemicals Co. | |
| Plaxpak | Plax Corporation | |
| Plicose | Harte & Co., Inc. | |
| Poly-Eth | Spencer Chemical Co. | |
| Poly-Eth Hi-D | Spencer Chemical Co. | |
| Polyfilm | Extruders, Inc. | |
| Poly-T | Tupper Corp. | |
| Polytone | Sun Chemical Corp. | |
| Resinite | Resin Industries, Inc. | |
| Resinol | Allied Resinous Products, Inc. | |
| Reynolon | Reynolds Metals Co. | |
| Tenite Polyethylene | Eastman Chemical Products, Inc. | |
| Visqueen | The Visking Corp. (Bakelite) | |
| Wynene | National Plastic Products Co. | |

UNITED STATES PLASTICS TRADE NAMES (*Continued*)

| Trade Name | Material | Manufacturer |
|---|---|---|
| Poly-Fiber Reinforced | reinforced polyester | Poly-Fiber, Inc., Div. of Calresin Corp. |
| Polyflex | polystyrene (flexible) sheeting | Plax Corp. |
| Polyfoam | polyurethane foam | General Tire & Rubber Co. |
| Polygard | stabilizer for rubber and plastics | Naugatuck Chemical Company |
| Polylite | polyester resin | Reichhold Chemicals, Inc. |
| Polyox | epoxy resins | Reichhold Chemicals, Inc. |
| Polypenco | nylon rods, tubes, filaments, sheeting, film | The Polymer Corp. of Penna. |
| Polyplex | resin adhesives, coatings | Heribert, Inc. |
| Polyprene | vinyl organosol finish | Interchemical Corp. |

Polystyrene:

| | |
|---|---|
| Ampacet | American Molding Powder & Chemical Corp. |
| Ampcolite | The Atlas Mineral Products Co. |
| Amphenol | American Phenolic Co. |
| Bakelite Polystyrene | Bakelite Co. |
| Boltaron | General Tire & Rubber Co. |
| Campco | Chicago Molded Products Corp. |
| Catalin Polystyrene | Catalin Corp. of America |
| Clearsite | Celluplastic Corp. |
| CP-1 | Cast Optics Corp. |
| Cycolac | Marbon Corp. |
| Dylene | Koppers Company, Inc. |
| Evenglo | Koppers Company, Inc. |
| Exon | Firestone Plastics Company |
| Fibertuff | Koppers Company, Inc. |
| Fostarene | Foster Grant Co., Inc. |
| General Plastics | General Plastics Corp. |
| Gilco | The Gilman Brothers Co. |
| Koppers Polystyrene | Koppers Company, Inc. |
| Loavar | Catalin Corp. of America |
| Lustrex | Monsanto Chemical Co. |
| Lustrex LX | Monsanto Chemical Co. |
| Lustrex Q-3022 | Monsanto Chemical Co. |
| Midlon H-I | Midwest Plastic Products Co. |
| Nixon Polystyrene | Nixon Nitration Works, Inc. |
| Plexene | Rohm & Haas Co. |
| Plio-Tuf | The Goodyear Tire & Rubber Co. |
| Polyflex | Plax Corp. |
| Resiston | Allied Resinous Products, Inc. |

UNITED STATES PLASTICS TRADE NAMES (*Continued*)

| Trade Name | Material | Manufacturer |
|---|---|---|
| **Polystyrene:** (*Continued*) | | |
| Resproid | | Respro, Inc. |
| Resoglaz | | Advance Solvents & Chemical Div. |
| Stex | | National Plastic Products Co. |
| Styrofoam | | The Dow Chemical Company |
| Styron | | The Dow Chemical Company |
| Poly-T | polyethylene film | Tupper Corp. |
| Polytool | polyester, epoxy, phenolic and polyurethane tooling compounds | Reichhold Chemicals, Inc. |
| Primal | acrylic emulsions | Rohm & Haas Co. |
| Protektol | protective strippable coating | Interchemical Corp. |
| Protovac | solubilized caseins | The Borden Company |
| Pyralin | cellulose nitrate sheets, rods | E. I. du Pont de Nemours & Co., Inc., Polychemicals Div. |
| Pyra-Shell | cellulose nitrate, acetate | Shoeform Co. |
| Pyroplax | cold-molded plastics | Cutler-Hammer, Inc. |
| Raycolite | phenolic-impregnated macerated molding material | Rayon Processing Co. |
| Redo | vinyl coated fabric | Goodall-Sanford, Inc. |
| Redux | adhesive for metal | Rohm & Haas Co. |
| **Reinforced Polyesters:** | | |
| Alsynite | | Alsynite Company of America |
| Apex | | Apex Electrical Manufacturing Co. |
| Aqua-glass | | Hawley Products Co. |
| Chem-O-Glas | | Chemold Company |
| Chemold | | Chemold Company |
| Conolon | | Narmco Resins & Coating Co. |
| Corrulux | | Corrulox, Div. of Libbey-Owens-Ford Glass Co. |
| Diall | | Mesa Plastics Co. |
| Duolite Polyesters | | Chemical Process Co. |
| Durolux | | Depew Mfg. Corp. |
| Estoglas | | Plastilight, Inc. |
| Gala | | George Morrell Corp. |
| Hexcel | | California Reinforced Plastics Co. |
| Kalwood | | Keller Products, Inc. |
| Laminac | | American Cyanamid Co. |

UNITED STATES PLASTICS TRADE NAMES (*Continued*)

| Trade Name | Material | Manufacturer |
|---|---|---|
| Reinforced Polyesters: (*Continued*) | | |
| Monoplast | Mastercraft Plastics Co. | |
| Narmcloth | Narmco Resins & Coatings Co. | |
| Plastaloy | The Atlas Mineral Products Co. | |
| Plastrong | Bassons Industries Corp. | |
| Plexolite | Plexolite Corp. of California | |
| Plexton | G. B. Lewis Co. | |
| Poly-Fiber Reinforced | Poly-Fiber, Inc., Div. of Calresin Corp. | |
| Resolite | Resolite Corp. | |
| Rigidon | Heil Process Equipment Co. | |
| Structoglas | International Plastics, Inc. | |
| Sy-Loy | General Tire & Rubber Company | |
| Syroco | Syracuse Ornamental Co. | |
| Syrocowood | Syracuse Ornamental Co. | |
| Trevarno F58 Series | Coast Manufacturing & Supply Co. | |
| Taylor | Taylor Fibre Co. | |
| Tropiglas | Russell Reinforced Plastics Corp. | |
| Woodite | Syracuse Ornamental Co., Inc. | |
| X-500 | Monsanto Chemical Co. | |
| Zenaloy | Zenith Plastics Co. | |
| Resimene | melamine resins | Monsanto Chemical Co., Plastics Div. |
| Resin XR-C | furfural casting resin | Furane Plastics, Inc. |
| Resinite | polyethylene film, tubing, rigid or flexible rods | Resin Industries, Inc. |
| Resinol | polyethylene molding material, film, rigid and flexible sheets, rods and tubes | Allied Resinous Products, Inc. |
| Resinox | phenolic resins and molding compounds | Monsanto Chemical Co., Plastics Div. |
| Resistoflex | polyvinyl alcohol | Resistoflex Corp. |
| Reslac | resinous lacquers | The Borden Company |
| Resloom | melamine resins (wool treatment); textile finishes | Monsanto Chemical Co., Plastics Div. |
| Resoglaz | polystyrene | Advance Solvents & Chemical Div. |
| Respro | adhesively integrated fibrous materials | The General Tire & Rubber Co. |
| Resproid | polystyrene impregnated fabric | Respro, Inc. |
| Reynolon | polyethylene film | Reynolds Metal Co. |

UNITED STATES PLASTICS TRADE NAMES (*Continued*)

| Trade Name | Material | Manufacturer |
|---|---|---|
| Rezyl | alkyd varnish; coating resins | American Cyanamid Company |
| R-4200 | phenolic casting resin | Monsanto Chemical Co., Plastics Div. |
| Rhoflax | plastic fabric coating | Rohm & Haas Co. |
| Rhonite | urea resins | Rohm & Haas Co. |
| Rhoplex | acrylic-ester emulsions | Rohm & Haas Co. |
| Rhotex | water-soluble resins | Rohm & Haas Co. |
| Richelain | phenolic; urea | Richardson Co. |
| Rigidon | reinforced polyester material and sheets | Heil Process Equipment Co. |
| Rucoam | polyvinyl chloride film and sheeting | Rubber Corp. of America |
| Rulan | flame-retardant plastic | E. I. du Pont de Nemours & Co., Inc., Polychemicals Div. |
| Ryercite | phenolic | J. T. Ryerson & Son, Inc. |
| Saflex | vinyl (butyral) materials; film; polyvinyl butyral | Monsanto Chemical Co., Plastics Div. |
| Santolite | aldehyde coatings | Monsanto Chemical Co. Plastics Div. |
| Santoloid | cellulose esters | Monsanto Chemical Co., Plastics Div. |
| Saraloy | an elastomeric copolymer based on vinylidene chloride | The Dow Chemical Company |
| Saran Wrap | transparent plastic film | The Dow Chemical Company |
| Saran: | | |
| Ace Saran | American Hard Rubber Co. | |
| Bolta-Saran | General Tire & Rubber Co. | |
| Dow Saran | The Dow Chemical Co. | |
| Lumite | Chicopee Mfg. | |
| Saran by National | National Plastic Products Co. | |
| Saran-Wrap | The Dow Chemical Co. | |
| Velon | Firestone Plastics Co. | |
| Scriptite | paper finishes | Monsanto Chemical Co., Plastics Div. |
| Selectron | polyester resin | Columbia Chem. Div. |

UNITED STATES PLASTICS TRADE NAMES (*Continued*)

| Trade Name | Material | Manufacturer |
|---|---|---|
| Silastic | silicone rubber | The Dow Corning Company |
| Skylac | aircraft lacquer | Monsanto Chemical Co., Plastics Div. |
| Solugums | synthetic resins | Solvol Corp. |
| Solvar | polyvinyl acetate | Shawinigan Products Corp. |
| Spencer Nylon | nylon-6 molding resins | Spencer Chemical Co. |
| S-polymers | butadiene-styrene copolymer | Esso Labs. |
| Spraymask | phenolic resin | Adhere, Inc. |
| Stacol | water-soluble resin | Glyco Products Co. |
| Stixall | casein glue | The Borden Company |
| Structoglas | reinforced polyester laminate | International Plastics, Inc. |
| Strux | cellular cellulose acetate | Aircraft Specialties |
| Styresol | styrenated alkyd resins | Reichhold Chemicals, Inc. |
| Styrex | styrene-acrylonitrile copolymer | The Dow Chemical Company |
| Styrofoam | polystyrene foamed plastic; expanded polystyrene | The Dow Chemical Company |
| Styron | polystyrene molding compound | The Dow Chemical Company |
| Styron 475 | polystyrene copolymer | The Dow Chemical Company |
| Suflex | safety glass interliner | Monsanto Chemical Co., Plastics Div. |
| Sullvyne Clad | vinyl sheeting laminated to metals | O'Sullivan Rubber Corp. |
| Sunform | polyester impregnated fabric | Electro-Technical Products Div., Sun Chemical Corp. |
| Super-Beckacite | pure phenolic resins | Reichhold Chemicals, Inc. |
| Super-Beckamine | melamine-formaldehyde resins | Reichhold Chemicals, Inc. |
| Super-Beckosol | isophthalic acid alkyd resins | Reichhold Chemicals, Inc. |
| Survival | moistureproof cellophane | American Viscose Corp.* |
| Sy-Loy | plastics reinforced polyester fiberglass material | General Tire & Rubber Co. |
| Sylphwrap | regenerated-cellulose wrapping | American Viscose Corp.* |

* For export.

UNITED STATES PLASTICS TRADE NAMES (*Continued*)

| Trade Name | Material | Manufacturer |
|---|---|---|
| Sylplast | urea-formaldehyde; urea molding compound | Sylvan Plastics, Inc. |
| Syntex | oil modified alkyd | Jones-Dabney Co. |
| Synthane | melamine sheet laminates, tubes, rods, molded laminates; phenolic laminates | Synthane Corp. |
| Synvar-Ite P | phenolic resins | Synvar Corp. |
| Synvar-Ite U | urea resins | Synvar Corp. |
| Synvarol | urea-base adhesive | Synvar Corp. |
| Syroco | reinforced plastics, molding compound | Syracuse Ornamental Co., Inc. |
| Syrocowood | reinforced plastics, molding compounds | Syracuse Ornamental Co., Inc. |
| Taylor Laminated Phenolic | phenolic reinforced laminated sheets, rods, and tubes | Taylor Fibre Co. |
| TEC | cellulose acetate | Tennessee Eastman Co. |
| Teflon | tetrafluoroethylene resins | E. I. du Pont de Nemours & Co., Inc., Polychemicals Div. |
| Teglac | alkyd coatings | American Cyanamid Co. |
| Tego | phenolic | Rohm & Haas Co. |
| Tempreg | low-pressure laminate | U.S. Plywood Corp. |
| Tenite Acetate | cellulose acetate molding compounds and extrusion composition | Eastman Chemical Products, Inc. |
| Tenite Butyrate | cellulose acetate butyrate molding compound and extrusion composition | Eastman Chemical Products, Inc. |
| Tenite Polyethylene | polyethylene molding and extrusion composition | Eastman Chemical Products, Inc. |
| Textileather | pyroxylin coated material; pyroxylin leather cloth | General Tire & Rubber Co. |
| Textolite | high-pressure laminate; decorative and industrial laminates; plastic laminated sheets, tubes, rods | General Electric Co., Chemical & Metallurgical Div. |

UNITED STATES PLASTICS TRADE NAMES (*Continued*)

| Trade Name | Material | Manufacturer |
|---|---|---|
| Thermocast | ethyl cellulose | Ernst Bischoff |
| Thiokol RD | nitrile rubber | Thiokol Corp. |
| Thor | foundry core binders | The Borden Company |
| Tolex | vinyl plastic leathercloth | General Tire & Rubber Co. |
| Tonox | hardener for epoxy resins | Naugatuck Chemical Div., U. S. Rubber Corp. |
| Trevarno F58 Series | reinforced polyester impregnated fabrics | Coast Manufacturing & Supply Co. |
| Tropiglas | reinforced plastics | Russell Reinforced Plastics Corp. |
| Tuffite | phenolic | S. R. Browne |
| Tygoflex | vinyl plastisol | U.S. Stoneware Co. |
| Tygon F | furane resin | U.S. Stoneware Co. |
| Tynex | nylon monofilament | E. I.du Pont de Nemours & Co., Inc., Polychemicals Div. |
| Ty-Ply | rubber-to-metal vulcanizing adhesives | Marbon Chemical Div., Borg-Warner Corp. |
| Uformite | urea dispersions | Rohm & Haas Co. |
| Ultraflex Resins | cellulose-plasticizing alkyds | Hercules Powder Co. |
| Ultron | vinyl film, flexible sheeting; polyvinyl chloride | Monsanto Chemical Co., Plastics Div. |
| Uniplast | phenolic | Universal Plastics Co. |
| Urac | resins for adhesives | American Cyanamid Co. |

Urea:
| | |
|---|---|
| Arodures | U. S. Industrial Chemicals |
| Beckamine | Reichhold Chemicals, Inc. |
| Beetle | American Cyanamid Co. |
| Catalin Urea | Catalin Corp. of America |
| Daka-Ware | Harry Davies Molding Company |
| Fabrez | Reichhold Chemicals, Inc. |
| Gala | George Morrell Corp. |
| Insurok | Richardson Co. |
| Lamicoid | Mica Insulator Co. |
| Lauxite | Monsanto Chemical Co. |

| Trade Name | Material | Manufacturer |
|---|---|---|
| **Urea: (*Continued*)** | | |
| Plaskon Urea | | Barrett Div., Allied Chemical & Dye Corp. |
| Pliofoam | | The Goodyear Tire & Rubber Co. |
| Plyamine | | Reichhold Chemicals, Inc. |
| Reptone | | Sun Chemical Corp. |
| Rhonite | | Rohm & Haas Co. |
| Richelain | | Richardson Co. |
| Sylplast | | Sylvan Plastics, Inc. |
| Synvar-Ite U | | Synvar Corp. |
| Synvarol | | Synvar Corp. |
| Uformite | | Rohm & Haas Co. |
| Urefoam | plastic foam | The Atlas Mineral Products Co. |
| Uskon | conductive rubber panels | U.S. Rubber Co. |
| Valite | bagasse plastics | Valentine Sugars Co. |
| Valtex | plastisol colors for print-embossing textiles | Interchemical Corp. |
| Varcum | phenolic | Varcum Chemical Corp. |
| Veloflex | vinyl-base leatherlike materials | Firestone Plastics Co. |
| Velon | saran filament; vinyl film sheeting and vinylidene chloride monofilaments | Firestone Plastics Co. |
| Velvasil | silicone fluids | General Electric Co., Plastic Div. |
| Vibramix | polyester molding compounds | Naugatuck Chemical Co., Div. U. S. Rubber Co. |
| Vibrathane | polyurethane | Naugatuck Chemical Co., Div. U. S. Rubber Co. |
| Vibrin | polyester resins | Naugatuck Chemical Co., Div. U. S. Rubber Co. |
| Vine-L | vinyl rigid sheets | Nixon Nitration Works |
| **Vinyl:** | | |
| Ampcoflex | | The Atlas Mineral Products Co. |
| Aroplaz | | Archer-Daniels-Midland Co. |
| Bakelite Vinyl | | Bakelite Co., Div. of Union Carbide Corporation |
| Boltaflex | | General Tire & Rubber Co. |
| Brasslyfe | | Bee Chemical Co. |
| Butacite | | E. I. du Pont de Nemours & Co., Inc. |

UNITED STATES PLASTICS TRADE NAMES (*Continued*)

| Trade Name | Material | Manufacturer |
|---|---|---|

**Vinyl: (*Continued*)**

| | | |
|---|---|---|
| Butvar | Shawinigan Products Corp. | |
| Calresin | Calresin Corp. | |
| Camargo | Breneman-Hartshorn, Inc. | |
| Cascorez | Casein Co. | |
| Clearsite | Celluplastic Corp. | |
| Denflex | Dennis Chemical Co. | |
| Diamond PVC | Diamond Alkali Co. | |
| Dow PVC | The Dow Chemical Co. | |
| Duran | The Masland Duraleather Co. | |
| Duxkin | Harte & Co., Inc. | |
| Elasti-glass | S. Buchsbaum & Co. | |
| Elastofoam | Elastomer Chemical Corp. | |
| Elvacet | E. I. du Pont de Nemours & Co., Inc. | |
| Elvanol | E. I. du Pont de Nemours & Co., Inc. | |
| Escambia PVC | Escambia Chemical Corp. | |
| Exon | Firestone Plastics Co. | |
| Fabrilite | E. I. du Pont de Nemours & Co., Inc. | |
| Fashon | General Tire & Rubber Co. | |
| Flamenol | General Electric Co. | |
| Flexiplast | Foster-Grant Co. | |
| Federan | Federal Leather Co. | |
| Formex | General Electric Co. | |
| Formvar | Shawinigan Products Corp. | |
| Frostone | President Suspender Co. | |
| Gelva | Shawinigan Products Corp. | |
| Gem-Flex | Gemloid Corp. | |
| Geon | B. F. Goodrich Chemical Co. | |
| Goodallite | Goodall-Sanford, Inc. | |
| Horco X | Hodgman Rubber Co. | |
| Koroseal | B. F. Goodrich Co. | |
| Krene | Bakelite Co., Div. of Union Carbide Corporation | |
| Lawnette | Yardley Plastics Co. | |
| Lemac | The Borden Co. | |
| Lemol | The Borden Co. | |
| Lifewall | The Pantasote Co. | |
| Lutrex | Foster Grant Co. | |
| Macolite | Detroit Macoid Corp. | |
| Macoprene | Detroit Macoid Corp. | |
| Marvibond | Naugatuck Chemical Div. | |
| Marvinol | Naugatuck Chemical Div. | |
| Multipruf | Elm Coated Fabrics Co., Inc. | |
| Nygen-Tolex | General Tire & Rubber Co. | |
| Opalon | Monsanto Chemical Co. | |
| Pantasote | The Pantasote Co. | |
| Placcolock | The Borden Co. | |
| Plastiflex | Calresin Corp. | |

UNITED STATES PLASTICS TRADE NAMES (*Continued*)

| Trade Name | Material | Manufacturer |
|---|---|---|
| Vinyl: (*Continued*) | | |
| Plastylite | | Plastylite Corp. |
| Plioflex | | The Goodyear Tire & Rubber Co. |
| Pliovic Series | | The Goodyear Tire & Rubber Co. |
| Plyamul | | Reichhold Chemicals, Inc. |
| Polectron | | General Aniline & Film Co. |
| Polyprene | | Interchemical Corp. |
| Resistoflex | | Resistoflex Corp. |
| Resinite | | Resin Industries, Inc. |
| Resproid | | Respro, Inc. |
| Reynolon | | Reynolds Metals Co. |
| Rucoam | | Rubber Corp. of America |
| Saflex | | Monsanto Chemical Co. |
| Solvar | | Shawinigan Products Corp. |
| Tolex | | General Tire & Rubber Co. |
| Tygoflex | | U.S. Stoneware Co. |
| Ultron | | Monsanto Chemical Co. |
| Veloflex | | Firestone Plastics Co. |
| Velon | | Firestone Plastics Co. |
| Versilan | | The Landers Corp. |
| Vine-L | | Nixon Nitration Works |
| Vinylite | | Bakelite Co. |
| Vinylseal | | Bakelite Co. |
| Vinyon | | Bakelite Co. |
| Visten | | The Visking Corp. (Bakelite) |
| V/L | | Nixon Nitration Works |
| V/L H | | Nixon Nitration Works |
| V/P | | Nixon Nitration Works |
| V/P H | | Nixon Nitration Works |
| Vygen | | General Tire & Rubber Co. |
| Vylene | | Elm Coated Fabric Co. |
| Vynafoam | | Interchemical Corp. |
| Wataseal | | Harte & Co., Inc. |
| Vinylite | vinyl copolymers; vinyl flexible sheeting; coated materials (paper); resins and plastics | Bakelite Co. |
| Vinylac | organic tackifiers for polyvinyl chloride emulsions | The Borden Co. |
| Vinylseal | vinyl-adhesive solution | Bakelite Co. |
| Vinyon | vinyl copolymer fiber, yarn | Bakelite Co.* |

* Also American Viscose Corp.

UNITED STATES PLASTICS TRADE NAMES (*Continued*)

| Trade Name | Material | Manufacturer |
|---|---|---|
| Viscasil | silicone fluids | General Electric Co., Chemical & Metallurgical Div. |
| Visking | plastic products | Bakelite Co., Div. of Union Carbide Corporation |
| Viskon | plastic impregnated non-woven fabrics | The Visking Corp. (Bakelite) |
| Visqueen | polyethylene flexible film, sheeting, tubing; plastic film | The Visking Corp. (Bakelite) |
| Vistanex | polyisobutylene rubber | Enjay Co. |
| Visten | vinyl sheeting and tubing | The Visking Corp. (Bakelite) |
| V/L | copolymer rigid vinyl | Nixon Nitration Works |
| V/L H | high impact copolymer rigid vinyl | Nixon Nitration Works |
| V/P | PVC rigid vinyl | Nixon Nitration Works |
| V/P H | high impact PVC rigid vinyl | Nixon Nitration Works |
| Vuepak | cellulose acetate rolls and sheets; cellulose acetate flexible sheeting | Monsanto Chemical Co., Plastics Div. |
| Vulcoid | phenolic-laminated vulcanized fiber | Continental-Diamond Fibre Div. |
| Vygen | vinyl molding materials | General Tire & Rubber Co. |
| Vylene | vinyl film, sheeting | Elm Coated Fabric Co. |
| Vynafoam | expandable vinyl plastisol | Interchemical Corp. |
| Woodite | reinforced plastics, molding compound | Syracuse Ornamental Co., Inc. |
| Wynene | vinyl extruded | National Plastic Products Co. |
| X-500 | reinforced-plastic resin | Monsanto Chemical Co., Plastics Div. |
| Zapon | pyroxylin lacquer | Atlas Powder Co. |
| Zenaloy | reinforced plastics | Zenith Plastics Co. |
| Zyrox | chlorine-base resins | Bakelite Co. |
| Zytel | nylon resin molding powder | E. I. du Pont de Nemours & Co., Inc., Polychemicals Div |

# INDEX

Skeist, Dr. Irving, 35
Slush molding, definition of, 11
Smith, W. Mayo, 260
Society of the Plastics Industry, 9
Specific gravity, 195, 207
    converted into ounces and grams per
        cu. in., 209
Specific heat table, 200
Spencer Chemical Company, statement
    of, 253
Spinnerettes, phenolic, 162
Strength-weight properties, of plastics and
    metals, 194
Styrene, 57
    modified types of, 290
Styrene-acrylonitrile, 71
Swimming pool, 55

Table mats, 154
Tables of properties explained, 14, 266
Teflon, 42, 43
    applications of, 139
Temperature resistance table, 196
Tenite acetate, prices of, 133
Tenite butyrate, 24
    prices of, 134
Tennessee Eastman Company, 15, 24
Tensile strength
    of fillers, 107
    of plastics, 196
Terephthalate polyesters, 61
Terms, for plastics, 5, 10
Tetrafluoroethylene, properties of, 44
Textile industry, plastics used in, 161
Textiles, treating of, 163
Textolite, 105
Thermal conductivity table, 198
Thermal expansivity table, 202
Thermoplastic, definition of, 4
Thermoplastics, list of, 6
Thermosetting, definition of, 4
Thermosetting resins
    future of, 256
    list of, 8
Thiokol, 37
Tools
    for forming metal, 173
    plastic, 36
Top operating temperature, 197
Tote pans, polyester, 178
Toys and sport items, plastics in, 163

Trade names
    for cold-molded compounds, 273
    for United States plastics, 272
Transfer mold, in open position, 182
Transfer molding, **183**
    press for, 183
Transportation industry, applications in,
    145
Trash can, polyethylene, 66
Trays and bowls, 155
Triallyl cyanurate, 57
Trifluorochloroethylene, properties of, 45
Tubing, polyethylene, 94

Union Carbide Corporation, Bakelite
    statement, 217
U.S.I. prices, 135
U.S. Industrial Chemicals Company,
    statement of, 254
United States Rubber Company,
    Naugatuck statement, 245
United States Tariff Commission,
    production table, 117
Urea-alkyd finishes, 90
Urea formaldehyde, **86**
Ureas, 86
    applications of, 141
    comparative properties of, 50
Urethanes See also Polyurethane
    applications of, 141
    foams, 72
Uses of plastics, 143, See also Specific
    applications

Vacuum forming, 192
Varnishes
    of alkyds, 64
    polyester insulating, 59
Versamid-epoxy adhesives, 88
Versamids, 37
Vinyl, cast on paper carrier, 270
Vibrin, prices of, 135
Vinyl, 143
    applications of, 176
    conveyor belt, 176
    family of, 73
    flooring, 1960 sales of, 262
    future of, 260
    qualities of, 74
    sheets, 102
Vinyl acetals, 75
    See also Polyvinyl acetal